Catalogue VI

1	The Suzhou astronomical chart	£80,000
2	The San Zeno Astrolabe	£1,200,000
3	Dürer	£500,000
4	Apianus	£1,200,000
5	Apianus	£12,500
6	Roemischer Kalender	£120,000
7	Danfrie	£75,000
8	Carrarino	£16,000
9	Tanner	£45,000
10	Rossi	£7,500
11	Rossi	£6,000
12	Toro	£6,000
13	Tranckius	£3,000
14	Pisani	£60,000
15	Brentel	£12,000
16	Heiden	£1,800
17	Dudley	£650,000
18	Seitz	£2,500
19	Cellarius	£250,000
20	Lucini	£10,000
21	Seller	£15,000
22	Vooght	£75,000
23	Oursel	£1,600
24	Anonymous	£3,500
25	Coronelli	£150,000
26	Lusvergh	£12,000
27	Tuttell	£28,000
28	Anonymous	£15,000
29	Aa	£1,800
30	Pigeon d'osangi	£20,000
31	Stampioen	£65,000
32	Andreae	£8,000
33	Franz	£12,000
34	Ferguson	£7,500
35	Henning	£7,000
36	Miller	£300
37	Frey	£1,600
38	Ferguson	£1,800
39	Naylor	£12,500
40	Robert de vaugondy	£7,500
41	Ferguson	£7,500
42	Nakanishi	£6,000
43	Dicquemare	£75,000
44	Donn	£12,500
45	Ferguson	£6,000
46	Beringer	£2,000
47	Flecheux	£30,000
48	André	£5,000
49	Anonymous	£45,000
50	Pâris	£2,200
51	Gautie	£500
52	Miersch	£5,000
53	Norie	£2,200
54	Bauer	£10,000
55	Shop sign	£3,000
56	Anonymous	£16,000
57	Malby	£350
58	Krotovii	£10,000
59	Fuller	£1,500
60	Flammarion	£2000

DANIEL CROUCH RARE BOOKS

Daniel Crouch Rare Books LLP
4 Bury Street, St James's
London SW1Y 6AB

+44 (0)20 7042 0240
info@crouchrarebooks.com
crouchrarebooks.com

ZODIACI
LINEA
ECLIPTICA

Daniel Crouch Rare Books LLP
4 Bury Street
St James's
London
SW1Y 6AB

+44 (0)20 7042 0240
info@crouchrarebooks.com
crouchrarebooks.com

MIX
Paper from responsible sources
FSC® C001785

ISBN 978-0-9567421-5-5

Catalogue edited by Daniel Crouch, Elena Napoleone and Nick Trimming
Design by Ivone Chao
Photography by Louie Fasciolo
Cover: item 4; p1: item 4; p4: item 4; p6: item 28; p196: item 19

Terms and conditions: The condition of all books has been described. Each item may be assumed to be in good condition, unless otherwise stated. Dimensions are given height by width. All prices are nett and do not include postage and packing. Invoices will be rendered in £ sterling. The title of goods does not pass to the purchaser until the invoice is paid in full.

Printed by Park Communications on FSC® certified paper. Park is an EMAS certified CarbonNeutral ® company and its Environmental Management System is certified to ISO14001. 100% of the inks used are vegetable oil based, 95% of press chemicals are recycled for further use and, on average 99% of any waste associated with this production will be recycled. This document is printed on Chromomat, a paper containing 15% recycled fibre and 85% virgin fibre sourced from well managed, sustainable, FSC® certified forests. The pulp used in this product is bleached using both Elemental Chlorine Free (ECF) and Process Chlorine Free (PCF) methods.The unavoidable carbon emissions generated during the manufacture and delivery of this document, have been reduced to net zero through a verified carbon offsetting project.

Catalogue VI

DANIEL CROUCH RARE BOOKS

Centaurus
Coruus
Crater
Hydra
Argonauis
Lanx meri
Virgo
Libra
Leo
Arcturus
Rosa
Crines Beronices Triche
Dorsum
Via lactea
Fera
Scorpius
Angueis
Bootes
Corona
Benenaz
Alioth
Ecliptica
Ophiuchus
Hercules
Draco
Cancer
Procyon
Gemini
Vrsa maior
Plaustrum
Sagittarius
Aquila
Lyra
Vrsa minor
Alrukaba
Stella polaris
Canicula
Canis maior
Cygnus
Cepheus
Cassiopea
Perseus
Erichthonius
Orion
Delphinus
Equus minor
Pegasus
Capricornus
Deltoton
cap. Medusæ
Taurus
Rigel
Lepus
Piscis notius
Aquarius
Andromeda
Aries
Pisces
Cetus
Eridanus
Effusio Aquarii
Acarnar

"Astronomy, at all events, is not disdained, but can be tolerated. It needs a great deal of thought; but if the universal theory of the heavens were to be reduced to instruments not requiring numbers and calculations, it would help to simplify the whole business"

Petrus Apianus, 'Astronomicum Caesarum', 1540, 'Address to the reader' (trans. - see item 4).

AN DE GRACE
Nombre d'Or
Cycle Solaire
Indiction Romaine
Festes du Mois
Nom du Mois
Signe du Mois
Lever du Soleil
Longueur du jour
Heures. Minutes
CADRAN ANNUEL DE CABINET.
Dimanche.
Lundy.
Mardy.
Mercredy.
Ieudy.
Vendredy.
Samedy.
Dimanche
Années du Seigneur.
Iours des Cendres.
Pasques.
Ascension.
Pentecoste.
Feste Dieu.
Avant.
Age de la Lune de 8. jour en 8. jour.
Soleil.
La Lune.
Mars.
Mercure.
Jupiter.
Venus.
Saturne.
Soleil.
TEMPUS EDAX RERUM
Pour trouver lage de la lune on cal cule lépact de lannée le quantieme du mois et le nombre des mois à comencer par Mars Jusqu'a Fevrier led. Calcul fera lage de la Lune, sil ne va pas jusqu'a trente sil va a trente il ni a point de Lune et si le dit calcul excede trente l'excedant fera lage de la Lune.
Fevrier qui a 28. jour en aura 29. en Bisexte et la Lune toujours egalle au contraire des autres Mois ou elle a toujours un jo. de moins
Les 4. tems arivent les Mercredys qui suivent les Cendres la Pentecoste Ste. Croix en Sept. et Ste. Luce en Decembre.
Dédié a Monsieur le Baron de Breteuil et de Preuilly, Premier Baron de Tourraine, Introducteur des Ambassadeurs et Princes Etrangers auprés du Roy.
Par son tres Humble et tres obeissant Serviteur le BOUTEUX.

Introduction

Catalogue VI represents something of a departure for Daniel Crouch Rare Books. In the year that marks 300 years since the passing of the Longitude Act, and the 25th anniversary of the World Wide Web, we thought it a good time to put together a collection of calculating machines from the first information revolution.

The paper scientific instruments within these pages do, however, have something in common with our normal offerings of maps and atlases: they are all attempts to answer the question "where am I?"

For centuries mankind has looked to the skies in attempts to answer this question both in terms of time and space. We have constructed star charts and planispheres to aid navigation, and astrolabes, dials and calendars to mark time and the movement of celestial bodies. We have done this for religious reasons - such as enabling astrological predictions in Song Dynasty China with the Suzhou Astronomical Chart (item 1); or to determine the date of Easter in a Mediaeval monastery in Verona (item 2) – and also in the pursuit of the pure "science which depicts and demonstrates the motions and locations of the stars" (item 14). We have made games to educate the young (such as items 27 and 50) and manuals for "A sure safety for Saylers" (item 9). It is this multiplicity of purpose, together with requirements for portability and ability to revise and update, which drew instrument makers to the low-cost flexibility of the printed image.

The term "paper instrument" ("instrumentle auff papir") was coined by Georg Hartmann in 1544. The impact of their arrival was such, that the makers of traditional objects in brass and ivory arranged for the prohibition of instruments "...covered with painted paper which does not endure... and is a mere deception through which the buyer is cheated" as "paper fraud" in the Nuremberg Statute Thirteen of 1608 (Schmidt). Whilst the instrument makers of northern Europe were ultimately unsuccessful in their attempts to close down the market in this new technology, they were, however, correct about the ephemeral nature of paper instruments: despite the extraordinary diversity of design present in the following pages, each of the items are known today in, at most, only a handful examples.

We would like to thank the following people for their assistance in producing this catalogue: Dr Justin Croft (item 59); Jonathan and Megumi Hill (item 42); Dr Stephen Johnston at the Museum of the History of Science, University of Oxford; Adam Douglas (item 9); Robert van Gent of the Institute for the History and Foundation of Mathematics and the Natural Sciences in Utrecht (items 22 and 31); Steven de Joode (item 16); Peter Kidd (item 2); Professor Richard Kremer at Dartmouth College (item 6); Richard Pegg at the Maclean Collection (item 1); Dr Ian Ridpath; and David Temperley (item 27).

We have included a glossary of the basic features of astronomy and time keeping on page 190.

The Suzhou astronomical chart

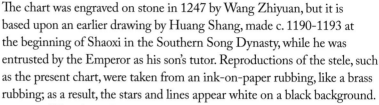

1 [Wang Zhiyuan after Huang Shang]

T'ien wên t'u [A Map of the Stars].

Publication
[Suzhou, 1247].

Description
Ink rubbing taken from a stele.
A rubbing of a thirteenth-century astronomical stele from Wen Miao Temple (Confucian Temple of Literati) Suzhou, Kiangsu, China; prepared for the instruction of a future emperor. The stele survives in the Suzhou Museum of Inscribed Steles.

Dimensions
1830 by 1000mm (72 by 39.25 inches).

References
Rufus, W.C. & Hsing-Chih Tien, 'The Shoochow Astronomical Chart', Ann Arbor, University of Michigan Press, 1945; Ridpath, Ian, 'Charting the Chinese Sky', http://www.ianridpath.com/startales/chinese3.htm.

The chart was engraved on stone in 1247 by Wang Zhiyuan, but it is based upon an earlier drawing by Huang Shang, made c. 1190-1193 at the beginning of Shaoxi in the Southern Song Dynasty, while he was entrusted by the Emperor as his son's tutor. Reproductions of the stele, such as the present chart, were taken from an ink-on-paper rubbing, like a brass rubbing; as a result, the stars and lines appear white on a black background.

"The planisphere depicts the sky from the north celestial pole to 55 degrees south. Radiating lines, like irregular spokes, demarcate the 28 xiu (akin to the Western Zodiac system). These lines extend from the southern horizon (the rim of the chart) to a circle roughly 35 degrees from the north celestial pole; within this circle lie the circumpolar constellations, i.e. those that never set as seen from the latitude of observation.

Two intersecting circles represent the celestial equator and ecliptic, which the Chinese called the Red Road and the Yellow Road respectively. An irregular band running across the chart outlines the Milky Way, called the River of Heaven – even the dividing rift through Cygnus can be made out. All 1464 stars from Chen Zhuo's catalogue are supposedly included (an inscription on the planisphere tallies the total as 1565, but this is clearly an ancient Chinese typographical error [and a recent count suggests that the stele depicts a total of 1436 stars]); not all of the stars show up on the rubbing, however." (Ian Ridpath).

The text below the chart gives instruction to the new emperor with information on the birth of the cosmos; the size and composition of both the heavens and the earth; the poles; the celestial equator (the Red Road) and the ecliptic (the Yellow Road); the sun; the moon, and the moon's path (the White Road); the fixed stars; the planets; the Milky Way (or the River of Heaven); the twelve branches; the twelve positions; and the kingdoms and regions.

It is difficult to ascribe a precise date to the rubbing; there were periods in the seventeenth century where rubbings were popular with the early Jesuits in the Kangxi court, and again in the eighteenth century in the Kangxi through early Qianlong courts, but equally in the late nineteenth and early twentieth centuries during European archaeological explorations of the region.

The present example is mounted on nineteenth century oriental paper, which would indicate that the rubbing was taken c. 1890, or earlier. Whilst several institutions, such as the Suzhou Museum of Inscribed Steles and the National Library of China in Beijing, hold similar rubbings, we are not aware of any other example on the market in the past 50 years.

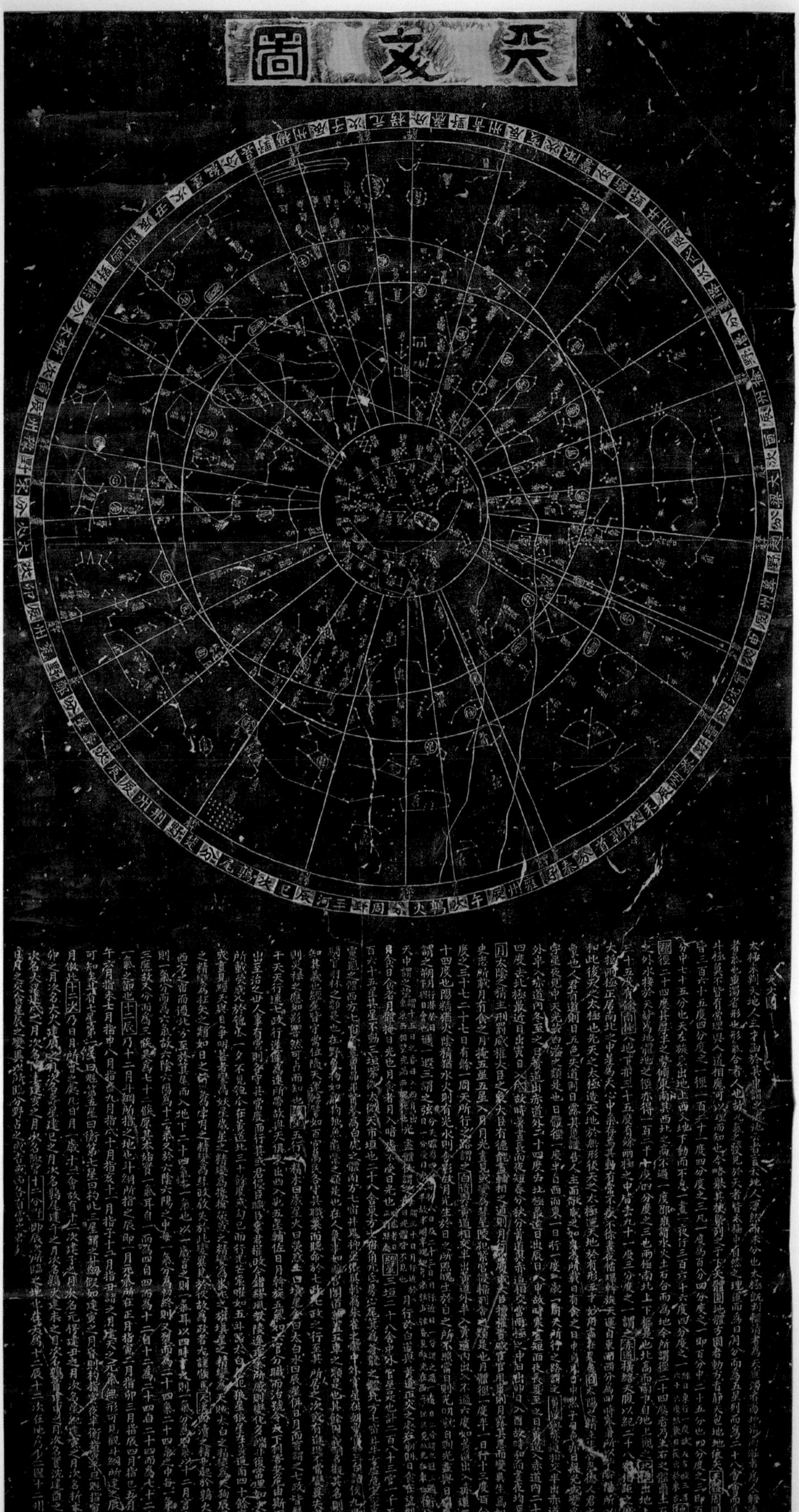

天文圖

A unique late Medieval/early Renaissance volvelle astronomical calendar

2 *[The San Zeno Astrolabe].*

Publication
[Verona, cloister of San Zeno, c. 1455].

Description
Ink and polychromy on wood and vellum.

Dimensions
Approximately 1280mm diameter.

A unique calendar, and the only object of its type to have survived from the Middle Ages.

Wall-mounted and hanging for over three centuries in the cloister of the Benedictine abbey of San Zeno, Verona, it was the primary timekeeper for the monks who saw and used it daily to organise their devotional schedule. Its three dials can be rotated by hand and chart the phases of the moon, the zodiacal calendar of the stars, the amount of daylight occurring in any given day of the year, and the feast days and times of the saints to whom the monks intended to pray.

Introduction

For at least three centuries this remarkable object hung on the wall in the cloister of the abbey of San Zeno, and it was placed in such a way that it would have been seen by all of the monks several times each day: as they left the dormitory for Matins at about midnight and as they returned to bed, as they returned to the church in the morning, and when they retraced their steps again to go back to bed in the evening. It would have been the monks' only way of telling the time – it was, in effect, their clock – because it told them what time the sun rose and set each day, how many hours of light and darkness there were, changing with the seasons, and thus allowed them to tell the time based on sunrise, sunset, and the position of the sun in the sky.

Datable to about 1455 – within a year of the printing of the Gutenberg Bible – the calendar marks the transition from the Middle Ages (generally considered to have ended around 1500 in northern Europe) to the Renaissance (generally considered to have begun about 1400 in Florence). As an object it is essentially medieval in character, yet the Zodiac illustrations are decidedly Renaissance in style.

It is also the major witness to the continued tradition of astronomical observation at Verona in the fifteenth century, a tradition that dates back to Pacificus (died 844), who invented a primitive form of astrolabe for telling the time during the night at Verona Cathedral.

To understand the San Zeno Calendar one needs first to understand a little about medieval time-keeping in general, and specifically about time-keeping within a Benedictine monastery. Astronomy and religion were inextricably linked in the Middle Ages; the date of the most important feast of the Christian ecclesiastical year, Easter – and every other feast whose date depended on it, such as Lent and Pentecost – was based on the variable date of a full moon occurring in March or April. Thus, at the very least, Church authorities needed to be able to predict in advance the relationship between the phases of the moon and the 365-day year.

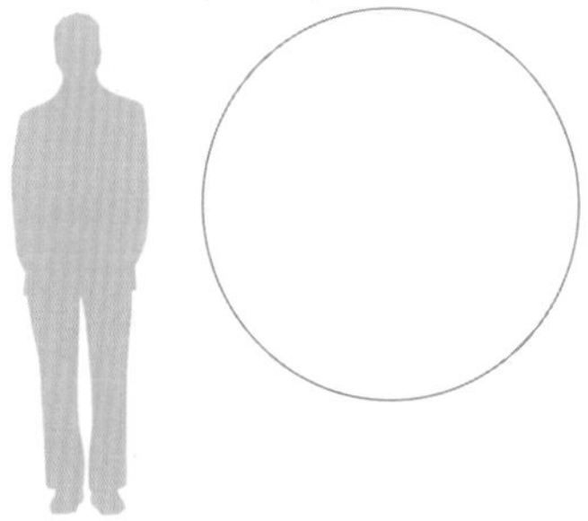

Questions of astronomical time-keeping were therefore crucial, and some of the greatest minds applied themselves to the problem, including the Venerable Bede in the eighth century. But, even today, the Eastern Church celebrates Easter on a different date than the West, due to differences in how the dates were calculated in the early Middle Ages.

Daily life in any Benedictine monastery, including San Zeno, was dictated by the liturgical "hours" (called Matins, Lauds, Prime, Terce, Sext, None, Vespers, and Compline), at intervals of roughly three hours from about midnight until about 9pm the next evening; seasonal variations in the length of the day and night were also of fundamental concern.

As early as the fifth century BC it had been realised that, although the solar year and the lunar month did not correspond neatly with one another (discussed in more detail below), the relationship between them would repeat every 19 years. Thus, if one could calculate data for an entire 19-year cycle it could be re-used in perpetuity, re-starting every 19 years.

As the Middle Ages progressed astronomical observation became more sophisticated. Increasingly precise instruments, such as astrolabes, were manufactured and greater numbers of scientific texts were translated into Latin from Arabic and Hebrew. By the mid-thirteenth century it was possible for King Alfonso X of Castile to commission the so-called Alfonsine tables of astronomical data: not only did these tables provide data for the full 19-year cycle, but they also provided data applicable to a wide variety of different latitudes in Europe, so that wherever one was, one could look up variable seasonal features (such as the length of the day and night) for one's own location. The tables contained data for a number of cities in Italy, including Venice, which is on the same latitude as Verona.

Knowledge that features of the world and the cosmos repeat themselves regularly – including seasons, phases of the moon, and tides – led to their representation on circular devices from a very early date: perhaps the most famous circular representation of time is the carved stone Mayan Calendar (which some people believed predicted the end of the world in 2012). But different cosmological features observed cycles of different lengths: the sun appeared to repeat a cycle lasting about 365 days, while the moon had a cycle of about 29½ days. The most efficient way of representing cycles that were out of step with one another was by means of a volvelle: a device that allowed the different cycles to be represented by rotating discs of different sizes.

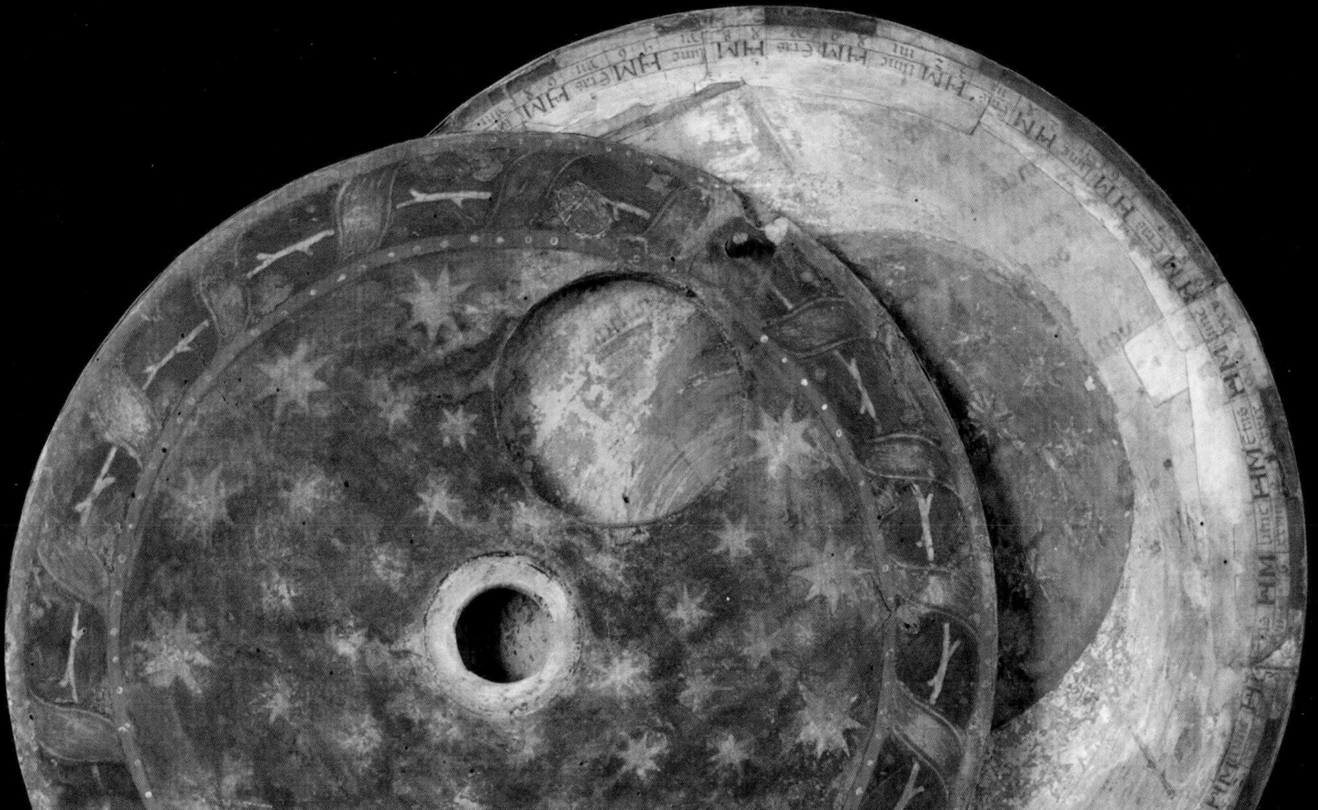

The Benedictine abbey of San Zeno had an illustrious history of astronomical scholarship, and thus it is less surprising that it should commission an astronomical calendar unlike any other known to have existed. We have not been able to find any reference to any other comparable medieval volvelle astronomical calendar, nor have we found any documentary evidence that any other ever existed. The closest comparisons are the famous astronomical clock in Prague, most of which dates from 1490, and heavily restored in more recent years, and the similar astronomical clock in St Mary's, Gdansk, dating from the late-1460s, which was severely damaged in 1945 and subsequently heavily restored.

Content

The various columns of letters, numbers, and text, from the outermost to the innermost concentric circle, are as follows:

1. The day of the month in Arabic numerals: 1 – 28 (February), 1 – 30 (April, June, etc.), or 1 – 31 (January, March, etc.), according to the modern (Gregorian) calendar; in black ink.
2. The day of the month in Roman numerals, with kalends, ides, and nones, according to the Roman (Julian) calendar; in red.
3. The Sunday Letters, "Litterae Dominicales": the first seven letters of the alphabet A – G repeated fifty-two times for the weeks of the year, starting at A on 1 January; in black except for 'A's, which are in red.
4. Saints' days and their liturgical gradings, plus a number of other astrological entries including the equinoxes and solstices, and immovable ecclesiastical entries, such as the earliest possible dates of Septuagesima and Easter; in black, with red for major feasts.
5. The Golden Numbers (16, 5, 13, 2 … 11, 19, 8) against various dates from 17 January – 15 February, and letters representing the possible dates of Easter, "Litterae tabulares" against 21 March – 25 April with [a] – u in black and a – q in red, to be used with a table indicating the date of Easter.
6. The age of the sign of the zodiac, in Arabic numerals 1 – 30; in red.
7. The Sidereal Months, starting at 1 January, consisting of the letters of the alphabet a – z, often with one or more letters repeated and followed by the Tironian symbols for 'et' and 'con', making a total of 27 or 28 days; in black.

The next three pairs of columns each give an increasingly long period of time:

8 – 9. The half-length of the night (i.e. from dusk to midnight, or midnight to dawn) in hours and minutes, varying from a maximum of

			[illegible]onie epi. Dux[x] [illegible]		
13	xviii	f	Ste Euphemie v. et mr.		
14	xvii	g	Tyburcii Valeriani et Maximi mr.	iii l	
16	xvi	A	Claus rogationum		
17	xv	b	Sci Aniceti ppe et mr.		
18	xiiii	c			
19	xiii	d			h
20	xii	e			i
21	xi	f			k
22	x	g	Sothere et Gaii ppe et mrm		l
23	ix	A			m
24	viii	b	Sci Georgii mr.	xii lc	n
25	vii	c	Marci euangeliste. Dux[x] min.		o
26	vi	d	Cleti et Marcelli ppe et mrm.	xii l	p
27	v	e			q
28	iiii	f	Sci Vitalis mr.	iii l	
29	iii	g	Petri mr de ordine p[...]. Claus pentec[oste]	xii l	
30	ii	A			
1	Kl	b	Philippi et Iacobi aplorum. Dux[x] min.		
2	vi	c	Alexandri the[...] mr		
3	v	d	Inuencio s[an]c[t]e crucis. D[ux] mi[n].		
4	iiii	e			
5	iii	f	[...] porta latina. Dux[x] min.		
6	ii	g	Johannis ante [...]. Dux[x] min.		
			[...]hael arch. Dux[x] [...]		

7 hours 45 minutes on 13 – 16 December (i.e. the Winter Solstice), to a minimum of 4 hours 15 minutes on 13 – 18 June (i.e. the Summer Solstice).
10 – 11. The full length of the night in hours and minutes, varying from a maximum of 15 hours 30 minutes on 13 – 16 December, to a minimum of 8 hours 30 minutes on 13 – 18 June; i.e. the lengths of night in this pair of columns are simply twice as long as those in the previous pair of columns.
12 – 13. The full length of the night plus half the length of the day, i.e. the length of time from dusk to the following midday, in hours and minutes, varying from a maximum of 19 hours 45 minutes on 13 – 16 December, to a minimum of 16 hours 15 minutes on 13 – 18 June.
14. Depictions of the signs of the zodiac, with two labels stuck on each (some now missing), one inscribed with the name of the sign (Aquarius, Pisces, Aries, etc.), the other with the word "Bonum", "Indifferens" or "Malum", indicating whether it is a good, indifferent, or bad time for blood-letting.
15 – 16. Of the next two concentric circles, the inner one contains column headings "Lune", "H"[orae, i.e. hours], "M"[inuta, i.e. minutes], and "Etas" (i.e. age), and the other contains the numbers 1 – 30 under the alternate Lune and Etas headings, and with hours and minutes columns with numbers rising from 0:0 to 12:0 and then decreasing back to 0:0, in increments of eight (0:0, 0:8, 1:6, 2:4 … 12:0, 11:12, 11:4 … 1:6, 0:8, 0:0).

By turning a pointer attached to the innermost disc so that it points to the age of the moon, a hole in this disc reveals a depiction of the phase of moon, from new to full and back again, with intermediate crescents showing its waxing and waning.

Artist

The artist of the miniatures has not been identified. The art historian Caterina Gemma Brenzoni of Verona University recently studied the calendar in relation to the restoration of the apse of San Zeno, which contains a remarkable fresco 24-hour clock-face on a wall to the left of the altar, numbered in both Roman and Arabic numerals, that presumably once had a mechanism to drive an hour-hand.

Copies of her unpublished work ('Ricerche inedite d'archivio e lettura storico artistica della decorazione dell'abside della basilica di San Zeno', Verona 2008-2009) are deposited with the Banco Popolare Archive, Verona, and in the Biblioteca Civica di Verona. She kindly informs us that the closest stylistic parallels that she found were by Lombard painters working in the middle of the fifteenth century, such as the 'Maestro Paroto's Madonna and Child with Saints' and the Crucifixion poliptych in the Bagatti Valsecchi Museum, Milan; the

Etas
HM
Lune
HM
Etas
HM
Lune

famous sets of 'Tarocchi' (Tarot cards) by the workshop of Bonifacio Bembo (Pinacoteca Brera, Milan); and works by the Zavattari brothers, such as the frescoes in the chapel of Queen Theodolinda, Monza Cathedral, executed by Ambrogio and Gregorio Zavattari in 1444.

Provenance

There is ample liturgical evidence that the calendar was made for the use of the Benedictine abbey of San Zeno, Verona:

The highest grade ("Duplex maius") feasts include:
21 March: Benedict, founder of the Benedictine Order.
12 April: The Deposition of Zeno, bishop of Verona.
21 May: The Translation of Zeno.
8 December: The Ordination of Zeno.
10 December: The Dedication of the Basilica of San Zeno.

The next highest ("Duplex minus") feasts include:
28 March: The Octave of Benedict.
5 September: Crescentianus, bishop of Verona.

The next highest feasts (with 12 readings) include:
23 March: Proculus, bishop of Verona.
29 April: Peter Martyr, who was born in Verona.
22 May [added]: Lupicinus, bishop of Verona.
13 July: Anthony Abbot, "the father of all monks" and probably (but the grading is damaged).
31 October: Lucillus, bishop of Verona.

The calendar is recorded attached to a wall in the cloister of San Zeno in the mid-eighteenth century (Giambatista Biancolini, 'Dei Vescovi e Governatori di Verona' [Bishops and Governors of Verona] (Verona, 1757), p. 22, in a section discussing the former bishop of Verona St Lupicino) with the following passage (translated from the Italian):

"A curious calendar is tucked into the wall of the loggia which leads from the dormitory of San Zeno monastery to the choir and the sacristy of the church [i.e. the East side of the Cloister]. This calendar is very beautiful, large, and accurate, written on paper [sic] on a circular panel that can be rotated for the convenience of readers, placed there about 1455 for use of the monks of San Zeno. In it one can only read the names of our sainted bishops San Proculo, San Lucillo, San Zeno and San Cerbonio. But it is unknown why it lacks San Lupicino whose sacred body, together with those of San Lucillo and the martyr San Crescenziano (who is recorded in the said calendar) rests in the said church since time immemorial, since in a list register of our sainted

bishops in a miscellaneous codex in the library of San Zeno, the oldest of the latter, is recorded the name of the said saint, by whose name is added in a more recent hand: 'whose body is in the church of San Zeno'."

If Biancolini is correct about the date of the placement of the calendar in 1455 (he must have had information no longer available, perhaps an inscription painted on the wall of the cloister or a now-lost document in the abbey archives) then it was doubtless commissioned by Gregorio Correr (1409 – 64), who was Abbot of San Zeno from 1448. A somewhat earlier date than 1455 is perhaps suggested by the absence of the feast-day (20 May) of St Bernardino of Siena, however: he died in 1444, was canonized in 1450, and the feast was quickly adopted by liturgical calendars throughout Italy.

San Zeno was plundered by Napoleonic troops in 1797, one result of which is that the three predella panels of Mantegna's San Zeno Altarpiece, commissioned by Abbot Correr and painted c. 1457 – 60, are today at Paris in the Louvre and at Tours in the Musée des Beaux-Arts.

By the early twentieth century the calendar was the property of the Conte Antonio Maria Cartolari of Verona (born 1843; see Vittore Spreti, 'Enciclopedia storico-nobiliare italiana: famiglie nobili e titolate viventi riconosciute …', II (1929), pp. 344-5), and it may have entered the noble family's collection during the Napoleonic upheavals through one of their ancestors: they are recorded as owning a portrait of an ancestor called Bartolomeo, who was a monk of San Zeno (inscribed "Bartholomaeus de Fanzago Cartulariis, S. Zenonis Majoris Ver. Cenobii Monachus filius Io[hannes] Baptistae e consilio Nobilium gubernatoris S. Montis Pietatis"; see Avena and Callegari, p. 29). It is not known exactly when the calendar left the Cartolari family collection (Conte Antonio Maria was born in 1843, married in 1869, and was apparently still alive in 1929 when the Enciclopedia cited above was published), but a portrait of a 'Woman with Green Vest, White Blouse and Red Choker' by Pietro Antonio Rotari was sold by the descendants of the Conte Antonio Maria Cartolari in the 1970s, and is now in the Norton Simon Museum, California.

Bibliography

Apart from Biancolini's brief 1757 description, there appears to be only one published account of the calendar, now almost a century old, which rarely has been referenced in print: A. Avena and G.V. Callegari, "Un calendario ecclesiastico veronese del secolo XVo", Madonna Verona, Anno XI, n.1: fascicolo 41 (Gennaio – Giugno, 1917), pp. 1 – 33.

The first printed star charts

3 **DÜRER, Albrecht**

Imagines coeli Septentrionales cum duodecim imaginibus zodiaci [and] Imagines coeli Meridionales.

Publication
Nuremberg, 1515.

Description
Two woodcuts, with fine original hand-colour, northern hemisphere: first state, without monogram (according to Meder); southern hemisphere: second state, with some corrections to the numbers, the rabbit's feet crossed and Orion's belt with three stars (Munich holds one, uncoloured, example of the first, proof, state of the charts).

Dimensions
445 by 610mm (17.5 by 24 inches).

References
Meder 259-260; Panofsky II, 365-366; '1471 Albrecht Dürer 1971', exh. cat. Nuremberg 1971, no. 309-310; Schneider, 'Erich, Dürer, Die Kunst aus der Natur zu "reyssen", Sammlung-Otto-Schäfer-II', exh. cat. Schweinfurt 1997/98, no. 78-79; Schoch/Mende/Scherbaum, 'Albrecht Dürer, Das druckgraphische Werk II', 2002, no. 243-244; Wörz, Adèle Lorraine, 'The Visualization of Perspective Systems and Iconology in Dürer's Cartographic Works', Oregon 2007 (Electronic dissertation: Permanent citation URL: http://hdl.handle.net/1957/3785).

Albrecht Dürer (1471-1528) produced these two celestial maps under the patronage of the Holy Roman Emperor Maximilian I, in cooperation with Johannes Stabius and Conrad Heinfogel. 'Imagines Coeli Meridionales', the southern hemisphere, and 'Imagines Coeli Septentrionales', the northern hemisphere, are the first printed scientifically-rigorous star charts. They were novel for the sixteenth century, combining accuracy of star-placement with classical constellation figures. "These two celestial planispheres can be seen as a representation of over two thousand years of intellectual thought. The constellation and celestial iconography inherited from Antiquity, Greek geometrical studies, and the Islamic scholarship focusing on spatial accuracy for charting the heavens all culminated in this work, aided by the aesthetic mastery of Dürer" (Wörz, p. 156).

The earliest printed depictions of the constellations were not true maps of the sky. Constellation figures were produced as woodcut diagrams, with stars positioned to adorn the figures, but not to portray the heavens. Only Dürer's planispheres included a coordinate system and attempted to accurately position the stars of the 48 constellations based on the star catalogue contained in Ptolemy's second century 'Almagest'.

The map of the southern hemisphere includes some cartouches and coats-of-arms, providing information about the collaborators and patrons. In the upper corners is a dedication to Cardinal Mattheus Lang von Wellenberg and his arms. The lower right corner shows Stabius's privilege for publication, granted by Maximilian I. In the lower left are the coats-of-arms of the three authors and a printed badge noting their names and tasks: 'Johann Stabius ordered (and edited), Conradus Heinfogel positioned the stars, Albertus Durer drew the images'.

Johannes Stabius (after 1460-1522) was professor of mathematics in Vienna. From 1503 he served as court historian and academic adviser to Maximilian I. In this function he forwarded several imperial commissions to Dürer, including the famous "Ehrenpforte" (Meder 251). Stabius and Dürer also collaborated on a woodcut world map in 1515.

Conrad Heinfogel (d.1517), an astronomer and mathematician from Nuremberg, is well known for his translation of Sacrobosco's 'De Sphaera' into German. He was also co-author of the two star charts of 1502/3 (ink drawings on vellum; Nuremberg, Germanisches Nationalmuseum) on which Dürer's maps are based. However, for the prints he updated the positions of the stars, reflecting the year 1499 or 1500.

The earliest known western maps of the skies of the northern and southern hemispheres with both stars and constellation figures are datable to c. 1440, bound in a manuscript preserved in Vienna (cod. Vind. 5415). They may have been based on two now-lost charts from 1425, once owned by Regiomontanus. The Vienna maps form

Imagines coeli Septentrionales cum duodecim imaginibus zodiaci.

the pattern for Heinfogel's manuscript charts and, through these, for Dürer's woodcuts. His planispheres were then printed several times and disseminated throughout Europe, influencing the star maps of subsequent Renaissance cartographers like Petrus Apianus (1495-1552; see items 4 and 5) and Johannes Honter (1498-1549).

According to Ptolemaic tradition, the twelve signs of the zodiac are displayed on the northern hemisphere and are to be read counter-clockwise – that is, as seen from space, or as they would appear on a celestial globe. The constellation figures are therefore shown from their back view. "Dürer depicts the constellation figures as moving in a dynamic, three-dimensional space. The representation of Libra especially exemplifies this depiction. Instead of ropes connecting the weights to the trays represented as straight lines, Dürer's figure seems to be floating in weightlessness" (Wörz, p. 174). Dürer decorated the four corners of the northern chart with portraits of four ancient authorities, dressed in their assumed national dress, each holding a celestial globe: Aratus representing the Greek, Ptolemy the Egyptian, Al-Sufi the Islamic, and Marcus Manilius the Roman tradition of astronomy.

The southern hemisphere is projected by using the same system, but it shows distinctly fewer stars and constellations than the companion piece. Large areas of this map are empty of constellations because they were not visible from the Mediterranean or Middle East, the area from where the sources of Ptolemy's 'Almagest' originated. Although the discoveries of the New World produced new observations of the southern firmament, these were not incorporated.

Dürer's interest and participation is certainly not limited to the lifelike drawings of the constellations and the decorative form of the map; rather, his mathematical-scientific interests also apply to the projection methods (see Schoch, p. 434).

Imagines coeli Meridionales.

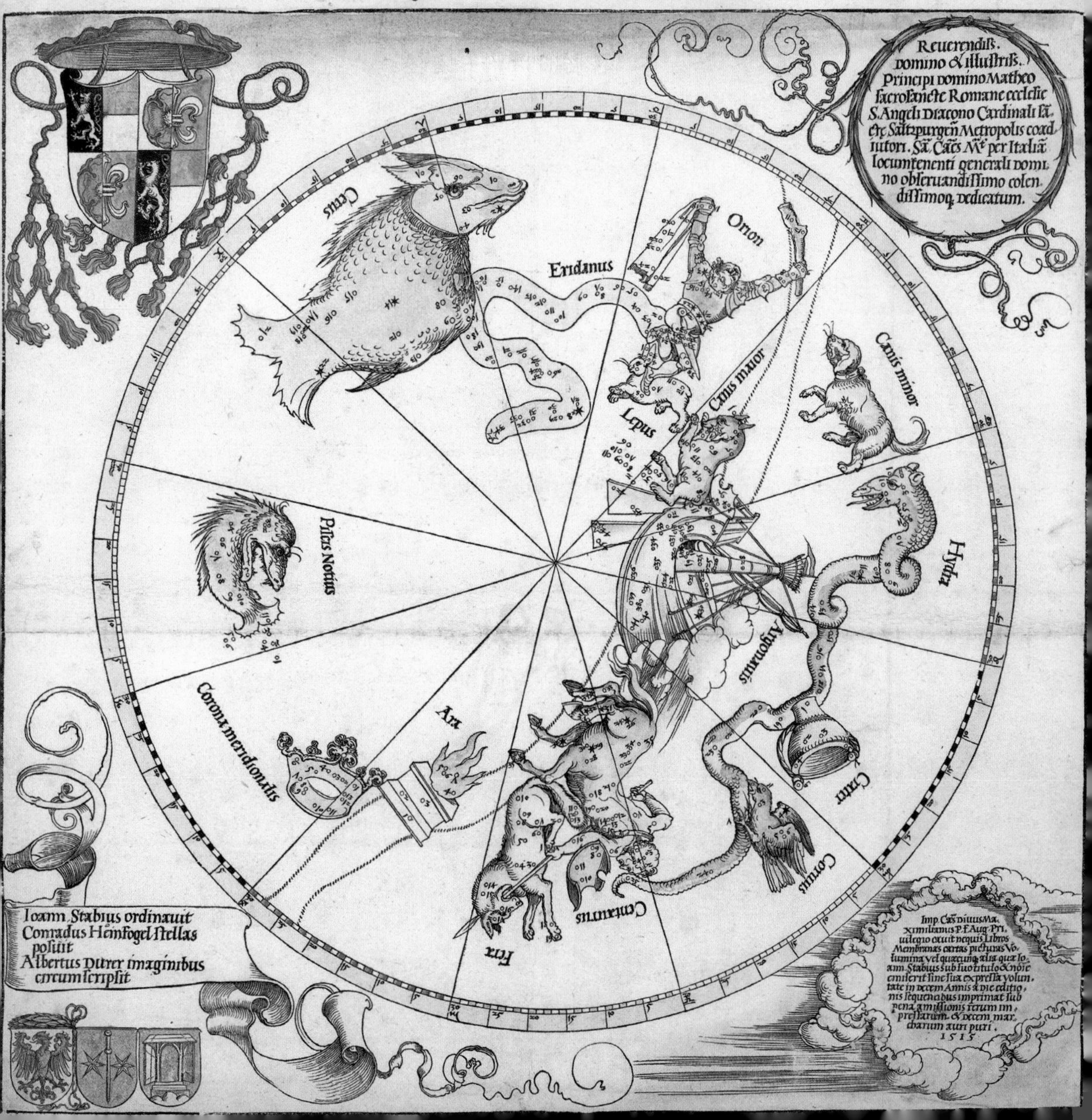

"The most spectacular contribution of the book-maker's art to sixteenth-century science"

4 **APIANUS, Petrus**

Astronomicum Caesareum.

Publication
Ingolstadt, Peter Apian, 1540.

Description
Folio (463 by 315mm), [60] ll., complete with the cancelled G3 bound at the end, title-page framed by a woodcut border, on verso of the same leaf woodcut coats-of-arms of the joint dedicatees Charles V and his brother Ferdinand of Spain, 53 eleven-line and 39 six-line historiated woodcut initials by Hans Brosamer, 36 full-page woodcut astronomical figures coloured by a contemporary hand, of which 21 have a total of 83 volvelles [complete], 39 [of 44] silk threads; and 8 [of 12] pearls, full-page woodcut arms of the author by Michael Ostendorfer on fol. O6. The leaf G3 is repeated, printed in black with variants, at the end of the volume, small letterpress cancel slip on recto of fol. K1 correcting the text, minor repair on fol. G3. Contemporary Venetian polished fawn calf on pasteboards, decorated with frames in gilt and blind, outer gilt frame with floral tools at corners, inner gilt frame with quadrilobes and small Aldine leaf tools at corner, remains of clasps.

Collation: A-F4; G5; H-N4; O6; [3].

References
Adams, A., 1277; Schottenloher, 'Landshuter Buchdrucker', 42; Benezit II, 332, & VIII, 49; Campbell Dodgson II, 242; DSB I, pp. 178-179; Lalande, p. 60; Gingerich 14; Stillwell 19; Van Ortroy 112; Zinner 1734; Solla Price, D. J. de, 'Science since Babylon', New Haven 1975, p. 104; Gingerich, Owen, 'Apianus's Astronomicum Caesareum', 'Journal for the History of Astronomy', 2 (1971), pp. 168-177; Poulle 1.83; Gingerich, O., 'A Survey of Apian's Astronomicum Caesareum', in Peter Apian, ed. by Karl Röttel, Buxheim 1995, p. 113.

First edition of "the most luxurious and intrinsically beautiful scientific book that has ever been produced" (D.J. de Solla Price, 'Science since Babylon', p. 104), in an extraordinary hand coloured example in first issue, as attested by the repeated fol. G3 and by the letterpress cancel slip on fol. K1r, preserved in a beautiful contemporary Venetian binding.

"[T]he most spectacular contribution of the book-maker's art to sixteenth-century science" (Gingerich, 'Apianus's Astronomicum Caesareum', p. 168).

The author of this popular textbook of astronomy is Peter Bienevitz (1501-1552), better known as Petrus Apianus (1495-1552), astronomer and professor of mathematics at Ingolstadt, a pioneer in the production of astronomical and geographical devices. The 'Astronomicum Caesareum' took Apianus eight years to produce and was printed in his private press at Ingolstadt.

The handbook is divided in two parts: the first (ll. B1-M3) includes 40 chapters with maps reproducing the position and the movement of celestial bodies, while the second part describes the meteroscope, an instrument designed to solve problems in spherical trigonometry, and relates the sighting of five comets. "The Astronomicum is notable for Apian's pioneer observations of comets (he describes the appearances and characteristics of five comets, including Halley's) and his statement that comets point their tails away from the sun. Also important is his imaginative use of simple mechanical devices, particularly volvelles, to provide information on the position and movement of celestial bodies" (DSB., I, p. 179). For the dissemination of calculating technology in a standardized and reproducible form, Poulle has compared the appearance of 'paper instruments' to nothing less than the advent of printing (see 'Les instruments de la théorie des planètes', 1.83).

The present example represents one of the most complete to ever have appeared on the market: the Horblit copy lacked 23 volvelles and one pearl, while the Honeyman copy lacked seven volvelles, one silk thread and nine pearls.

CANCER
GEMINI
TAVRVS
ARIES
PISCES
AQVARIVS
CAPRICORN
SAGITTARIVS
SCORPIVS
VIRGO
LEO
LATITVDO LVNAE SEPTENTRIO
LATITVDO LVNAE MERIDIOLIS
VMBRA TERRE
CAVDA
CAPVT

F III

IVLIVS
AVGVSTVS
IVNIVS
SEPTEMBER
OCTOBER
NOVEMBER
DECEMBER
IANVARIVS
FEBRVARIVS
MARTIVS
ANNI CVRRENTES
ANNI CVRRENTES
VMBRA TERRE

¶ Cautela obseruanda in dispositione rotarum.

Operandi modus huius secundi instrumenti verus qdem & certus est, quoties annus currens siue propositus in arcu limbi inferioris rotæ ab indice X Y procedendo secundum dierꝝ ordinem, usqꝫ ad 29 diem Ianuarii, horam 12, Mi. 44 siue stellam lunæ sic depictam ✳☽ reperitur. Annus ille cum filo (vt prius dictũ est) signatur, eidemqꝫ denuo index XY adducitur, qui inuariatus ad operationis finem sic perdurabit. Si uero post primam siue radicalem indicis locationem annus ꝓpositus à stella prædicta (supputatione secundum dierum ordinem facta) usqꝫ ad indicem X Y occurrat, iam dictæ stellæ centrum inspice, ꝑ huncqꝫ filũ tende, cui subducis indicem T. Mox deinceps filum ducatur per ꝓpositum siue currentem annum, ubi intersectio fili cum circulo T diem tantũ, aut diem horamqꝫ dabit. Dies ille tandem in limbo Ianuarii requisitus, cum filo signatur, eidemqꝫ denuo ostensor X Y subiungitur, ita autem rota illa ultimum sui locum sortita est. Atqui nunc mihi uideor satis superqꝫ positionem rotæ X Y declarasse, admonens interim, ut similia de rota Z V intelligantur, qualia de rota X Y prodita sunt, interesse tamen hoc vnum quod hic considerandus erit index Z V, & centrum stellæ iuxta 27 Ian: diem signatæ cũ charactere draconis sic ✳☊

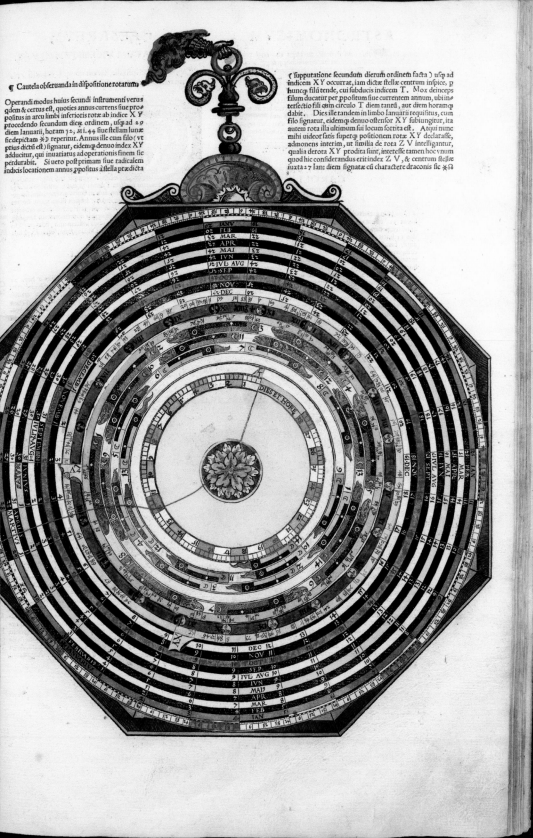

ENVNCTIATVM TRICESIMVM SEPTIM.

Cyclum Solarẽ, Literam dominicalem, annunq; Bisexti-lem, Interuallum & concurrentes, per instrumentum præ-sens velocissimè consequi.

Solaris vnde dicatur.

CYCLVS SOLIS COMPREHENdit 28 annos. Solaris vocat⁹, nõ ideo, quia Sol tãto tẽporis interuallo cursum suũ ꝑficiat signiferũ peragrãdo, sed qđ in 28 annis varietates vniuersæ quæ in litera Solari, id est, dominicali, anno Bisextili, diebusq; concurrentibus eueniunt ad sua principia pristinumq; statum reuertuntur. Aequo annorũ curriculo Bisextilis vna cum communi anno nullas non ferias seu dies hebdomadæ occupant, id est, tanto annorũ lapsu omnes literæ Calendarii dominicales fiunt, ex bisextilibus duobus integra septimana conflatur. Annus autem Solaris diebus 365 constat Iulio Cæsari primum obseruatus, Huius principium cum à meridie summas, sequentis anni principium vesperi post meridiem cæpturum est eiusdem diei quo prius cæpit, Secundus annus media nocte auspicabitur eiusdem diei, aliquid amplius iam promouens, Tertius non eundem magis diem sed auroram sequentem exordio suo vendicabit, sicut & quarto anno eiusdem diei meridies rursus principium dabitur, quamobrẽ dies integra intercalatur quarto quouis anno, id quod fit 6 Kalendas Martii, iterumq; annus incipit in eiusdem diei meridie velũt antea. Intercalatio ista nullibili commodius fieri potest, quàm in Februario, eò quod mensis ille omnium breuissimus sit, quamobrem Sexto Kalendas Martias, qui est 24 Februarii dies hoc confieri assolet. Scribitur autem sexto Kalendas bis, literaq; F bis repetitur, quam ob causam annus intercalaris etiam Bisextilis vocatur, quasi Bis sex Kalendas Martias habens. Illi vero duo dies pro vno numerari solent. Tanta autem intercalationis huiusmodi necessitas incumbit, vt nisi fieret, dies natiuitatis Dominicæ aliâs in spacio 728 annorum in diem Ioannis Baptistæ recisurus, reliqua vero festa per dimidium annum euariatura sint. Quanq̃ autem singulis quatuor annis intercalatio iteretur, nihilominus tamen, quia annus non ad vnguem adeo 365 dierum & 6 horarum est, ephemeris seu Calendarium, sicut videre licet, adhuc inemendatum nobis durat, velut in sequentibus dicetur fusius. E cyclo Solari, literam dominicalem, annos & Cõmunes & Bisextos, Diesq; cõcurrentes venamur.

Annus Bisextilis quis sit & vnde dicatur.

Operandi modus.

¶ Per figuram sequentem indagare qui cupiet ea, primum è propinqua hic tabula propositi numeri centenarium minorem anno post Christum accepto eliget. Numerus huic centenario collateralis Solaris cyclus vocabitur, eundem in instrumenti limbo extremo seu ampliori videns cũ indice X exprime. Annum post hac in circulo spirali propositum require, ab inuento limbum vsq; extimum recta traiicito, in quo numerum cycli Solaris in interiori literam dominicalem reperies. Si litera dominicalis vna dumtaxat offenditur, annum dices communem, si duplex, annus bisextilis nuncupabitur. Prior autem seu superior literarum dominicalis erit à anni principio in 24 Februarii diem, Secunda vel inferior à 24 die Februarii in finem anni vsq;. Quemadmodum anno nati Redemptoris nostri reperiuntur 9 prope radicem (qui numerus si Dionisio abbati, cognomẽto exiguo, fidem habemus) eo tempore Cyclus Solaris extitit. D C literæ dominicales, quarũ D vsq; ad Matthiæ festum dominicas docuit, C ad anni exitum.

Exemplum CAROLI. Imperatoris.

¶ CAROLI Imperatoris nati Centenarius est 1500, quo in tabula perspecto 25 iuxta Cyclus scz Solaris exhibet, quem numerũ 25 in limbo exteriore querenti E D literæ dominicales offerentur, indicantes CAROLVM esse anno Bisextili genitum.

Exemplũ Regis FERDINANDI.

¶ Regẽ FERDINANDVM anno currenti 1503 natum nouimus. 1500 centenarius dat 25, vt antea, in tabula, quæ in limbo quæsita, index X signet, in circuloq; spirali 3 reliquis annis inuentis, ab hiis directè ad limbum exteriorem promouendo, ibidem 28 cyclus videlicet Solaris, in proximo litera dominicalis A inuenietur.

Rhomæ cõditæ cyclus Solaris, litera dominicalis, interuallum &c̃ quę extiterunt.

¶ Quo pacto & ante Christum sit agendum vno exemplo docebẽris. Tempus igitur Romæ conditæ 753 anni completi ante Seruatorem fuisse feruntur. Centenarius inde maior 800 acceptus, & in tabula examinatus 21 collateralia dabit, quibus in limbo quæsitis, index X sublocabitur, 753 deinde ab 800 subtracta 47 relinquunt annũ currentem, in quo vrbs extrui cæpit. In circulo igitur gyroso 47 requisita, supra se cyclum Solarem 12, literamq; Dominicalem G huic numero congruum ostendent. Bisextilem annum alia quoq; ratione & expeditissima potes scire sic. Si propositum annorum numerum per 4 diuidas & nihil redundet, annus propositus Bisextilis est, sed hoc in annis post Christum numeratis. Ante vero hoc pacto agis. Propositum à centenario maiore demes, dempti summam deinde per 4 secabis, velũti in hoc priori vrbis fundatæ exemplo patet, in quo Rhoma tertio anno post Bisextum condita videbatur, cum enim 753 annos post fundationem scz ad Christum elapsos ab 800 subtrahas, 47 remanent, quibus diuisis per 4 supersunt 3, quæ annum tertium post Bisextilem fuisse indicant, Retro ergo à Christo computanti, 754 anni completi occurrunt. Literę Dominicalis subinde variatæ causa est duplex. Vna quod in anno Bisextili 24 die Februarii, f, f, litera bis confestim iteretur, vnde contingit necessariò, sequentes literas vniuersas integro diei spacio transponi, velũti hoc exemplo. CAROLVM Cæsarem anno Bisextili ortum accepim⁹ 24 Februarii, quo die literæ incipiunt diuersificari siue mutari dominicè, Vicesimoquarto enim die f litera apparet, diem Lunæ referens, quoniam E dominicalis in 24 vsq; diẽ fuit. Quãdoquidẽ aut intercalaris nomine F litera 25 diei quoq; tribuitur, f hoc loco dies Martis appellabitur, tametsi g hucusq; Martis signaturã gesserit. Qm̃ autẽ annus ita totus vno die nunc super aggregato procedat, nõ illepide à germanis ain Schalt iar dicitur, Schalten enim Germani ꝓpriè vocãt, qđ latini circũloquẽtes, manus ꝓmouere vel ꝓtrudere, vel vt sic dicã, ꝓgere vocãt, fur schiben, Shaltẽ enim & furtschibẽ idem diuersis natiõibus est. Alterã causam efficit finis anni principiũq; A litera signatum vtrumq;. Sequela siquidẽ literarũ A A duarũ facit vt dominicalis nõ variari non possit, sicut in anno Bisextili apparet, vt Anno Domini 1502 dominicalis litera B habita est, oportuit ergo literã A diem Saturni possedisse, est autẽ A litera diei 31 Decẽbris. Cũ itaq; nouissima Decembris Sabati dies sit, necessario primã sequentis anni (in quo nat⁹ est rex FERDINANDVS) qui semper ab A incipit dominicã diẽ fuisse cõuincitur, ideoq; A litera quæ in anno FERDINANDI dominicalis esse debebat, mutata est. Cũ iã pleræq; de dominica die meminerimus, nõ videbatur abs re esse, si adhuc manifestiora de eadẽ festiuitate dominica in sequẽtib⁹ sui vsum fr[illegible]tiorẽ exhibitura in pręsentia tractarem. Christiana itaq; ecclesia, quod Iudei Sabatũ, dominicũ diẽ nominauit, a Saturni in Solis diẽ digressa nõ temere, cũ enim Solis die Christ⁹ & nat⁹ sit & mortis victor, nos eodẽ die vitę triumphans restituerit, qs miretur? nõ potius hũc diẽ quàm Sabbati? in quo nihil tale nobis euenerit colere quid cũ Iudeis festiuitate nõ participaremus? à qbus omnis nostra religio abhorrere merito debet. A Iudeis autẽ dies Solis prima Sabbati vel feria prima, antiquitus dies Solis, sicut & nobis (der Sonnentag) appellatur, velũti Iudei rursus secundã Sabbati, quã veteres diẽ Lunę, nos (den Montag) dicimus. Restat nũc vt dicamus de internullo breuibus. ¶ Interuallũ spaciũ est, dierũ illud quod inter natiuitatis festũ & dominicã Esto mihi vel Quinquagesimã intercidit, reliqui vero dies à natiuitate vsq; ad proximã dominicam CONCVRRENTES nominantur. Cũ autẽ per literas dominicales hacten⁹ interuallũ & festa mobilia inueniri solita sint, alium hoc loco inquirẽdi modũ præscribã, ita vt se vltro & sine negotio querẽtis offerãt. Cõcurrentes tantũmodo per regulã inuenire docebo. Regula. Literam dominicalem intuere, quæ si A est, cõcurrentem o esse scito, Si B tũ cõcurrens est 1 &c̃. vt patet hoc versu.

A o. B 1. C 2. D 3. E 4. F 5. G 6.

Hoc adiecto de anno Bisextili, cuius litera dominicalis prior sedulo accipi debet secunda neglecta. Quod ad festa mobilia & interuallum attinet, in sequenti enunctiato transigetur, vbi de paschate verba fient.

SEQVVNTVR RADICES CENTENARIORVM CYCLI SOLARIS.

TAB V
CYCLI
LARI

Centenarii annorum ante & post Christi aduentum. Ann.	Radices post Christum annis labẽtibus respondẽtes.	
Christi	9	Chri
100	25	10
200	13	20
300	1	30
400	17	40
500	5	50
600	21	60
700	9	70
800	25	80
900	13	90
1000	1	100
1100	17	110
1200	5	120
1300	21	130
1400	9	140
1500	25	150
1600	13	160
1700	1	170
1800	17	180
1900	5	190
2000	21	200
2100	9	21
2200	25	22
2300	13	23
2400	1	24
2500	17	25
2600	5	26
2700	21	27
2800	9	28
2900	25	29
3000	13	30
3100	1	31
3200	17	32
3300	5	33
3400	21	34
3500	9	35
3600	25	36
3700	13	37
3800	1	38
3900	17	39
4000	5	40
4100	21	41
4200	9	42
4300	25	43
4400	13	44
4500	1	45
4600	17	46
4700	5	47
4800	21	48
4900	9	49
5000	25	50
5100	13	51
5200	1	52
5300	17	53
5400	5	54
5500	21	55
5600	9	56
5700	25	57
5800	13	58
5900	1	59
6000	17	60
6100	5	61
6200	21	62
6300	9	63
6400	25	64
5600	13	65
6600	1	66
6700	17	67
6800	5	68
6900	21	69
7000	9	70

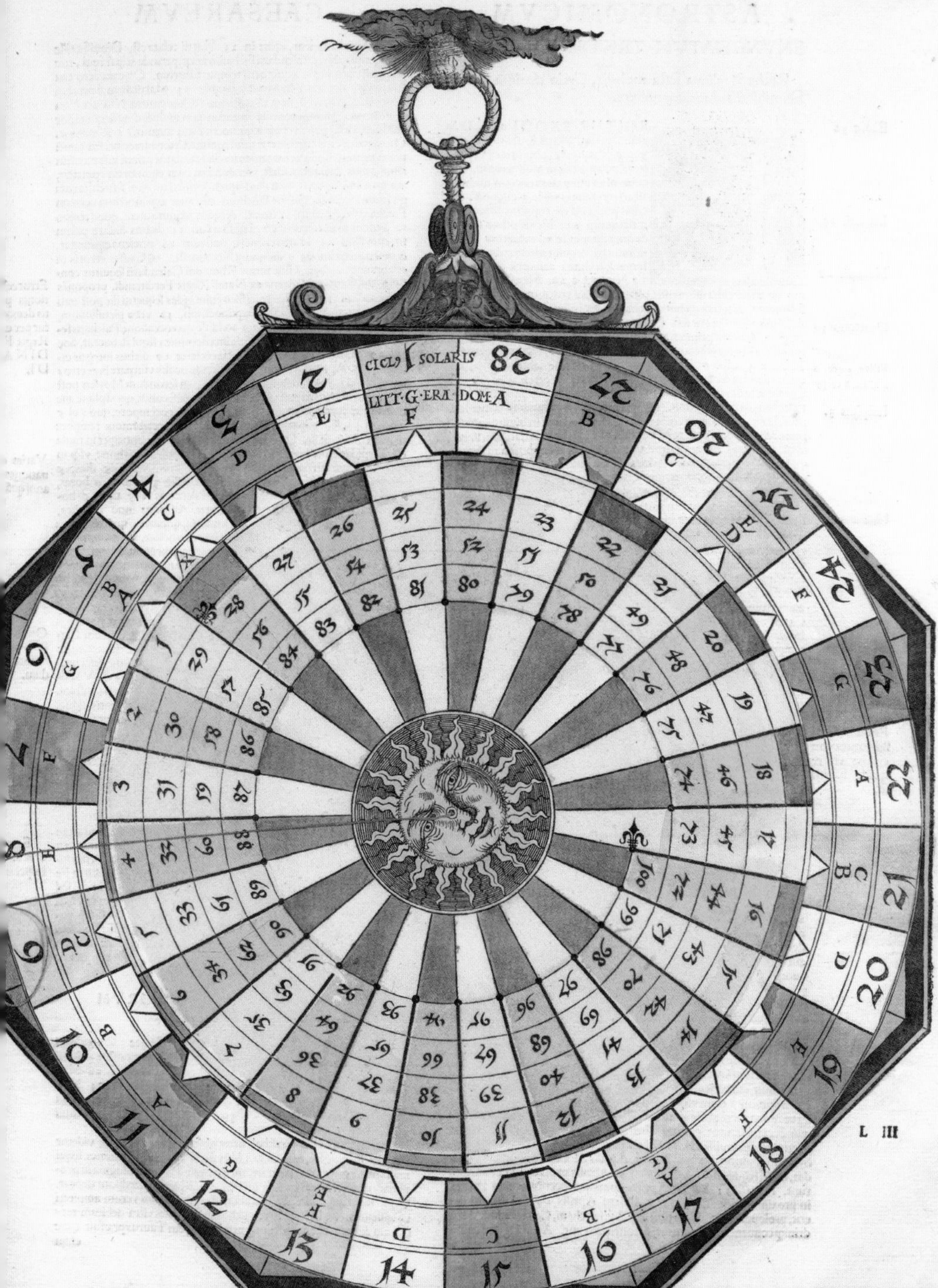
CICLI SOLARIS
LITT·G·ERA·DOM·A

The 1540 and 1550 Latin editions' of Apianus's 'Cosmographia' bound in one volume

5 **APIANUS, Petrus; Gemma Frisius**

Cosmographia, per Gemmam Phrysium, apud Lovaniensis Medicum ac Mathematicum ...

Publication
Antwerp, Arnoldo Berckmano [Birckman]; [and] Gregorio Bontio [de Bonte], 1540 [and] 1550.

Description
Two works in one volume, quarto (225 by 150mm), woodcut globe on title, numerous woodcut illustrations and diagrams, five with volvelles, woodcut historiated initials and publisher's device at end, manuscript leaf on vellum over pasteboard, spine rubbed.

A compilation comprising the 1540 and 1550 Latin editions, two volumes in one. Quarto, 62 leaves and 68 leaves respectively (complete), large woodcut of a globe to both titles, numerous woodcut maps, charts, and diagrams, the 1550 edition with the large folding cordiform map, both editions featuring woodcuts with volvelles as follows: first work c2v (1 attachment, 1 volvelle); h1r (3 volvelles); m1r (2 volvelles); second work c2v (1 attachment, 1 volvelle); D1v (1 attachment, 3 volvelles, 2 threads); H2r (2 volvelles); O3r (2 volvelles).

References
Van Ortroy 31 & 39; Sabin 1752; Shirley, World 82.

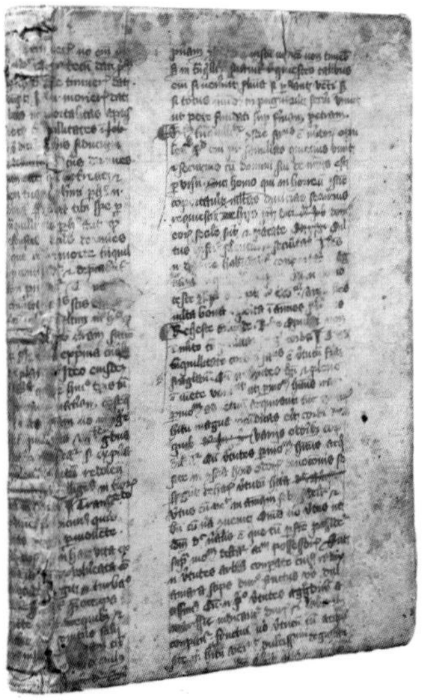

One of the most important German contributions to geography of the Renaissance and one of the first works to base geography on mathematics and measurement.

Peter Bienevitz (1501-52), better known as Petrus Apianus (1495-1552), was professor of mathematics and astronomy, holding chairs at Ingolstadt and Innsbruck. First published in 1524, the 'Cosmographia' was his first major work. It covers "the division of the earth into climatic zones, the uses of parallels and meridians, the determination of latitude, several methods for determining longitude including that of lunar distance, the use of trigonometry to determine distances, several types of map projections, and many other topics" (Karrow). Further, from 1533, editions of the 'Cosmographia' also included Gemma Frisius's treatise on topographical triangulation, in which he was the first person to propose it as a means of locating and mapping places: a landmark in the history of cartography.

The 'Cosmographia' is said to be one of the most popular books on cosmography ever published. It went through no fewer than 45 editions, was published in four languages, and was manufactured in seven cities, by at least 18 printers. This popularity derived principally from its maps and discussion of the New World, but also for its ingenious use of volvelles. Indeed, Frisius's revisions to the work include a fourth volvelle showing the phases of the moon, not present in the original edition.

The large world map, a reduced version of Apianus's celebrated cordiform world map 'Charta Cosmographica' after Waldseemüller's map of 1507, is important for being one of the earliest to show the entire east coast of North America. The map displays the eastern side of North America as a narrow landmass, named "Baccalearum," after the cod fisheries off the coasts of New England and Canada. It employs a truncated cordiform projection, much used by Renaissance cartographers to represent the relationship between the Americas and the Old World, and maintains the tantalizing possibility of a northwest passage to Asia over the top of North America. The map is also notable for being the first printed map to depict the Yucatán as a peninsula rather than an island, anticipating Ruscelli's 1561 map of New Spain. Cuba and Hispaniola are shown as huge islands. Also prominent are the Mountains of the Moon, considered the source of the River Nile. Signs of the zodiac and the Ptolemaic climatic zones border the map. Zeus and Mars, wearing the coats-of-arms of Charles V, Holy Roman Emperor, are shown atop the map while wind-heads at the south represent the traditionally believed plague-bearing nature of those winds.

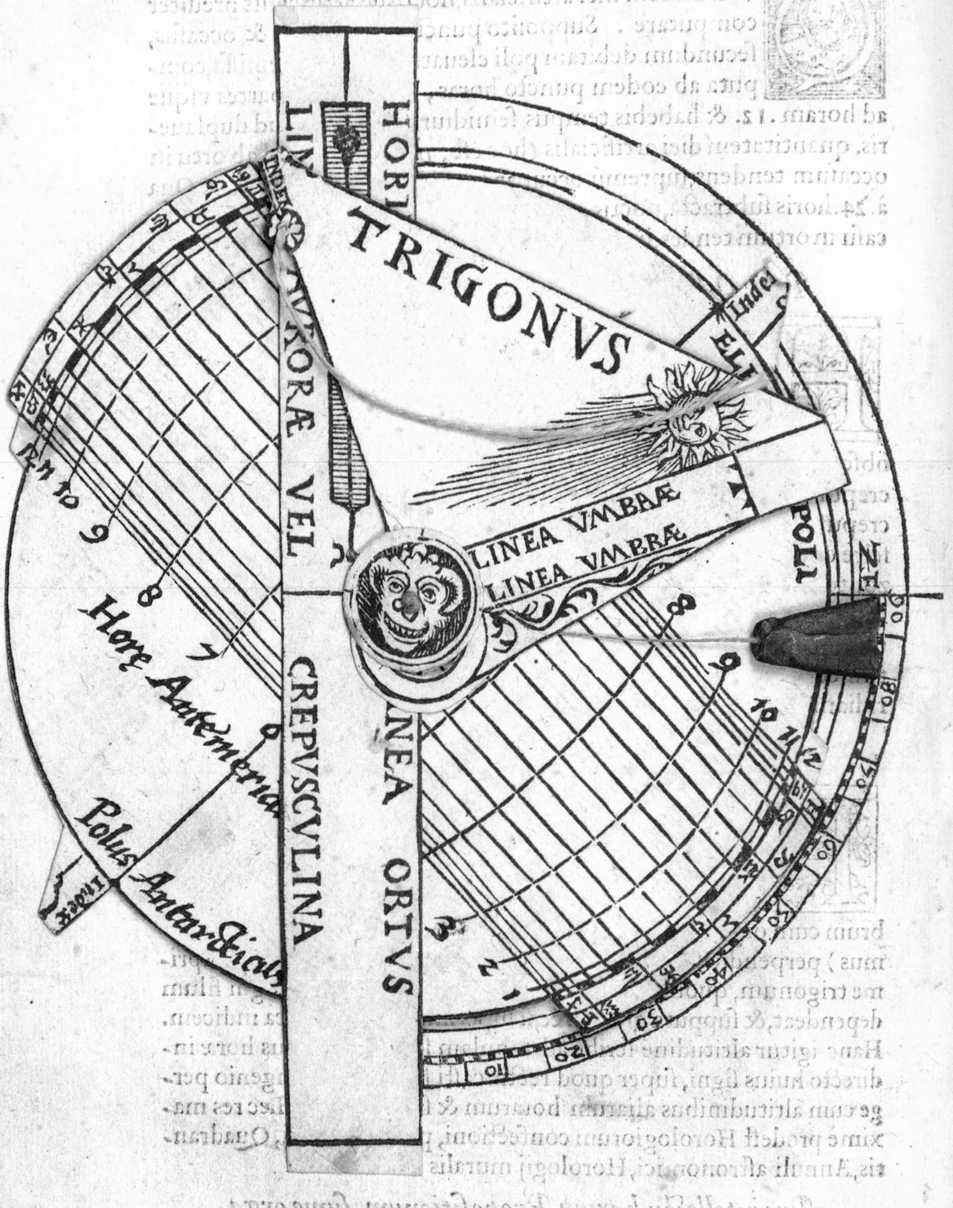
TRIGONVS
LINEA VMBRAE
LINEA VMBRAE
AVRORAE VEL
CREPVSCVLINA
LINEA ORTVS
Horae Antemeridianae
Polus Antarcticus
POLA
10
9
8
7
6
8
9
10
11
12
3
2
1

PRIMA PARS

Sphæra Mundi.

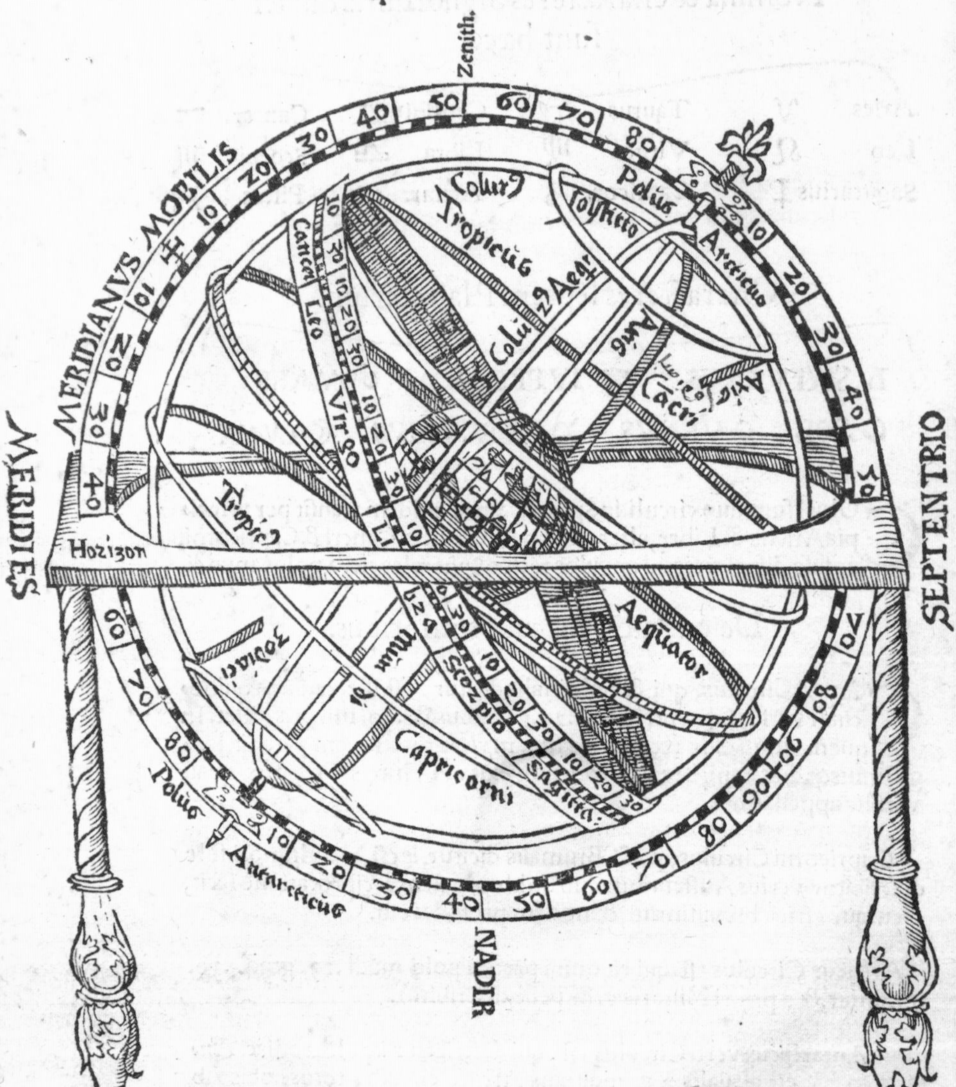

De quinq; Zonis. Cap.IIII.

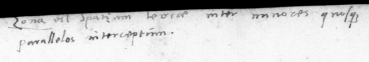

QVom terrę & aquę supficies sit vna, & sphęrica (quod eius vmbra, cū certa opaci corporis sit species, in luna ri eclipsatione apertissime demōstrat) & in medio mū di immobilis cōstituta, quinq; cœlestis sphærę circulos quemadmodum sphęra, in cōuexitate sua cōplectitur. Aequinoctialem sc3 & Tropicos & Arcticos circulos. Qui pręter æquinoctialē, in cœlo quinq; zonas, toti dēq; in terris plagas cōstituunt. Quarū duæ circa polos extremæ frigo re semp horrentes, vix habitabiles existunt. Tertia in omniū medio in ter tropicos sita, propter continuū solis discursum, & ob radiorū solis per pēdicularitatē, terra seu plaga adusta, & male aut ægre habitabilis, ratio ne discernitur. Reliquę duę q̄ tropicis arcticisq; circulis interiacēt, tem peratę & habitabiles. Temperātur enī calore torridę zonæ, & extrema rū frigore, quarū nos alterā incolimus, alterā Antœci & Antichtones.

Diuisionis præmisse formula in plano extensa.

A deluxe, illuminated and coloured example of a rare paper instrument

6 *Roemischer Kalender auss der Geometrica, auff alle jar sampt den beweglichen und unbeweglichen Festen nach den Sontags Buchstaben zuverstehen.*

Publication
[?Nuremberg or Augsburg, second half of the sixteenth century].

Description
Woodcut and typographic broadside, seven lines of letterpress text, large central woodcut roundel illustrated with signs of the zodiac, sun and moon phases space, topographical panorama, and feast days, volvelle at centre, two smaller roundels in lower corners, type-ornament border within outermost black border, coloured and illuminated by a contemporary hand, thick paper, the volvelle printed on pastepaper, verso of edges strengthened, a few neat tears repaired on verso, a few small areas of loss, some colour lightly rubbed.

Dimensions
458 by 347mm (18 by 11 inches).

References
Cf. the similar, but more complicated, Holbein/Münster sheet reproduced in Dackerman's 'Prints and the Pursuit of Knowledge', Harvard, 2011, pp. 306-7.

A wall calendar with volvelle. Although few survive today, calendars formed a regular part of the print trade from the fifteenth century onwards and were produced at various levels of sophistication and expense. They range from simple, cheaply produced versions to elaborate examples of great artistry, such as Hans Holbein's Sun and Moon Instrument (1534). The present example is a deluxe production: its large size is impressive; the illustrative elements, such as the astrological signs and topographical panorama, are finely executed; and it offers a complex range of calculations with the volvelle. Furthermore, the present example has been carefully finished with colouring and gold highlights. The panorama, although schematic, appears to depict the Mediterranean, from Arabia (with a mosque surmounted by a crescent) in the east to the Iberian Peninsula in the west. The calendar is known in only one other copy, at the Herzog August Bibliothek in Wolfenbüttel, which lacks the volvelle and is uncoloured.

Content
1. Outermost two circles: Sunday letters, feast days.
2. Next three circles: days of the month, months, zodiacal signs, showing longitude of sun in the zodiacal signs over the course of the year, starting with Sun at beginning of Aries on 10 March.
3. Next two circles: lengths of day, depending on the hours of sunrise/sunset, and the hours of the day in Roman numerals. For example, if the sun rises at 8 a.m. (on left) and sets at 4 p.m. (on right), the day length will be eight hours.
4. Next ten circles, with moving central volvelle with attached sector, divided into "Nachtlenge" (lower pink section) and "Tagelenge" (upper yellow section). For example, for the outermost circle, from 15 May through 11 July, the sun rises at 4 a.m. and sets at 9 p.m. giving a day length of 17 hours. The pointer on the volvelle is set to the hour of the mechanical clock (the "Grosse Uhr") and then read on the yellow or the pink sections the hour of the day or night, as counted from sunset or sunrise (the "Kleine Uhr"). Nuremberg counted hours starting at sunrise. Many towns to the east counted hours starting at sunset (Bohemian or Italian hours). The volvelle and the 10 circles permit conversion between these 3 hour-counting schemes, shifting through 9 sections of the year to adjust for the varying day lengths.
5. Small, lower right circle, "Planetenstund", illustrates which planet is ruling each hour of the day, as day lengths shift from 16 down to 8 hours. The other small, lower left circle calculates the Sunday letter for any year. The instructions say to start counting at the cross, but do not indicate what year this is. The "Schaltjar 25" is confusing, since 1524 was the Schaltjar. The cross should be 1557, 1585 or 1613.

Römischer Kalender auß der Geometria/ auff alle jar/ sampt den beweglichen vnd vnbeweglichen Festen nach den Sontags Buchstaben zuverstehen/ wie dann der vnter Zirckel außweist/ Auch wie die Sonn das gantze Jar durch die zwölff himlischen Zeichen/ Deßgleichen wann sie auff vnd nider gehet. Sampt der vergleichung der Grossen vnd Kleinen Vhrn/ vnd zu welcher zeit der tag zu vnd abnimmt/ Wie der mitler Zeiger in neun zirckelrissen der tagleng getheilt/ als 8. 9. 10. 11. 12. 13. 14. 15. 16. anzeigt. Vnd wann man auff solchen Zeiger acht hat/ in welchem Monat wir seind/ vnd ob der tag zu oder abnimt/ wie darob zu sehen/ so zeigt derselbe Circkelkreiß alle stund des tags vnd nacht/ die vergleichung der Grossen gegen der Kleinen Vhr an. Deßgleichen auch ist zu sehen/ im Planetenzirckel/ wie sich die 12. Planetenstunden/ mit der Kleinen vnd Grossen Vhr verjüngen vnd vergrössern/ bey tag vnd nacht.

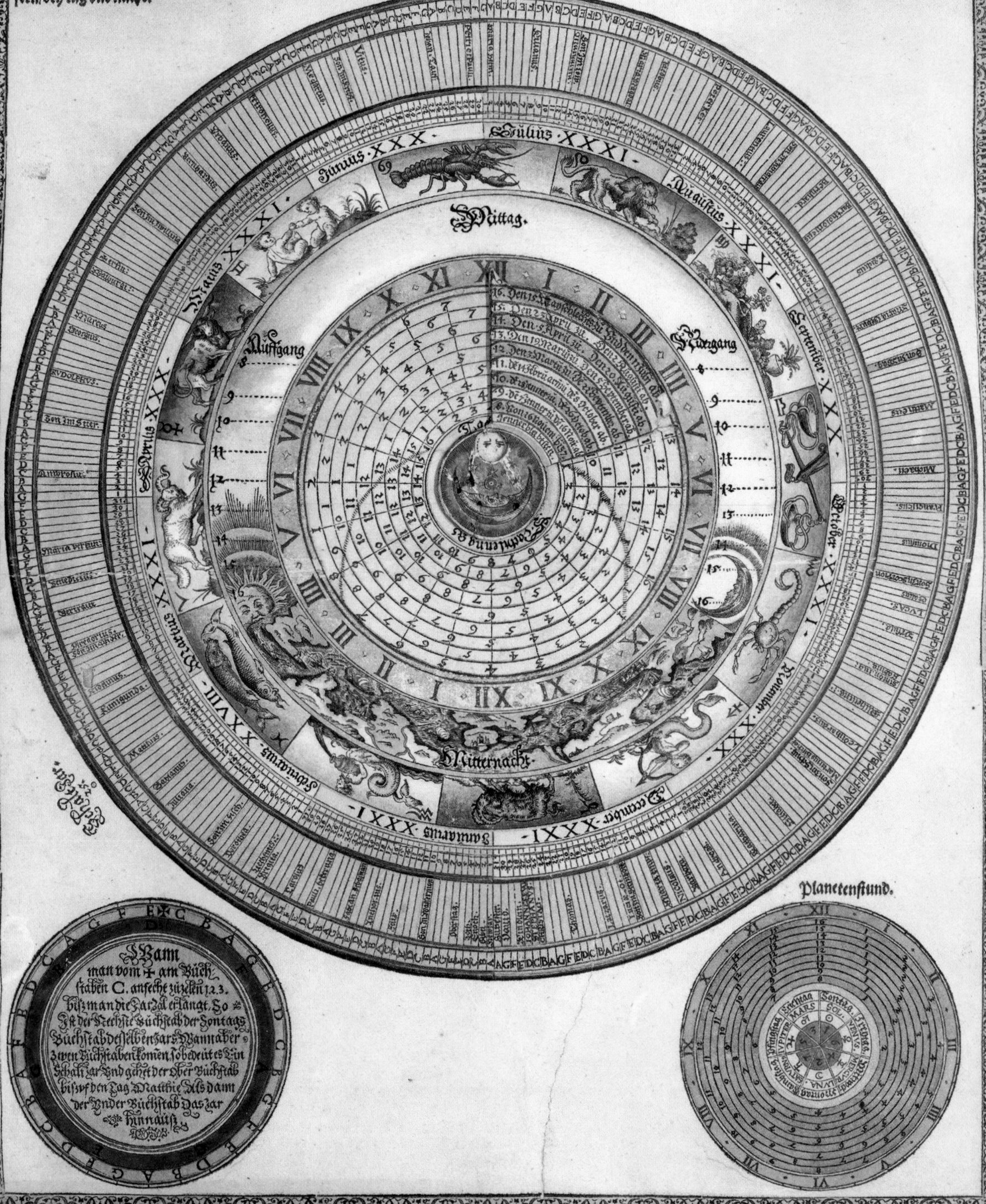

A rare sixteenth century paper astrolabe signed by the famous instrument maker Philippe Danfrie, and dated 1578

7 **DANFRIE, Philippe**

[Astrolabe].

Publication
Paris, Philippe Danfrie, 1578.

Description
Engraving mounted on a solid oak board, suspension by brass ring, missing a few small areas of printed paper on the rete.

Dimensions
Diameter 216 mm; depth 18mm.

References
Turner, A.J., 'Paper, Print and Mathematics: Philippe Danfrie and the making of mathematical instruments in late sixteenth century Paris', in 'Studies in the History of Scientific Instruments', 1989, pp. 22-42; Gunther, 'The Astrolabes of the World', 1932, pp. 358-359; Daumas, 'Les instruments scientifiques aux XVIIème & XVIIIème siècles', 1953, p. 24.

Philippe Danfrie (c. 1532-1606) was born in Brittany and moved to Paris in his twenties, where he became a partner in a printing and bookselling business. He designed a new typeface in cursive script, which was given the name of "caractère de civilité". He later studied mathematics, became an "ingénieur", and was appointed royal die cutter for coins of the realm. Danfrie took a special interest in inexpensive alternatives to brass instruments. He is known for some 20 mathematical instruments, notably his astrolabes printed on paper, and for his invention of the graphomètre, on which he published in 1597.

We are only aware of five other surviving Danfrie paper astrolabes: one dated 1578, incomplete (missing one of the seven plates [with brass rete]) sold at Christie's South Kensington in 1998; another dated 1578 belongs to the Service hydrographique de la Marine; one dated 1584 described by Tesseract; another dated 1584 belongs to the Museum of the History of Science Oxford; a further 1584 at the National Museum of American History, Smithsonian Institution, Washington DC.

Horizon Rectus
Linea

The Gregorian Calendar

8 **CARRARINO, Antonio**

Theorica della Compositione dell'Universo et delle cause della Nuova riforma dell'anno.

Publication
Rome, 1582.

Description
Engraving with etching, signed and dated in the lower right part of the plate, on laid paper with watermark "Easter lamb in the double circle", small woodworm holes and minor defects, skilfully repaired.

Dimensions
245 by 315mm (9.75 by 12.5 inches).

References
Rossi, L. F. de, 'Indice Dele Stampe', Rome, 1729, p. 12, No. 14.

A rare separately published plate containing information on cosmography and the new Gregorian Calendar.

This extremely rare plate was published in the year 1582 – the inception of the Gregorian Calendar. The work is dedicated to Cardinal Luigi d'Este (1538-1586), a great patron of the arts and sciences, and gives a brief overview of contemporary cosmographical thought and the reasons for the adoption of the new calendar.

To the centre of the work is a depiction of a Ptolemaic universe – the prevailing model of the universe at the time – with the earth and the elements (water, air, and fire) at its centre, surrounded by ten spheres: the Moon, Mercury, Venus, the Sun, Mars, Jupiter, Saturn, the Stars, the Universe, and the Prime Mover (i.e. God). Below are depictions of lunar and solar eclipses together with an armillary sphere. Below this is a representation of the Julian and Gregorian calendar for the year 1582. To the left and right is a text on the veracity of the Ptolemaic model of the Universe. To the lower right is a brief text on the reasons for the adoption of the new calendar, of which the overriding one was religious. The date for the celebration of Easter had, by the sixteenth century, shifted by some ten days from the original date as enshrined in the Treaty of Nicaea (AD 325); the Catholic Church saw this drift as undesirable. To achieve the recalibration, the reform altered the calendar through two fundamental measures. The first consisted of the drastic and immediate shift of the date to the astronomical position, suddenly jumping ten calendar days; therefore in 1582, from Thursday 5th October there was a jump to Friday 16th October. The Pope's second measure was to modify the leap years' rule in order to avoid that the day would shift again in the future.

Antonio Carrarino (fl.1581-1615) was an Italian author and engraver from Orvieto. He appears to have moved to Rome in the early 1580s, where he produced several important scientific and medical works.

A crucial and extremely rare astronomical work, previously known only in one incomplete example in the British Museum that is missing a considerable part of the engraved surface.

THEORICA DELLA COMPOSITIONE DELL'VNIVERSO ET DELLE CAVSE DELLA NVOVA RIFORMA DELL'ANNO

Fatta da m. Antonio Carrarino.

Auuertiranno i benigni lettori che si e posta la Sfera materiale in quest'opera per mostrar a ciascuno i quattro punti principali di essa Sfera i quali dalli dotti sono chiamati Cardinali, & in questi punti essendoci occorsi misterij Grandi tirate da queste occasione seruiranno per cognitione delle cause della nuoua riforma dell'Anno come chiaramente nelli discorsi si uede.

AL' ILL.MO ET R.MO S.R DON LVIGI D'ESTE CAR.LE DELLA S.TA ROMANA CHIESA.

Volendo io far uedere al Mondo la Theorica della compositione dell'Uniuerso, & delle cause della nuoua riforma dell'Anno, ho deliberato di publicarla sotto il nome di V. S. Ill.ma perche si come l'opera è composta di materie nobilissime, così non hò io saputo trouare scorta ne più nobile, ne più eccelsa di lei. Degnisi per sua benignità accettar gratam.te questa mia fatica, & me insieme per suo humiliss. & diuotiss. Seruo, che per tale me le dedico, & dono, pregando N. S.re Dio che la faccia compitamente felice.

Di V. S. Ill.ma & R.ma

Humil.mo et diuot.mo Seruo
Ant.o Carrarino.

DIVISIONE DI TVTTA LA SFERA DELL'VNIVERSO NELLE SVE PARTI PIV PRINCIPALI

Con l'aiuto del Omnipotente, et eterno Iddio daren principio alle nostre considerationi intorno alla Sfera del Mondo douiamo primieramente sapere, che questa gran machina, di cui parliam, et che noi Mondo chiamiamo, fu da quel sapientissimo, et potentissimo Architetto, che con diuina prouidentia, et arte di nulla la produsse, fabricata così ampia, et così capace; acciò che ella commodamente chiudere, et contener dentro di se potesse, tà tante et sì diuerse cose, che in marauigliosa varietà, parimente egli creò di nulla, et lasciò soggette al ben ordinato gouerno della Natura. Onde se bene in diuersi modi si può considerare questa machina diuisa, principalmente et sostantialmente in due parti, ò uero Regioni: l'una delle quali celeste si domandi, et diuina; et l'altra elementare, et men nobile. La prima, si come trasparente, luminosa, et ben regolata nella più alta parte dell'vniuerso si fa vedere; così parimente immortale, perpetua, et libera da corrottione è ella per sua natura: quantunque quella diuina assoluta potentia, che la produsse, possa et distruggere, et ridurre in nulla.

L'altra parte poi domandata elementare, si come varia, fallace, et ignobile nel più basso sito di questa della machina si stà riposta, così medesimamente sottoposta à corrottione, et per conseguentia frale, et caduca si dee stimare. Hor ciascheduna delle dette Regioni si diuide in altri parti, percioche l'elementare uien ad esser posseduta da quattro elementi, da i quali ella è così chiamata. questi sono il fuoco, l'aria, l'acqua, et la terra; de i quali quattro corpi, come sempli, et puri so composti tutti gli altri corpi inferiori, ò più nobilmente ò manco, secondo 'l grado delle cose generabili, et corrottibili, alla compositione, et destruttione delle quali, essi concorrono con il mezo de i quattro gran ministri della Natura, che sono il caldo, il freddo, l'humido, e 'l secco, et quanto alle figure, à i siti, et alle grandezze loro, ne dirò più di sotto.

Diremo phora, che la terra si troua grauissima, come quella nella quale discese s'adunaro, et rimase ogni purgamento, et ogni feccia, et parte più grossa degli altri elementi, et conseguentemente di tutto 'l Mondo. però che hauendo per lor natura tutte le cose graui hauuto impeto d'andare al basso verso 'l centro dell'vniuerso; si come per il contrario le leggieri di discostarsene più che possono; viene la terra per la sua grauezza à restringersi per se stessa verso 'l detto centro, nè tutta insieme punto da quel si muoue. posciache per esser sommamente graue, nò può muouersi verso 'l cielo, ne dal cielo parimente può ella essere più di quel che sia, trouandosi nel centro stesso.

L'acqua poi per esser ancor in lei più la grauezza, che la leggerezza, quantunque men graue sia che la terra, nò dimmeno uolentieri ancor ella cerca d'andare à basso. Et non è dubbio alcuno, che se la terra non la impedisse, la quale, come graue ha occupato il più basso luogo, si ridurrebbe ancor ella al centro del Mondo tutto. Ma sendo ella impedita dalla terra, come si è detto, non potendo far più, si posa sopra di essa terra: et la circonderebbe d'ogni intorno, se per le ragioni che per breuità le lascio, nò fusse necessitata à lasciarla scoperta per molte parti. L'aere poi che sta diffuso sopra della terra, et dell'acqua, uolentieri sopra innalzandosi con la sua leggierezza, salirebbe sino all'estremo della Regione elementare; se non gli fusse ciò diuietato dal fuoco, che come più leggieri, l'altissimo sito si ha occupato tra gli elementi. Onde l'aere sotto del fuoco restando, cinge d'ogni intorno l'acqua, et la terra, come si è detto; nel qual luogo stando, non ha egli maggior impeto di discender che di salire. Ma il fuoco, come ellemento di maggior purità, et di più schietta leggierezza, sopra dell'aria ha il suo luogo, et con la Regione celeste si accosta, et confina, et l'aria per ogni parte racchiude, et circonda. Hora tornando alla Regione celeste, lucida, et chiara, la quale à nissuna varietà, ò mutatione obligata, saluo che al mouimento di luogo à luogo, sta meritamente in alta parte collocata, eccelsa, et sublime, in modo che la Regione elementare d'ogni intorno circonda et racchiude, parimente ancor ella in più parti è diuisa. Conciosia che secondo gli Astrologi dei nostri tempi, contiene in se dieci Sfere, ò Orbi, ò Cieli che gli uogliamo chiamare; de i quali l'uno cinge, et circonda l'altro, saluo che l'ultimo uerso noi, ch'è quel della Luna il quale per esser il più basso, non può circondare alcun altro Cielo, ma solo cinge d'ogni intorno la Sfera del fuoco. Parimente il decimo cielo, per essere il più sublime di tutti agli altri cieli naturali, nò ha sopra di se altro cielo naturale, che lo giri, et racchiuda: dico, naturale, perche se ben ha sopra di se il cielo empireo il quale habbiamo da creder che sia il luoco beato della felice patria degli eletti; tuttauia per esser egli sopra della natura, et nò sottoposto à natural mouimento nò ha da cader nella considerazione degli Astrologi né nel numero con altri cieli naturali.

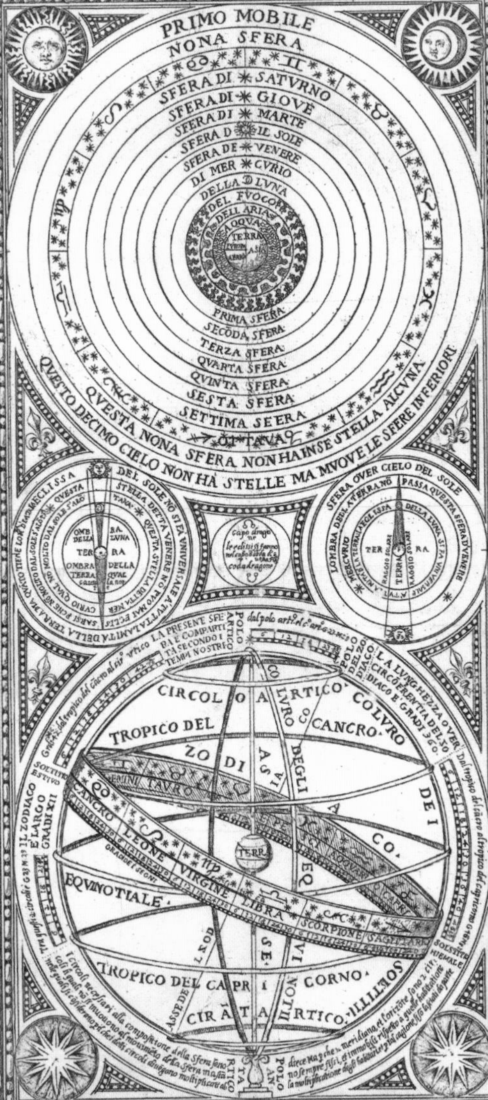

COME SI POSSA PROVARE CHE LE SFERE CELESTI SIANO DI NVMERO DIECI

Douiam sapere che da tutti i Filosofi, et antiqui, et moderni, che di tal cose hanno trattato, si tiene per cosa fermissima, che le stelle nò si mouino per se stesse, essendo cosa in uero fuora di ragione che disgiunte da i lor orbi, si muouino per se medesime, come quasi à uolontà. Ma tengan ferma oppenione che le si muouino al mouimento de i lor orbi, nei quali stieno infisse, nella guisa che noi veggiamo star saldi i nodi in una traue di legno; di maniera che si come mentre che tal nodi nò si separano da quella traue non si muouono punto per se stessi separatamente; ma son mossi insieme con essa traue, mantenendo sempre la medesima distantia l'vno dall'altro: così dicono questi Filosofi, che adiuien delle Stelle, non essendo quelle altro, che parti più spesse, et più dense de i lor orbi; li quali per la loro rarità, non mostrano la loro lucidezza; la quale si uede ben risplendere ne i corpi delle stelle, per esser quiui più adunata, più condensata, et più spessa. Segue dunque da questo che al mouimento d'un orbe, si habbian da mouere tutte le stelle, che sono in quello; conseruando sempre tra di loro, le medesime lontanze, et le stesse figure, che insieme faranno. Veder dico quelli antiqui Astrologi, che il Sole et la Luna, et cinque altre stelle, che sono Saturno, Gioue, Marte, Venere, et Mercurio Variauano sempre distantia di giorno in giorno l'una con l'altra, dalla qual uariatione, furono domandati Pianeti, la qual parola significa nella lingua Greca, quanto nella nostra errabondi, et peregrinanti; conclusero che per forza bisognaua che ciascheduno di questi sette Pianeti, hauesse ritenuto un orbe suo proprio nel quale si mouesse. Et che oltra di questi sette de un altro facesse di mestieri almeno, che mouesse tutte l'altre stelle. Le quali perche si uedeuano conseruar sempre infra di loro le medesime figure et distantie diedero occasione di far giudicio che in uno stesso cielo potesser esser mosse, et portate.

Et questo tal cielo chiamorono la Sfera stellata, et da alcuni fu domandato il firmamento, quasi perche ferme si trouino le stelle in esso senza punto uagare ò uariare distantia, nella guisa che li pianeti fanno. Questa sfera stellata fu per gran tempo dagli Astrologi giudicata per la più alta, et suprema di tutte, in modo che sopra di lei non fusse nè la decima, nè la nona, et primo mobile la domandauano. Et perche il spacio mi manca nò posto gli Autori et lor argomenti citarui ma seguirò con dirui che venuti poi nuoui Astrologi li quali hanno conosciuto che questa ottaua sfera hà tre mouimenti il primo vien da leuante a ponente il secondo vien per il contrario di questo, et l'ultimo da lor chiamato appressamento, et discostamento. Et così con molti argomenti discorrendo, che con la moltiplicatione dei mouimenti, bisognaua moltiplicare ancora gli orbi, hanno concluso, et affermato, che sopra le debbiano essere due altre sfere che sono la nona, et la decima come per la presente figura. Benche ne nella decima ne nella nona in loro stesse nò habbiano alcuna Stella, niente dimanco coi lor mouimenti seruono marauigliosamente alle stelle tutte, percioche tutta quella machina celeste composta di tanti orbi, ha un ordine, et una corrispondentia, diffusa et penetrata per tutti gli orbi, in modo che con marauigliosa concordia, si aiutano l'uno l'altro a beneficio commune et à produttione di uari effetti quaggiù da basso. Hor tornando al primo mobile ouer decimo cielo ancora che nò habbia in se stella alcuna nò dimeno nò indarno si muoue, ma per causa di mouere il Sole, la Luna, et altre stelle in 24 hore intorno alla terra da leuante à ponente sotto del decimo cielo. Segue la Nona sfera priua ancor ella di stelle. la quale si muoue da ponente verso leuante et ha uirtù di mouer seco ancora le sfere che le sono inferiori. Segue appresso di detta sfera l'ottaua, questa oltra li 2 mouimenti, ch'ella ha per virtù della decima, et della nona, si muoue ancora per uirtù propria mouendo in gran parte insieme con la medesima uirtù le sfere che le so sotto, il cui mouimento chiamato gli Astrologi appressamento, et discostamento. Segue doppo questo cielo stellato la sfera di Saturno, nominata così, da una stella nominata Saturno, che sola si troua in lei, et parimente nissuna sfera ha più stelle che una da cui prende il nome saluo che la stellata. Hor tornando dico oltra li mouimenti che ha per uigore et uirtù delle tre che sopra le sono, è mossa ancora dalla sua propria intelligentia, facendo il suo integro riuolgimento da ponente verso leuante ritornando in ponente in 30 anni solari la sudetta sfera di Saturno, et questo differisce dall'altre sfere che le so superiori, che doue quelle fanno parte de i lor mouimenti à quelle che so lor sotto, questa per il contrario nò muoue col suo riuolgimento altra sfera, si come parimente nò lo fanno le altre sfere, che le so sotto. Segue poi la sfera ouer cielo di Gioue che per uirtù della propria intelligentia in 12 anni solari finisce il suo integro riuolgimento. sotto questo è il cielo di Marte il quale in anni 2 finisce il suo corso integro. La Sfera del Sole di poi lo finisce in 365 giorni, et quasi 6 hore. Segue doppo 'l Sole Venere, et poi Mercurio secondo i lor mouimenti mediocri s'aggguagliano al Sole. L'ultimo cielo è questo della Luna che è più prossimo verso di noi il quale per 27 giorni, et 8 hore finisce quasi il integro corso.

DE I CIRCOLI DELLA SFERA SOPRA AI SVOI IIII PVNTI PRINCIPALI

Di molti circoli si concorrono alla compositione della sfera materiale come si uede nella presente figura et per quella politia iscrittione sotto di essa la qual sfera con la presente la Theorica del primo Mobile. Delli quali sue circoli cinque sono i quali nelle intersecationi loro eguale et proportionale costituiscono in detta sfera 4 punti chiamati punti cardinali nelli quali ui sono stati essequiti i maggiori Misteri della nostra salute dechiarati nella seguente cartella ò uero Iscrittione. Hor dico il circolo equinottiale et il Coluro degli equinottij si intersecano in parti eguale con angoli retti una delle quale intersecationi è nel principio di Ariete, et l'altra nel principio della libra. Il tropico del Cancro, et del Capricorno s'intersecono con il Coluro dei i solstitij si come ciascheduno per se stesso potrà nella designata sfera comprendere imperò che le 4 intersecationi che fanno li sudetti tropici et coluro solo 2 delle loro intersecationi si prendono cioè quelli che s'intersecono anco con la linea [illegible] distesa in luogo per il mezo del zodiaco imperoche la intersecatione fatta nel principio del cancro si chiama punto del solstitio estiuo qual nasce dal tropico del cancro l'altra intersecatione fatta nel principio [illegible] capricorno è detto Punto del solstitio hiemale gli altri due punti sono nelle sudette intersecationi del equinottio [illegible] degli equinottij uno detto punto uernale nel principio di ariete, et l'altro autunnale.

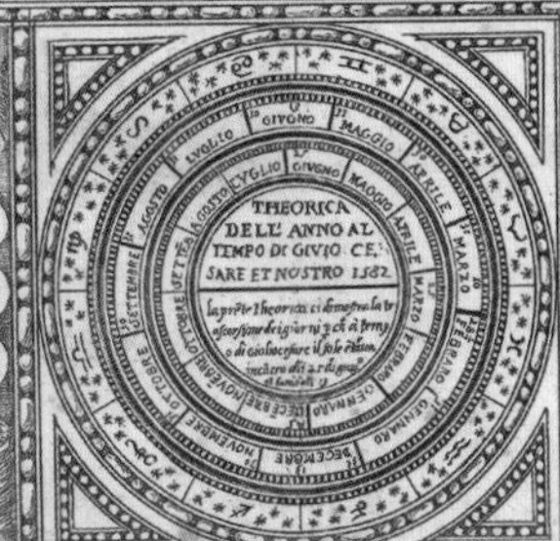

DELLE CAVSE DELLA NVOVA RIFORMA DELL'ANNO

Nelli 4 antedetti punti della sfera ci sono stati essequiti i maggiori Misteri della nostra Salute imperò che nel Equinottio della primauera, fu la Incarnatione di IESV XP̃O fu la sua Passione et fu la sua Resurrettione. Nell'Equinottio Autunnale fu la Natiuità della Vergine MARIA, et la essaltatione della † Nel Solstitio estiuo ci nacque il Precursor Giouanbatista, furono martirizzati I Principi delli Apostoli Pietro, et Paolo per dar principio alla Chiesa Romana, et ci fu con grand'allegrezza del mondo uisitata la Vergine MARIA. Nel solstitio Hiemale ci nacque IESV XP̃O, ci fu concepita la Vergine MARIA, et la Stella apparse al mondo per condurre i Doctissimi Magi d'oriente ad adorar IESV XP̃O et presentarlo con doni Pretiosissimi. Et perche la CHIESA SANTA CHATTOLICA ROMANA I Spirata dallo SPIRITO SANTO uuole che le dette Festiuità si celebrano nelli detti quattro punti dechiarati nell'anticedente tauola, et in questa Theorica apiede della presente opera. Per esser trascorsi tanti giorni, che non si celebrauano più in detti punti, Però la S. di N. S. PAPA GREGORIO XIII ha ordinato che si esseguisca questa Riforma accio le sudette festiuità ritornino a esser celebrate nelli suoi proprij tempi.

In Roma appresso l'Autore l'Año 1582.

"Golden gem for geometricians: a sure safety for saylers, and an auncient antiquary for astronomers and astrologians"

9 TANNER, Robert

A Mirror for Mathematiques: A Golden Gem for Geometricians: A sure safety for Saylers, and an auncient Antiquary for Astronomers and Astrologians. Contayning also an order howe to make an Astronomicall instrument, called the Astrolab, with the use thereof. Also a playne and most easie introduction for erection of a figure for the 12 houses of the heavens. A work most profitable for all such as are students in Astronomie, & Geometrie, and generally most necessarie for all learners in the Mathematicall artes. The contents of which booke you shall find in the next page.

Publication
London by J[ohn]. C[harlewood]. and are to be sold, by Richard Watkins, 1587.

Description
Small quarto (192 by 137mm), 56 leaves, title within typographic border, 16 woodcut figures in the text, woodcut headpieces and initials, ink inscription at head of sig. B1 (the first page of text) recording the gift of the book from John Galloway to Peter Smart on 9 Sept 1666; manuscript arithmetical workings in the margins of sigs. I3v – I4r, apparently in the same hand; marginal note in an earlier hand on sig. L1v, board edges a little rubbed, minor paper repairs to a few outer corners (sigs. A1–3, B1, B4) not affecting text, title page a little dusty, a little marginal soiling elsewhere, but an excellent copy, generally clean, well-margined, and unwashed, early nineteenth-century sprinkled calf by W. Pratt, spine richly gilt in compartments, twin black morocco lettering pieces, sides ruled in gilt with a French fillet, gilt fleurons at inside corners, gilt inner dentelles, marbled endpapers, old red edges. First and only edition, variant imprint (another imprint of the same year has "solde by Richarde Watkins").

References
Adams and Waters, 'English Maritime Books', 3519; STC 23674.5; Taylor, 'Mathematical Practitioners', 67 (without details); Waters, 'Art of Navigation', pp.166–167.

The book includes "A particular description of some parte of America, as by travaile is found out", with a description of the characteristics of the natives, emphasizing that they are in possession of gold yet do not value it highly. Published on the eve of the Spanish Armada in 1588, the book is dedicated to Charles, Lord Howard of Effingham, Lord Admiral of England, Commander of the English naval forces against the Armada; he was also among the biggest subscribers to Sir Walter Raleigh's scheme to colonise North America.

Justin Winsor, in his 'Narrative and Critical History of America', lists this work as being among the 34 publications in English relating to America prior to the enlarged edition of Hakluyt (1598), and one of only 14 of English origin. Yet the title appears neither in Sabin nor in any of the great Americana collections (Church, Boies Penrose, Streeter, etc.) nor in others where it might have been expected, such as Macclesfield.

This rare early English work largely on the planispheric astrolabe was published only two years after John Blagrave's pioneering 'The Mathematical Jewel'. "Like Blagrave's, [Tanner's] astrolabe could be made in paper, wood, or brass, thus combining portability with cheapness or robustness. At the end of his book he included for seamen some rules for forecasting the weather by the state of the sun and moon. It is hard to say whether or not the works on astrolabes and the instruments were much used at this time by seamen: their appearance at this conjunction was certainly symptomatic of the growing sense in England of the practical value of a knowledge of astronomy: as Captain Smith recommended the use of astrolabes and astrolabe quadrants it would seem that in the seventeenth century they were certainly taken to sea by responsible navigators" (Waters).

The 4. part is the Voluel so called, contayning the Zodiack of the 12. signes, with their degrées and numbers, from 10. to 10. also the most noble fixed starres, very necessarie to those which iudge of starres, which is called of the *Arabians* Alencabuth, but in Latine Aranea or Rete, signifying a cobwebbe or net, whose fardest and extreame part béeing hollow, is said to bee the waie of the Sunne, or the Ecliptica. And about the beginning in the same Zodiack, is left a certaine little tooth, which the *Arabians* call Almuri, but in Latine a poynter out, because it is that which poynteth out the degrées described in the Limb.

You must know that all signes with their degrées, and starres which are contained betwéene the Equinoctiall circle and the center of the Astrolab are called Septentriall, and that all which are without towarde the Circle of Capricorne, are called Meridionall.

At the last all these thinges are ioyned together, with Rules and Indexes, as followeth.

The Ruler or Voluel, which is turned in the back of the Astrolab, which Ruler is called Alhiada or mediclinium, in the which are put two little pynnes or Tables, to take the height of the Sunne in the day, and of the stars in the night, of which one side, which goeth thorow, by the Center of the Astrolab, is called ỹ lyne of trust, because it bringeth credit of thinges practised there.

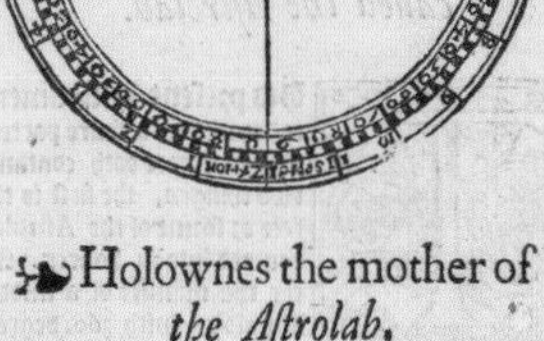

Holownes the mother of *the Astrolab.*

IN the second place commeth the backe of the Astrolab, in which the degrées of the altitudes of euerie fourth part of the circle, with their numbers from 10. to 10, vnto 90. do offer themselues. After those do followe the degrées of the Zodiack, seruing with their numbers from 10. to 10. for euery signe adding 30. to the which immediatly do cleaue ỹ names of the signes. Afterwarde the dayes of the yéere do fo-

low distinguished, with the numbers, monethes, and their names, after the order & custome of the Church: betwéene which, the Altimetricall Lather, for the dyuers Geometricall deuisions hath his place: and that there might be no voide roome, in the heade and top of the Lather spoken of, the bowes or ares of vnequall houres béeing discribed to shew themselues.

Of this let thys Fygure folowing be taken.

The author is described in the title as "Gent. Practitioner in Astrologie & Phisick", and the book includes astrological instructions, for which an astrolabe was also useful. Tanner had previously written 'A Prognostication for 1584', printed by the partnership of Richard Watkins and James Roberts, who held a 21-year patent given to them by Elizabeth I for almanacs and prognostications. On the present occasion, however, Richard Watkins alone acted as bookseller. The printer was John Charlewood, who entered the book in the Stationer's Register on 6 April 1587. Charlewood may have had Roman Catholic connections: in 1581 and again in 1583 he styled himself servant or printer "to the right honourable Earl of Arundel", i.e. Philip Howard, the dedicatee Lord Charles Howard's cousin, who was either traitor or saint depending on one's religious allegiance. Charlewood was indicted in the early part of his career for unauthorised publications but, later in 1583, he secured an exclusive licence from the Stationers' Company for the printing of playbills (the earliest such entry in the registers), suggesting a newfound respectability. This is the only recorded work printed by him for Watkins.

Rare. ESTC locates a total of seven copies with either imprint in Britain and four in North America, to which Adams and Waters add the Prinz Hendrik Maritime Museum copy in Rotterdam. No copy appears in auction records, according to ABPC, going back to 1960. The only copy we can trace in commerce in the last 50 years is the Horblit copy (same imprint as this, title washed and fore-edge remargined, nineteenth-century half morocco), which was sold to H. P. Kraus in 1974 and offered for sale in their catalogue 168, item 186.

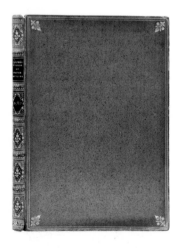

The Figure belonging to the Chapter aforesaide.

The 30. Chapter dooth teache the height of a thing erected vpon a hyll, of which height, the lower ende and top are seene, the eye beeing in a vallye to measure it.

Nowe it resteth to showe howe the measure of any height in a high place, (put case a Hyll may be comprehended of vs in a lowe place, put case a Wallie) this séemeth to bee hard; but reason searcheth euery way ef nature. Euery thing therefore, which rysing from ẏ vppermost part of the

earth is carried vpward, and the top béeing eleuated on high, dooth passe ouer the euennes of the playn lying about it, is height, which height, if sometimes from an vnlike place it méete with Wallies and hylles in measuring. First, let the measurer séeke out in ẏ low place or Wally the naturall Horison, of his station or place, that is, some thing which hath some playnes, equall distant to the Horison, in which he may finish the worke of his measuring, which béeing founde, let him first consider the height of the hyll by two places or stations, according to the instruction going before, then let him marke the height of the Towre and hyll together by the same instruction, and then let him substract ẏ height of the hill, from the height of ẏ whole added togeather, and the residue shalbe the height of the Towre.

¶ The 31. Chapter doth teache to try the measure of lengthes, by the Astrolab or Quadrant.

Knowledge béeing hadde of thinges spoken of the height of thinges standing perpendicular or stooping forward, you shall easily vnderstande these fewe thinges of ẏ measuring of Playnes according to the length which we haue sette downe. For thou hast learned by the length knowne, the height vnknowne, héere contrariwise by the height knowne, you shall knowe the length vnknowne of the Plaine. When therefore you would measure a Plaine, whose ende is seene, whether it be to be come vnto or no, according to the length, by the office of the Astrolab or Quadrant. First of all dispose the measuring Rodde, which in any case must be the same length, as thy stature is of from the eye to the foote, which rodde deuide by some measure knowne to thée, and the best deuision of it, is into 12. equall partes, which béeing disposed, stand in one ende of the Plaine according to the length to be measured, and the Astrolab béeing hanged vp, heaue vppe or put downe the Inder, vntill you sée by ẏ holes of bothe the Tables, the other limit or ende of the Plaine, on the ouerthwart part, which séene, reckon diligently the poyntes cut off by the lyne of trust, which are almost alwayes the poyntes of ẏ turned shaddow, for then the length of the Plaine is greater then the rodde of ẏ measurer: by the poyntes therefore cut of aboue found out, deuide 12. and the number accounted will declare to thée of what quantitie the part of the measuring rodde is, in respect of the length of the Plaine which is measured, for if the line of trust shall fall iustly vppon the

The man as sundial

10 **ROSSI, Teodosio**

Horihomo di Theodosio Rossi da Piperno, per il quale ogni huomo stando al Sole per l'ombra sua propria, ò altra, poul conoscere l'hore tutto l'ano.

Publication
Rome, Alittenio Gatti, 1590.

Description
Engraving with etching, dated and signed in the lower central part of the plate, on laid paper with watermark "pilgrim in the circle", light stains to central upper and lower part, trimmed to upper neatline.

Dimensions
300 by 435mm (11.75 by 17.25 inches).

References
Jannicola, Giuseppe, 'Teodosio Rossi da Piverno al Quirinale' in 'Citta' Comprensorio', April 2001, pp. 16-17.

A fine example of this extremely rare sheet.

Teodosio Rossi (1550-1630) was born in Priverno and moved to Rome, where he studied mathematics and astronomy under the Jesuit astronomer Christopher Clavius; he was also known to have corresponded with Tycho Brahe. As well as contributing to works on jurisprudence, astronomy and geography, his most notable achievements lie in his work on gnomonics, most notably in designing the "tetracycle sundial" for the Barberini family, one of the first works by the renowned architect Francesco Borromini.

However, the present work was the publication that established his name: the 'Horihomo', literally 'man clock'. The work was in essence a portable clock, almost like a pocket watch for the traveller. The man himself is turned into the gnomon, as is illustrated to the left of the print. To the centre is a table of months of the year together with the declination of the sun. The work would appear to have been well received as it is mentioned in the 'Almanacco Perpetuo' by Rutilio Benincasa, published in 1593, as "... a work that is very useful and delightful and also beneficial and necessary to anyone and particularly to astronomers, physiognomers, physicians ...".

The work is dedicated to Onorato Gaetani (or Caetini), the Sixth Duke of Sermoneta, Knight of the Golden Fleece, General of the Papal Infantry and a distinguished naval commander in the wars against the Turks.

HORIHOMO

di Theodosio Rossi da Piperno, per ilqual' ogn' huomo stando al Sole per l'ombra sua propria, ò altra, puol' cognoscere l'Hore tutto l'ano.

All' Ill.mo et Eccell.mo Sig.r Honorato Caetano Duca di Sermoneta &c.

VARII sonno stati li modi (Eccell.me Sign.r) ritrouati dalli ingegni humani percognoscere l'hore, uedendo la grand' utilità, et necessità d'esse, non m'intratterrò dicendo di quelli congegnati con cōtrapesi, n'anco di quelli da poluere, essendo per causa, et p effetto naturali; dirrò ben di quelli quali solo meritano il nome d'horloggi, alliquali io spesse uolte pensando non posso contenermi di non prorompere nelle parole d'Ouidio. Felices animæ q. bus haec cognoscere primum Inq. domos supum scandere cura fuit. dellaqual sorte d'horloggi sonno stati inuentati più modi da uarij auttori delli quali diffusamente ne tratta il Clauio nella sua Gnomonica, Ma perche non tutti, nè sempre si possono hauere tali horloggi

Vndarum intacta telis ...

Per questo hò pensato di mandare in luce questo mio Horihomo, cioè ch'un huomo stando però al sole in logho piano per l'ombra del suo corpo, ò d'altra cosa, puol cognoscere l'hore. Ilche pensando douer'essere non men' utile, che necessario, hò uoluto publicarlo sotto il nome di V. Eccell: como quella ch'intendendosi di cose celesti, sente gran' diletto dal discorso d'esse. Pregandola ch'all'hora si pensi ch'io sia sodisfattissimo di queste mie fatighe, quando uedrò che le riceuerà con la solita prontezza d'animo, con che basciandoli humilissimamente le mani fò fine. Di Roma il dì 25. di Febraro. 1590

Di V. Sig. Ill.ma et Eccell.ma

Humiliss.mo Ser.r

Theodosio Rossi da Piperno

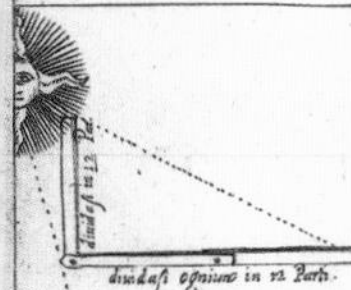

Alli 3 di Giugno essendo l'ombra longa 4 parti trouo hore 16.

Hore

	Giorni	9	10	11	12	13	14	15	16	17	18	19	20	21	22	23	24	Giorni	
	22	1031 3/4	64 1/4	30 5/6	19	12 3/4	8 4/6	5 5/6	4 1/4	4 1/3	6	8 5/6	13	19 4/6	32 1/6	68 3/4	Sempre infinita.	22	Giugno
	16	1031 3/4	64 1/4	30 5/6	19	12 3/4	8 4/6	5 5/6	4 1/4	4 1/3	6	8 5/6	13	19 4/6	32 1/6	68 3/4		28	
	9		64	32 11/12	19	13	9	6 1/12	4	4	6	8	13	19	31	68		5	Luglio
Giugno	3		75	30	20 3/4	13	9 1/6	6 2/6	4	4 4/5	6	8	13	19	31	68		11	
	28		97	36	21 4/6	14 2/3	9 4/6	6 5/6	4 3/5	4 4/6	6	8	13	19	31	68		17	
	21		114 1/6	41	23	15 2/6	10 1/4	7 1/4	5 1/4	4 1/6	6	8	13	19	31	68		24	
	15		171 4/6	48 1/6	25 3/4	16 2/4	11 1/5	7 4/5	5 5/6	5 1/12	6	8	13	19	31	68		30	
	9		82 1/12	56 1/2	28 1/4	17 5/6	12	8 2/6	6 1/12	5 7/12	6 3/6	8	13	19	31	68		5	Agosto
Maggio	3			74 2/6	32 1/12	19 1/3	12 4/6	8 5/6	6 11/12	6	6 4/6	9	13	19	31	67		11	
	27			97 3/4	36 11/12	21 4/6	14 2/6	10	7 5/6	6 4/5	7 1/3	9	13	19	31	67		18	
	21			152 1/6	44 3/4	23 1/6	15 11/12	11 1/6	8 2/3	7 1/3	7 3/4	9	13	19	31	66		24	
	18			687	56 3/6	28 1/4	17 3/4	12 3/6	9 2/3	7 2/4	7 3/4	9	13	19	30	65		30	
	12				75 1/4	32 3/6	19 11/12	13 2/4	10 2/3	8 3/4	8 3/5	10	13	19	30	64		5	Settembre
Aprile	5				114 1/3	39 1/4	22	15 2/6	11 7/12	9 3/4	9	10	13	19	30	63		11	
	30				180	48 1/6	26 11/12	17 3/4	11 5/6	10 2/3	9 3/4	10	13	19	29 1/4	62		18	
	24				687	44 1/2	27	18	12 4/6	11	10	11	14 4/6	19	29 2/4	61		21	
	21					61 1/4	29 11/12	19 3/6	14 1/4	11 4/6	10 4/5	11 4/6	14 1/4	19 1/5	29 11/12	61 1/4		24	
	18					91 1/6	39 1/4	23 1/6	15 1/6	11 5/6	12	12 1/4	14 5/6	19 1/6	30	61		27	
	12					137 1/6	44 3/4	25 1/4	18 1/6	14 2/6	12 4/6	13 2/6	15 2/6	20 1/6	30	61		3	Ottobre
Marzo	6					343 3/4	56 1/6	29 5/6	20 3/4	15 11/12	13 4/5	14 1/4	16 1/4	20 11/12	30	61		9	
	28						75 3/4	34 5/6	23 3/6	17 1/6	15 2/6	15	17	21 4/6	30	61		15	
	22						114 1/6	41 1/6	25 3/4	20	17 1/6	16 3/4	18	22	30	61		21	
	16						171 5/6	52	29 4/5	21 5/6	18 2/7	17 3/4	19 1/4	23 1/6	31 3/6	68		27	
	10						687 3/4	68	32 11/12	24 1/6	20	18 3/4	19 11/12	24 1/6	34	68		2	Nouembre
Febraro	4							85 2/6	39 1/4	27	21 4/6	20	21 3/6	25 3/6	35	68		8	
	29							114 1/6	45 1/3	30 2/3	23 2/6	21 4/6	22	25 3/4	36	68		14	
	23							151 5/6	52	32	24 4/6	22 3/4	23 1/6	26 5/6	37	69		20	
	18							229	61 4/6	34 1/2	25 3/4	23 3/4	24 1/6	27 2/6	38 2/6	69		26	
	12							687 3/4	68	37 1/6	28 1/4	24 4/6	24 5/6	28	39 1/4	75		2	Decembr.
Gennaro	6								73 1/4	41 1/6	30	25 3/4	25 3/4	29	40	76		8	
	31								80	42 1/2	31	26	26	30	41	77		14	
	25								82 3/4	42 3/4	31	26 1/4	26 1/5	30 4/5	41 1/5	77 3/4		19	
Decembre	22	R							82 3/4	42 3/4	31	26 1/4	26 5/6	30 4/5	41 2/5	77 3/4		22	

Horizonte orientale — Crepusculina — Commune — Parti dell' ombre

innanzi Mezzodi dopo

Quest' horihomo serue p 150 miglia intorn' à Roma: com'a dire.

Albano	Nargni
Anagni	Norcia
Amelia	Nocera
Aquila	Notturu
Aquino	Perugia
Arezo	Pesaro
Arimini	Piperno
Asisci	Pisa
Beneuento	Rauenna
Bracciano	Roma
Camerino	Riete
Capua	Sauona
Cisterna	Sora
Faenza	Subiaco
Fabriano	Sermoneta
Fermo	Siena
Firenza	Spoleti
Foligni	Terracina
Forli	Terni
Fondi	Tiuoli
Gaeta	Trento
Genua	Valmontone
Lucca	Velletri
Macerata	Veroli
Montalto	Vetralla
Napoli di Cap.	Viterbo
Niza	Vrbino

QVĀDO ci uolemo seruire di quest' Horihomo bisogna hauere un' bastone, ò filo eguale all'altezza nostra, et cōpartirlo in 12. parti eguali: Et uolendo sape l'hore andaremo in luogo piano al posibile esposto al sole, et farremo un' segno in terra sopra ilqual' metteremo il calcagno, et stādo dritto, sēza berretta, notaremo il fine dell' ombra nostra, et dopò la misuraremo col detto filo, pche se nel' horihomo trouato il mese, et giorno proprio, ò più uicino cercaremo la longhezza dell' ombra propria, ò più uicina, et p essa guardando dritto fin in capo del' horihomo hauerremo l'hora, potrai anchora seruirti dl' ombra d'un bastone diuiso in 12. parti, come uedi nell' esempij.

Ad Lectore Epigramma B. C.

Quisquis per campos, syluas, tractusq. viarum
Errat, uel propria gaudet inesse domo:
Possit ut horarum ex umbra dignoscere cursum

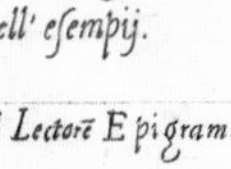

Seu sol Eous, seu micet occiduus,
Hisce Theodosij numeris tibi regula monstrat
Quae nuquam fallax, nec peritura manet.

R

Il presente horihomo è calculato pgradi 42 d'altezza di Polo, serue però 150 miglia uers Ostro, et Tramōtana.

In Roma L'Anno 1590 Con Priuilegio Alittenio Gatti Formis.

An unrecorded solar calendar

11 **ROSSI, Teodosio**

Arcus Semidiurni ad Omnes Utriusque Poli supra Horizontem Altitudines.

Publication
Rome, Cesare Capranica, 1591.

Description
Engraving with etching, dated and signed on the lower part of the plate, laid paper with watermark of a "lily in a circle", trimmed to neatline, small worm holes skilfully repaired.

Dimensions
410 by 550mm (16.25 by 21.75 inches).

References
Jannicola, Giuseppe, 'Teodosio Rossi da Priverno al Quirinale' in 'Citta' Comprensorio', April 2001, pp. 16-17.

This fascinating broadside deals with the duration of the sun's semidiurnal arc for places throughout the northern hemisphere. In theory, if one knew one's location, one could – by using the table – gain an accurate date.

To the left and right of the table is a list of months, days (with every third day marked), and signs of the zodiac (with every third day marked). These form four columns, with two to the left and two to the right. The first column begins with 24 September and ends with 22 December; the second 21 March to 22 July; the third 24 September to 22 June; and the fourth 21 March to 22 December. The table is divided into 90 columns in three sections. Each column marks a degree of latitude from zero (i.e. the equator) to 90 (the North Pole). Each column is subsequently subdivided into hours and minutes of the duration of each semidiurnal arc. To the left and right of the table is a list of cities in the northern hemisphere with their respective degree of latitude. For example, the Maluku Islands (latitude 0 degrees) are situated upon the equator and, according to the table, have a constant semidiurnal arc lasting six hours throughout the year (i.e. the transit of the sun across the sky from sunrise to sunset is 12 hours). 'Londimu Angl.' (London) is placed upon the 53rd degree of latitude, with the length of the semidiurnal arc ranging from six hours on 21 March (the Vernal Equinox) to eight hours 22 minutes on 22 June (the Summer Solstice).

The work is dedicated to Rudolph II of Augsburg, Holy Roman Emperor from 1576 to 1612, alchemist and patron, a character who was always attentive to scientific innovations of his time. In the dedication to Rudolph II, Teodosio Rossi states that he had consulted the studies on the semidiurnal arc by Cristoforo Clavius, who was his astronomy master in Rome.

No institutional examples are recorded by the OCLC.

INVICTISSIMO ROM IMPERATORI RVDOLPHO II. CAES. AVG. THEODOSIVS RVBEVS.

In bonam felicitatis partem ānumerandū duxi, Imp. Potentiss., cum Camillo Caetano Patriarcha Alexandrino a Gregorio XIIII Pont. Max. Nuncio Apostolico ad tuam Caes.m Maiestatē destinato in Germaniam proficisci, ut pręclara occasione fruerer tui vidēdi, et hāc uniuersalē arcuū semidiurnoꝝ tabulam à Christophoro Clauio Gemano Societatis Iesv presbytero celeberrimo Mathematiū Doctore, et pręceptore meo charissimo, non citra laborē et ingens studiū primum excogitatā, quę ad oēs tā Australes, quām Septentrionales Poli eleuationes accōmodata existit, et nullo ferme negotio adhibito, docet quibusq; horis in quibuslibet mundi partibus oriatur et occidat, quam Zodiaci partem singulis diebus diurna solis lux pnect, Hanc eandem à me absolutam exornatam typis aeneis incisam, imprimendam curaui, ut tuę C. M. Mathematum et omnium liberalium artium studiosę inprimisq; Moecęnati, dicarem. Quam si benigno, ut spero, vultu susceperis, Caesaream Clementiam expertus, ad maiora in dies, et tuo conspectu digniora pvocabor. Vale.

ARCVS SEMIDIVRNI AD OMNES VTRIVSQVE POLI SVPRA HORIZONTEM ALTITVDINES.

Menses	Dies	Gradus	Signa	Signa	Gradus	Dies	Menses	0	1	2	3	4	5	6	7	8	9	10	11	12	13	14	15	16	17	18	19	20	21	22	23	24	25	26	27	28	29	30	Menses	Dies	Gradus	Signa	Signa	Gradus	Dies	Menses
								H. M.	H. M.	H. M.	H. M.	H. M.	H. M.	H. M.	H. M.	H. M.	H. M.	H. M.	H. M.	H. M.	H. M.	H. M.	H. M.	H. M.	H. M.	H. M.	H. M.	H. M.	H. M.	H. M.	H. M.	H. M.	H. M.	H. M.	H. M.	H. M.	H. M.	H. M.								
[illegible]																																														

Menses	Dies	Gradus	Signa	Signa	Gradus	Dies	Menses	31	32	33	34	35	36	37	38	39	40	41	42	43	44	45	46	47	48	49	50	51	52	53	54	55	56	57	58	59	60	61	Menses	Dies	Gradus	Signa	Signa	Gradus	Dies	Menses
								H. M.	H. M.	H. M.	H. M.	H. M.	H. M.	H. M.	H. M.	H. M.	H. M.	H. M.	H. M.	H. M.	H. M.	H. M.	H. M.	H. M.	H. M.	H. M.	H. M.	H. M.	H. M.	H. M.	H. M.	H. M.	H. M.	H. M.	H. M.	H. M.	H. M.	H. M.								
[illegible]																																														

Menses	Dies	Gradus	Signa	Signa	Gradus	Dies	Menses	62	63	64	65	66	66½	67	68	69	70	71	72	73	74	75	76	77	78	79	80	81	82	83	84	85	86	87	88	89	90	Menses	Dies	Gradus	Signa	Signa	Gradus	Dies	Menses
								H. M.	H. M.	H. M.	H. M.	H. M.	H. M.	H. M.	H. M.	H. M.	H. M.	H. M.	H. M.	H. M.	H. M.	H. M.	H. M.	H. M.	H. M.	H. M.	H. M.	H. M.	H. M.	H. M.	H. M.	H. M.	H. M.	H. M.	H. M.	H. M.	H. M.								
[illegible]																																													

DIES SIVE LVX CONTINVA

QVANTITAS DIEI, ET NOCTIS IN HEMISPHAERIO BOREALI.

SOLE EXISTENTE IN SIGNIS BOREALIBVS:

ARCVS semidiurnꝰ, id ē medietas diei ī āgulo cōmuni, id ē sub data Poli altitudine, et ī regione dati gr. zodiaci uel datę die reꝑitꝰ.

ARCVS cōmunis, id ē medietas reliqꝰ arcu semidiurno ex H. 12. dēpto.

SOLE VERO AVSTRALIA SIG. PERCVRRENTE:

ARCVS seminocturnꝰ in eodē cōmuni angulo inuenitur.

ARCVS semidiurni reliqꝰ arcu seminocturno ex horis 12. detracto.

VBICVNQVE SOL EXISTAT.

ARCVS semidiurnꝰ duplicatꝰ totū arcū diurnū, id est, totā diei quantitatē efficit.

ARCVS seminocturnꝰ duplicatꝰ totū arcū nocturnū, hoc ē, totā quantitatē noctis constituit.

EXEMPLVM.

SOLE existente in gr. 12. ♉ uel in gr. 18. ♌, hoc est, die 3 Maij, uel 11 Augꝰ, ad altitudinē poli Arctici gr. 42.

ARCVS semidiurnꝰ reperitꝰ in cōmuni angulo H. 6. M. 58.

ARCVS seminocturnꝰ est H. 5 M. 2. q. relinqꝰ arcu semidiurno H. 6 M. 58 ex horis 12. detracto.

ARCVS diurnꝰ cōtinet H. 13 M. 56. duplū uidelicet semidiurni arcus H. 6. M. 58.

ARCVS nocturnꝰ cōplectiꝰ H. 10. M. 4. nimirū duplū arcꝰ seminocturni H. 5. M. 2.

SOLE uerò existente in gr. 12. ♏ uel in gr. 18. ♒, hoc est, die 5 ♎bris, uel 7 Februarij, ad eandē altitudinem poli Arctici gr. 42.

ARCVS seminocturnꝰ in eodē āgulo cōmuni inuenitur H. 6. M. 58.

ARCVS semidiurnus est H. 5. M. 2. q. relinqꝰ arcu seminocturno H. 6 M. 58. ex horis 12 subtracto.

ARCVS diurnꝰ habet H. 10. M. 4. duplū scilicet arcus semidiurni H. 5. M. 2.

ARCVS nocturnus constat H. 13 M. 56. q. numerus duplus est arcus seminocturni H. 6. M. 58.

SVPERIOR. PMISSV
ROMAE AN. DNI M.D.XCI.
Cęsaris supra...ia formis.
cū priuilegio.

TEMPVS ORTVS, ET OCCASVS SOLIS IN HEMISPHAERIO BOREALI.

ORTVS Solis post mediā noctē, more Astronomorum, indicitur per arcum seminocturnum.

OCCASVS Solis post meridiē, more etiā Astronomorum, per arcū semidiurnum exprimitꝰ.

ORTVS itē Solis post occasū more Italorū, monstratꝰ per arcū nocturnū.

OCCASVS deniq; Solis post ortū, more Babyloniorū, per arcū diurnū exprimitꝰ.

EXEMPLVM

DIE 3. Maij, uel 11 Augusti, ad altitudinē poli Arctici gr. 42.

ORITVR Sol H. 5 M. 2. post mediā noctē: qa tantus est arcus seminocturnus.

OCCIDIT Sol H. 6. M. 58. post meridiē: qa tantus est arcus semidiurnus.

ORITVR item Sol H. 10 M. 4. post occasum: quia tantus est arcus nocturnus.

OCCIDIT denique Sol H. 13. M. 56. post ortū: quia tantus est arcus diurnus.

TEMPVS MERIDIEI, ET MEDIAE NOCTIS IN HEMISPHAERIO BOREALI.

MERIDIEM post Solis occasū indicat arcꝰ semidiurni ex H. 24 detractus.

MEDIA noctē post occasū Solis exhibet arcꝰ seminocturnꝰ.

MERIDIE aūt post Solis ortū mōstrat arcꝰ semidiurnus.

MEDIA deniq; nocte post ortū Solis relinquit arcꝰ seminocturnꝰ ex H. 24 detractus.

EXEMPLVM.

DIE 5. ♎bris, uel 7. Februarii, ad altitudinē poli Arctici gr. 42.

MERIDIES fit H. 18 M. 58. post Solis occasū quod tēpus relinquꝰ arcu semidiurno H. 5 M. 2. ex H. 24. detracto.

MEDIA nox fit H. 6. M. 58. post occasū Solis: qa tantus est arcus seminocturnus.

MERIDIES itē post Solis ortū contingit H. 5. M. 2. quia tantus est arcus semidiurnus.

MEDIA nox deniq; post ortū Solis fit H. 17. M. 2. quod tēpꝰ relinquꝰ arcu seminocturno ex H. 24. detracto.

DIERVM, ET NOCTIVM CONTINVARVM INITIVM, AC FINIS IN HEMISPHERIO Boreali.

INITIVM cuiuslibet diei cōtinui cōtingit tot dieb. āte diē 22. Iunii, quot ī dimidiato nꝰ totius diei cōtinui existunt.

FINIS uerò totidē dieb. post diē 22. Iunii contingit.

INITIVM cuiuslibet noctis cōtinuę fit tot dieb. āte diem 22. xbris, quot ī dimidiato nꝰ totius diei continui cōtinēt. Nam noctes continuę sunt fermè dieb. cōtinuis ęquales.

FINIS uerò totidē dieb. post diem 22. xbris contingit.

EXEMPLVM.

AD poli Arctici altitudinē gr. 68.

INITIVM diei continui dierū 42. incidit in diē 21. ferè ante diē 22. Iunii, id est, in diem 1. Iunii ferè.

FINIS uerò ī diē 21. post diē 22. Iunii, hoc est, in diē 13. Iulii ferè incidit.

INITIVM noctis continuę dierū quoq; 42. incidit in diē 21. ante diē 22. xbris, hoc est, in diē 1. xbris ferè.

FINIS autem in diem 21. post diē 22. xbris, id est, in diē 12. fermè Ianuarij incidit.

QVANTITAS DIEI, AC NOCTIS, TEMPVS ORTꝰ, ET OCCASꝰ SOLIS: TEPꝰ MERIDIEI, ET MEDIĘ NOCTIS: DIERꝰ, DENIQ;, ET NOCTIVM CŌTINVARVM INITIVM, AC FINIS IN HEMISPHERIO AVSTRALI.

OMNIA, quę ex eadē tabula eruunꝰ ut in hemisphęrio Boreali, si ea, quę de signis Borealib. diximus, de Australib. dicta intelligꝰ, et quę de Australib. tradita sunt, trāsferantꝰ ad Borealia.

EXEMPLVM

ARCVS semidiurnꝰ, ad altitudinē poli Antarctici gr. 42. Sole existēte in gr. 12. ♏, uel in gr. 18. ♒, reperitꝰ in tabula cōtinere H. 6. M. 58. quēadmodū in hemisphęrio Boreali Sole existēte in gr. 12. ♉, uel in gr. 18. ♌.

ARCVS itē seminocturnꝰ, ad eādē poli Antarctici altitudinē gr. 42. Sole existēte in gr. 12. ♉, uel in gr. 18. ♌, cōtinet H. 6 M. 58. quēadmodū ī hemisphęrio Boreali, Sole existēte ī gr. 12. ♏, uel in gr. 18. ♒.

DIES cōtinuꝰ dierū 42. initiū habet die 1. xbris, finē uerò die 12. Ianuarii, ubi polus Antarcticus eandē gr. 68. quēadmodū de nocte continua in hemisphęrio Boreali diximus.

NOX continua illīc incipit die 1. Iunii, terminatꝰ aūt die 13. Iulii: quēadmodū de die cōtinuo dictū ē in Boreali hemisphęrio.

An early perpetual calendar

12 **TORO, Ortensio**

Rota Perpetua per trovar a quant hore si leva il sole e quando e mezzo giorno.

Publication
[?Rome], Nicolas van Aelst and Giovanni Battista de Rossi, 1594.

Description
Engraving with etching, laid paper with watermark of a bird in a double circle with the letter N, trimmed to within neatline.

Dimensions
400 by 480mm (15.75 by 19 inches).

A rare perpetual calendar giving the times of the sun's rise and midday.

The plate consists of a large wheel in the centre of which is the coat-of-arms of Cardinal Pietro Aldobrandini, to whom the work is dedicated. This, in turn, is surrounded by a calendar, with each month bearing two sets of three columns each. The first set gives the date together with the hour and minute of the sun's rising, with the second set giving the date and time for midday.

The explanation below the title reads:

"To find at what time the sun rises, and what hour and minutes is midday, for example find the month of March, say the 1st of March, the sun rises at 12 hours and 35 minutes, and then follow day by day, month by month perpetually, bearing in mind that 'D' stands for day, 'H' hour, and 'M' minute".

The explanation is at first somewhat confusing, however the times marked upon the instrument should be read as the amount of time lapsed between the sun's setting and its rising: therefore on 11 March (the Vernal Equinox on the chart) the first column reads 12 hours and zero minutes, with the second column 17 hours and 59 minutes, i.e. midday is almost 18 hours after sunset. The date of the Vernal Equinox also suggests that the calendar was based upon the Julian model; the new Gregorian calendar, which had been introduced in 1582, had reset the Vernal Equinox to 21 March, the date agreed upon at the Treaty of Nicaea in AD 325.

The work is dedicated to Pietro Aldobrandini, Pope Clement VIII's nephew, who was elected Cardinal in 1593. Unfortunately, little is known about the work's author, Ortensio Toro.

We are unable to trace any institutional examples of the work.

ROTA PERPETVA PER TROVAR A QVANT HORE SI LEVA IL SOLE E QVANDO E MEZZO GIORNO

DICHIARATIONE

Volendo trouare a quante hore leua il Sole, e quanti minuti, e a quante hore e minuti e il mezzo giorno per essempio trouate Marzo e dite il primo di Marzo leua il Sole a H·12 M·35 e sequitate trouate il medesimo e dite il mezzo giorno sara a H·18 M·15 e sequitate di giorno in giorno di mese in mese perpetuamente hauertendo che la littera D significa giorno H hore M minute.

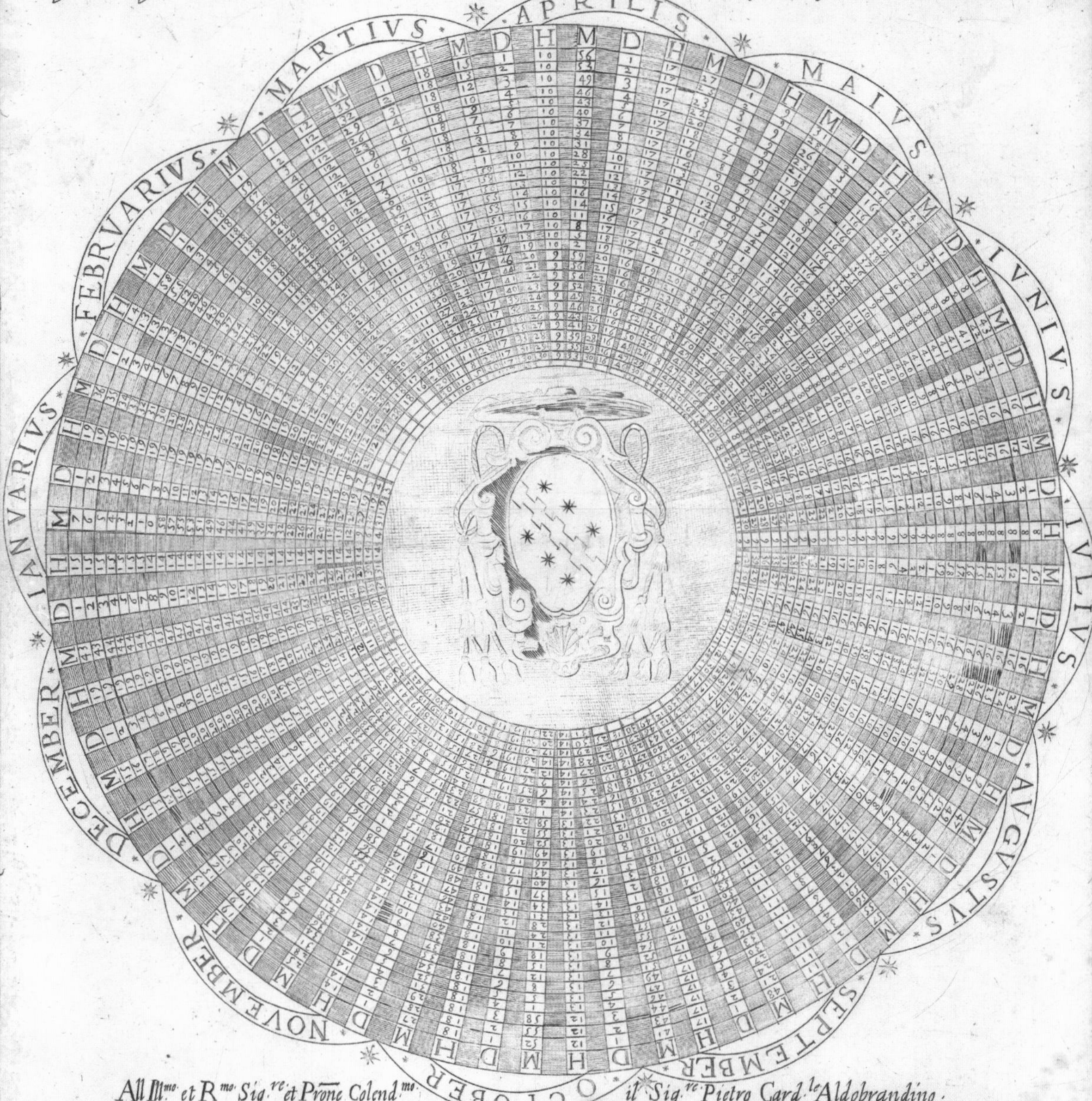

All Ill.mo et R.mo Sig.re et Prone Colend.mo il Sig.re Pietro Card.le Aldobrandino.

Hauendo piu uolte deliberato dar qualche segno ha V·S·Ill.ma del deuoto animo mio con questo picciol saggio di cosi poca operetta della mia professione la quale ancor che di poco momento rispetto alla grandezza sua ho dedicata a quella conferma fede che la benignita sua togliera ogni difetto et gli dara credito euigore degnesi dunq accettar con lanimo suo generoso questa mia picciola fatiga ancor che pouera et meschina per che scaturisca da un pouero suo Vassallo il quale di amore et fidelta non cede a qual si uoglia altro ser.re de V·S Ill.ma alla quale pregando sempre ogni maggior felicita et esaltatione se li dona et bascia le mani di Roma il di 3 de Decembre 1594.

D V·S· Ill.ma et R.ma
Fid.mo Ser.re et Vassallo Hortensio Toro da S.to Oresto.

Nicolo uan Aelst formis. con licentia di Superiori. Giouanni Batta de Rossi in piazza Nauona formis

Rare pillar sundial dedicated to Heinrich Rantzau, an associate of Tycho Brahe

13 **TRANCKIUS, J[oachim]**

[Pillar Sundial] Cylindrus Horarius Convexus Maior.

Publication
Perleberg, 1st March, 1596.

Description
Engraved paper sundial, trimmed to neat line, small tear to upper left corner skilfully repaired.

Dimensions
290 by 230mm (11.5 by 9 inches).

A rare sheet for a pillar sundial.

A pillar, or shepherd's, sundial indicates time from the sun's altitude, which is also dependent on the latitude and the season of the year. The present sheet was made for the latitude 53 degrees (the latitude for the German town of Perleberg). Once mounted on to a cylinder or pillar, the dial must be set to the correct date by rotating a knob on the top so that the metal gnomon lies immediately above the symbol for the appropriate month, which is marked along the bottom of the column. To use the sundial, it is positioned so that the shadow of the gnomon falls vertically down the column. The time will then be indicated by the position of the tip of the shadow relative to the curved hour lines that are marked on the column.

The present example is also embellished with the signs of the zodiac, a table providing information upon the signs of the zodiac with the ruling planets, and a scale giving the altitude of the sun and moon above the horizon.

Tranck dedicates the instrument to Heinrich Rantzau or Ranzow (Ranzovius) (1526–1598) who was a German humanist writer and statesman, a prolific astronomical author and an associate of Tycho Brahe. He was Governor of the Danish royal share in the Duchy of Holstein, a wealthy man and celebrated book collector. Rantzau is perhaps best remembered as a patron of scholars. His own 'Tractatus astrologicus de genethliacorum thematum' appeared in 1597, and went through five editions by 1615. In his time, he was regarded as a generous supporter of artists and writers in Lübeck, many of whom he engaged to write memorials of his father.

We are only able to trace one institutional example: that held by the Musée de Chateau de Pau (P1279). An example is mentioned in 'Catalogue de vente d'une belle collection d'estampes colligée par Benj. Petzold', No. 1213, held in Vienna in 1842, which describes the work as "superbe épreuve d'une pièce très rare".

CYLINDRUS HORARIUS
CONVEXUS MAIOR.

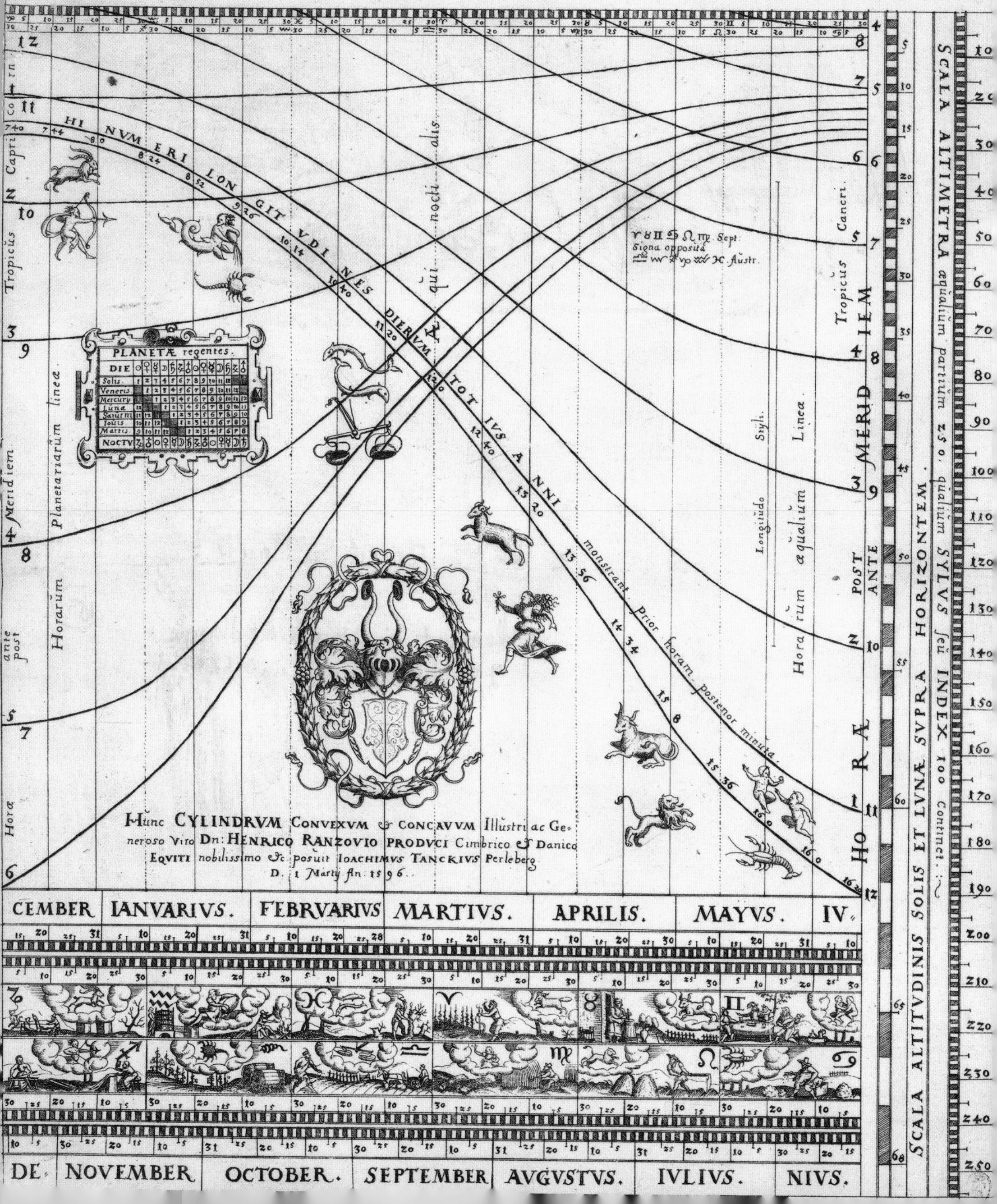

“The science which depicts and demonstrates the motions and locations of the stars”

14 **PISANI, Ottavio**

Octavii Pisani Astrologia seu Motus, et Loca Sideerum. Ad Serinissimum Dominum Cosmum Medicen.

Publication
Antwerp, Robert Bruneau, 1613.

Description
Folio bound in plano (500 by 500mm), 46 [?of 47] printed leaves and plates, many with volvelles, including Medici arms on title, dedication, and engraved portrait of Pisani by Wiericx, two moving parts replaced in facsimile, several repaired tears, small areas of damp staining to a few leaves, seventeenth century limp vellum. A full collation is available upon request.

References
Riccardi, App. V, col. 124, and App. VII, col. 71; Carli and Favaro, Bibl. Galileiana, 85; Caillet III, 8700; Houzeau-Lancaster I, 2942; cf. Kepler, Gesamte Werke xvii, 76-77; Galileo, Opere XI, 592.

A spectacular example of the art of the book, containing what is probably the first accurate and large-scale representation of the “Medicean Stars” (the four moons of Jupiter). The discovery of celestial bodies orbiting something other than the earth, first announced by Galileo in 1610, dealt a serious blow to the then-accepted Ptolemaic planetary system.

Ottavio Pisani (1574-after 1613) was reluctant to wholly abandon the idea of a geocentric universe and based his work on the Ptolemaic system. He was, however, familiar with the discoveries of Copernicus, Galileo and Kepler, and was a correspondent of the latter two. In October 1613 Pisani wrote to Kepler, “Galileo is really a heavenly Amerigo [Vespucci] in that he has found new stars in the heavens, and in particular the Medicean stars. I however am drawing the theory of the motion of the stars around Jupiter, like a satellite, in the epicycle of Jupiter. I have devised a new way of drawing the whole globe ... and have thus made a new cosmographical map ...”. Writing to Galileo on 7 November 1613, he says that he spent 200 scudi and ten years of his life on the book. Indeed, Pisani seemed keen to impress his scientific credentials on his readers, and explained the title ‘Astrologia’ not as astrology, but as “the science that depicts and demonstrates the motions and locations of the stars”. He was also a cartographer and engraved a world map in 1637 (see Bagrow, ‘History of Cartography’ p. 265).

The multitude of finely engraved diagrams in the ‘Astrologia’ illustrate the motion of the planets by a very complicated system of superimposed volvelles, intricately cut-out and in some cases totaling nine moveable parts.

“This rare atlas is a magnificent example of book production, and one has the impression that every copy must have been expressly assembled by the author; the collation, if it can be called that, is such that it could simply have been left to a binder” (Macclesfield catalogue).

& centrum circuitus planetæ, aut semidiam
Hæc autem differentia maxim … ationem instru-
ctorum; cateræ verò par … s est quod
tabulas & theori … em
cateras proport
In latitudi
rentis; M
artò, in

atur tabulæ, se
emet supp
n numer
ositio
delin
atis

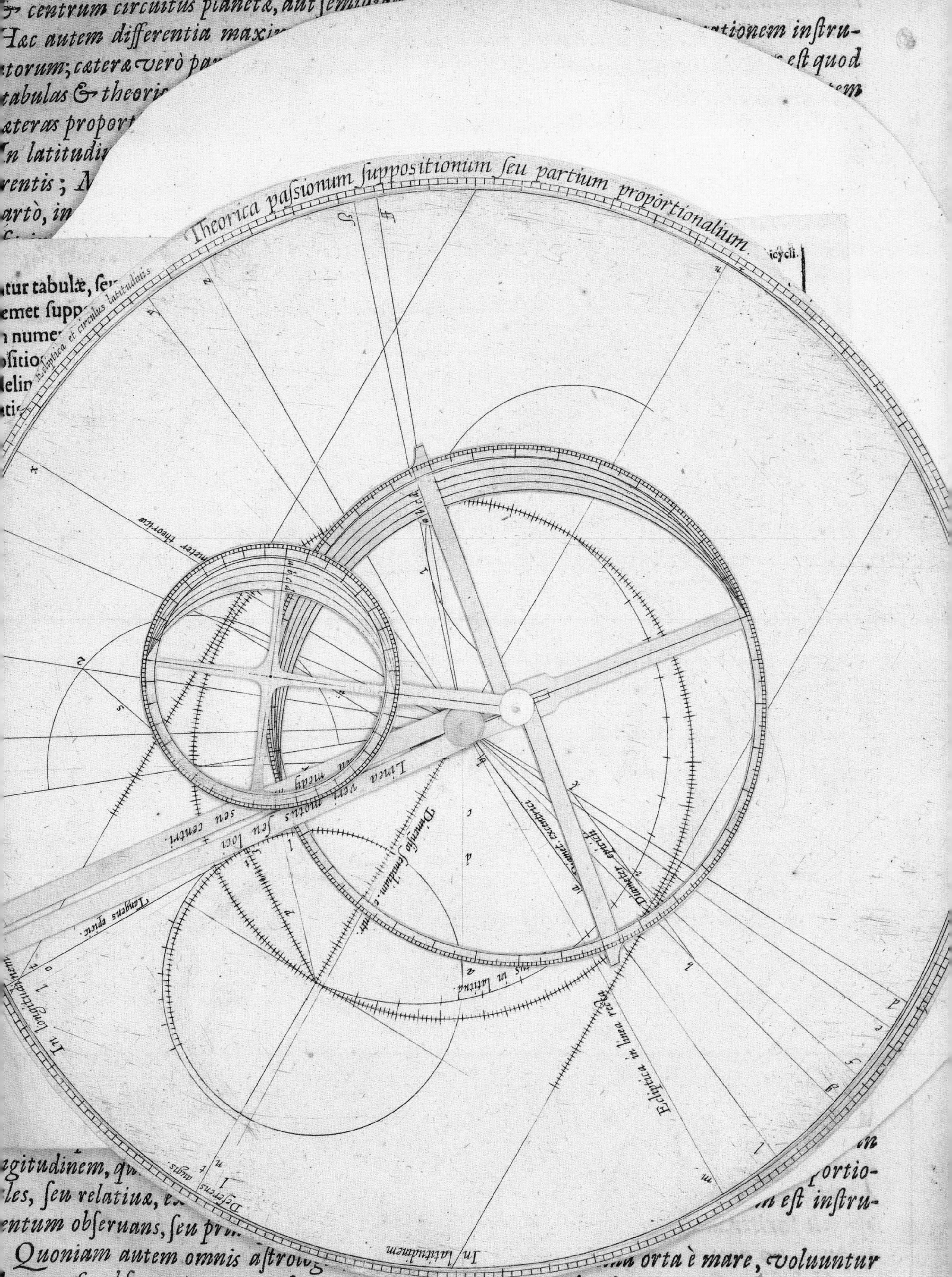

gitudinem, qu … portio-
les, seu relatiuæ, ex … m est instru-
entum obseruans, seu pri
Quoniam autem omnis astrolog … ena orta è mare, voluuntur
mare: sic obseruationes ex instrumento orta voluuntur ad instrumentum; …

Given inconsistencies in bibliographic description, and that the book is composed of differently sized sheets with numerous intricate movable illustrations, comparing collations is difficult. A careful comparison of the copy held by the Museo Galileo in Florence with the present example reveals that, using the pagination supplied for their digital reproduction, the present book is without the star chart at p. 70 in their copy, although this is duplicated at p. 40, and present in that position in our example. The present book also lacks a circular pointer on p. 57, and part of the volvelle on p. 36 (both replaced in facsimile). Interestingly, recent research has suggested that the Museo Galileo example was sent by Pisani to Galileo, asking him to present it to the Medici court in order to obtain some financial support for the author.

Rare. We have been able to trace eighteen examples of the work in institutional holdings, together with three further copies that have appeared on the market since the end of the Second World War (Sotheby's 2005 and 1952, and Lathrop Harper 1964).

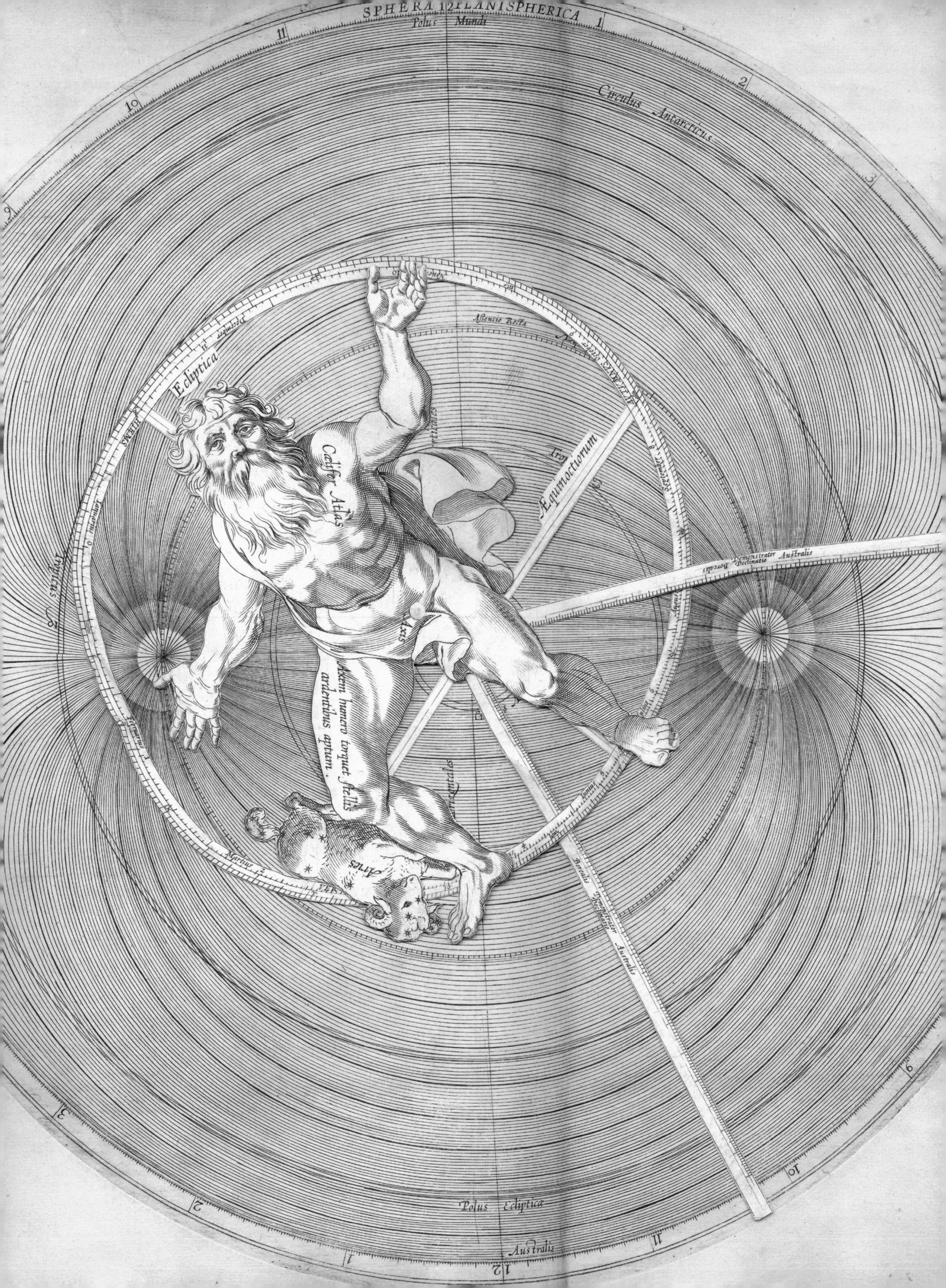
SPHERA PLANISPHERICA
Polus Mundi
Circulus Antarcticus
Ecliptica
Assencio Recta
Æquinoctiorum
Cælifer Atlas
Axis
Axem humero torquet stellis ardentibus aptum.
Aries
Demonstrator Australis
Declinatio
Borealis
Polus Ecliptica
Australis

Rare treatise on the chalice sundial

15 **BRENTEL, Georg**

Conus Solaris Concavus, das ist ein holer innwendiger Kögel oder Kelch.

Publication
Lauingen, Jacob Winter, 1615.

Description
Octavo pamphlet (200 by 165mm), 12pp., three engraved plates, of which two are folding (lacking one dial plate).

Reference
Dackerman, p. 300.

A rare treatise on the chalice, or conical, sundial.

The Bavarian painter and printmaker Georg Brentel (1580-1638) issued around twenty printed instruments, engravings and woodcuts with brief manuals, including this treatise on conical sundials. Brentel most likely relied upon the expertise of the priest-scholar Georg Galgemair, with whom he had close links between 1608 and Galgemair's death in 1619. He may also have consulted the works of Apian and Hartmann, as he is known to have copied Hartmann's cruciform sundial, and refers to Apian within the present treatise.

Brentel's first conical sundial of 1608 is a rather simple affair which tells the time from the altitude of the sun and measures heights and distances. The rotating engraved dials added to the 1615 pamphlet allow the user to convert from local to planetary hours, to allow for astronomical predictions. The treatise itself provides detailed instructions upon the construction of the instrument, together with a tutorial upon the dial itself. The dial was to be reinforced with parchment, then rolled and glued into the shape of a cone, and mounted upon a wooden base, as illustrated on the plate.

Although the present example lacks a dial plate present in the Harvard copy, it does include Franz Ritter's rare sundial plate, which first appeared in his work 'Speculum Solis' of 1607. The plate consists of a compass rose and ten sundials, including his unusual sundial world map.

Although there are several institutional examples of the pamphlet, we are only able to trace three examples that include the plates: housed at Harvard Art Museum, The University of Cincinnati, and Nuremberg University.

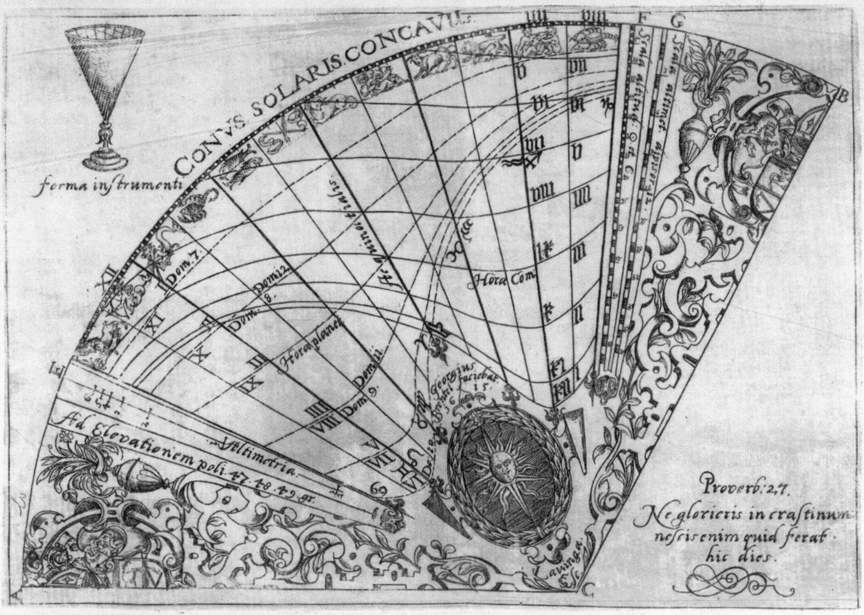
CONVS SOLARIS CONCAVVS
forma instrumenti
Scala altimet. dupsi
Horæ Com.
Horæ planet.
Dom. 7.
Dom. 9.
Altimetria
Ad Elevationem poli 47. 48. 49. gr.
Proverb: 2,7.
Ne glorieris in crastinum: nescis enim quid ferat hic dies.

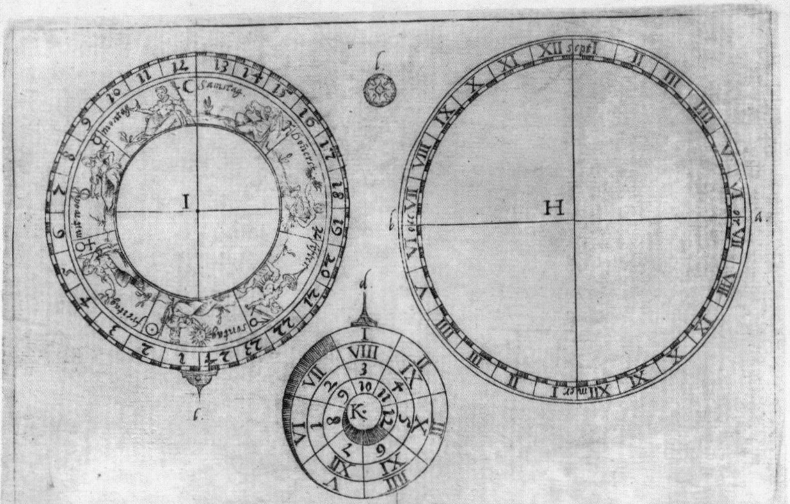
I
H
K
Samstag
Montag

Exempel: den 10. alten / oder 20. newen Jenners / befind ich auff der Tafel / daß die Sonn ist im ersten Grad deß Wassermans / darauff rucke ich das Perlein am Faden / vnd wolt nun gern vor Mittag vmb 9. Vhr der gemeinē Stund wissen die Juden Stund: lege demnach darauff den Faden / so zeigt mir das Perlin an die 2. Judenstund.

Ein ander Exempel: wir lesen Mat. 27. vnd Mar. 15. cap. vmb die 9. Stund rüfft Jesus laut vnd sprach: Eli / Eli / ꝛc. mein Gott / mein Gott / warum̃ hastu mich verlassen / das ist geweßt am Freytag / der 3. Aprill / da man gezehlt nach Christi Geburt 33.

Wann ich nun in der Tafel such den 3. Aprill / alten Calenders / so find ich in zwar nit (dann die Monatstag sein nur von 5. zu 5. Tagen eingeschriben) darumb nimb ich zwischen dem 1. vñ 5. Aprill. vngefehrlich das Mittel / also: im 1. Aprill laufft die ☉ im 21. Grad deß ♈. im 5. aber im 25. Grad: zwischen 21. vnnd 25 ist das Mittel 23. Grad. Demnach zeuch ich den Faden in der Scheiben auff den zodiacum, vnd rucke das Perlin auff den 23. Grad deß ♈. laß das Perlin vnverruckt am Faden / vnd lege solches auff die IX Stund / vnnd ziehe den Faden durch die vssere Stunden hinauß / vnd befinde / daß mir der Faden halb siebene vnser gemeinen Stunden anzeigt.

Ein ander Exempel: wir lesen Mat. 20. die Gleichnuß / so Christus seinen Jüngern erzehlt vom Hausvatter vnd Arbeittern im Weinberg / da stehet: das Himmelreich ist gleich einem Hausvatter / der am Morgen (das ist / da die Soñ auffgangen) außgieng / Arbeitter zu mieten in sein Weinberg / ꝛc. Vnd vmb die dritte Stund gieng er abermal auß / vnd fand andere müssig stehen am Marckt. Item vmb die 6. auch vmb die 9. ja auch vmb die 11. Stund / vnd fand andere müssig stehen.

Nun dise Stunden mit vnsern zuvergleichen / müssen wir wissen / in welchem Zeichen vnd Grad die Sonn ist / so befind ich auß Bartolomæi Sculteti Diario, daß Christus der Herr dise Gleichnus erzehlt nach seiner angenommenen Menschheit vnd Geburt imm 33. Jahr / den 22. Martii / Sontags: befinde also auß der Tafel / daß die ☉ im 11. Grad deß ♈ jrn Lauff hat: rucke demnach in der Scheiben das Perlin auff den 11. Grad deß ♈. vñ handle darmit / wie in vorgehendem exempel: so befindet sich / daß die 3. Stund beynahe vnser 9. die 6. den Mittag / die 9 ein wenig vber 3. die 11. aber halbe sechsin / das ist / 1. Stund vor vndergang der Sonnen anzeigt.

Hiemit will ich disen Bericht beschliessen / den kunstliebenden Leser Gottes gnedigem Schutz vnd Schirm befelhend.

ENDE.

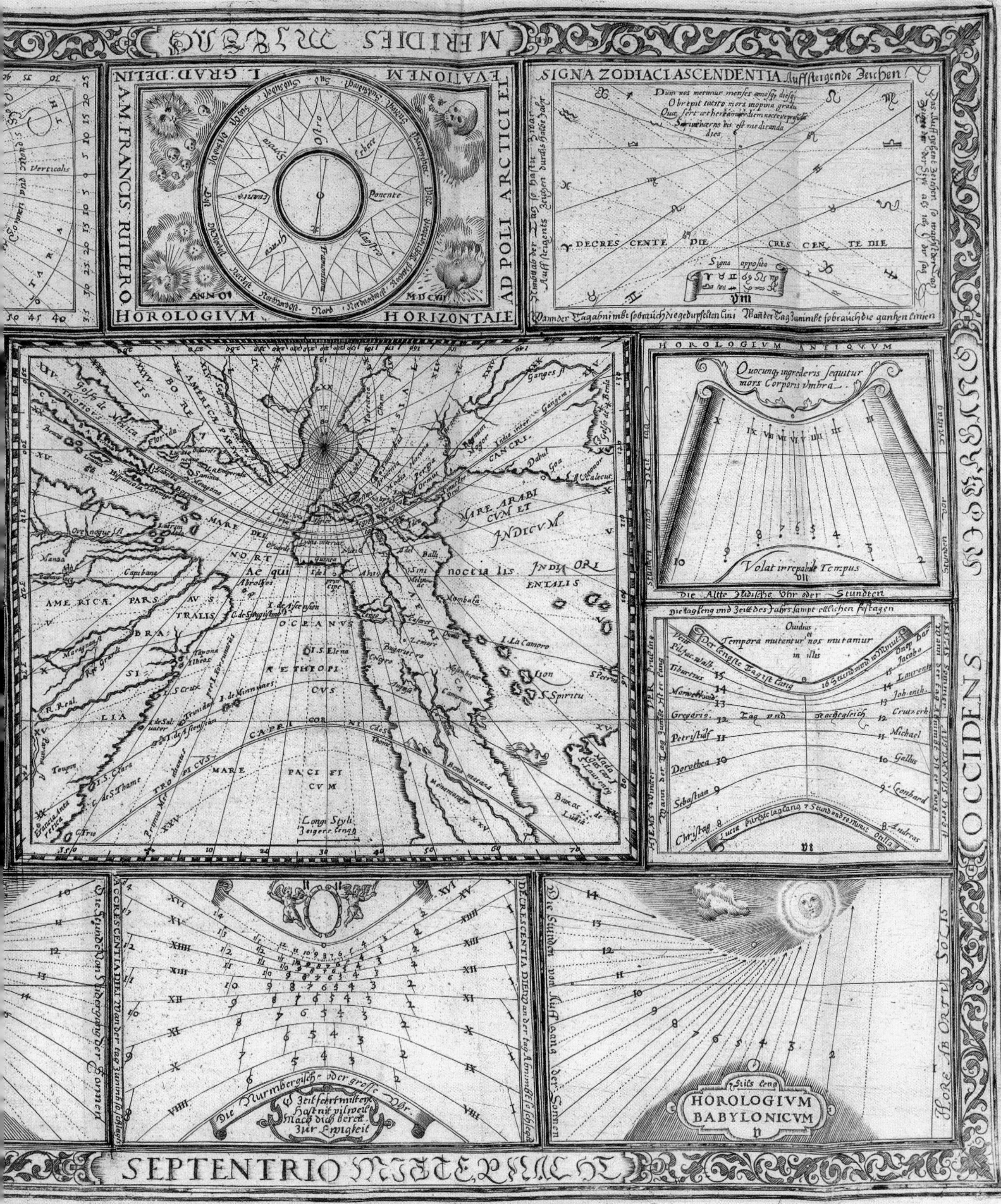
MERIDIES
HOROLOGIVM HORIZONTALE
A.M. FRANCIS RITTERO
AD POLI ARCTICI ET
ANNO MDCVII
SIGNA ZODIACI ASCENDENTIA Auffsteigende Zeichen
DECRES CENTE DIE
CRES CEN TE DIE
HOROLOGIVM ANTIQVVM
Quocunq ingrederis sequitur mors Corporis umbra
Volat irrepabile Tempus
Die Altte Jüdische Uhr oder Stundten
Ouidius
Tempora mutantur nos mutamur in illis
MARE ARABI CVM ET INDICVM
AMERICA PARS AVSTRALIS
OCEANVS AETHIOPICVS
MARE PACIFICVM
Longi Styli Zeigers leng
Die Nurmbergisch oder grosse Uhr
HOROLOGIVM BABYLONICVM
OCCIDENS
SEPTENTRIO MITTERNACHT

An apparently unrecorded dial

16 **HEIDEN, Jacobus ab [HEYDEN, Jacob van der] [after ?WELPER, Eberhard]**

[Sundial] Praeterit hicce dies, nescitur origo secundi, an labor, an reqvies: sic transit fabula mundi.

Publication
[Strasbourg, c. 1630].

Description
Engraved sundial, parts of upper margin restored, with minor loss to text.

Dimensions
195 by 270mm (7.75 by 10.75 inches).

References
Aked, C. K., and Severino, Nicola (ed.), 'International Bibliography of Gnomonica', West Drayon and Lazio, 1997.

A rare horizontal paper sundial.

The sundial was the work of Jacob van der Heyden (c. 1580-1636), an engraver and publisher of maps and scientific works in Strasbourg during the first half of the seventeenth century. He is known to have cooperated with such eminent figures as Jacob Bartsch, Isaac II Habrect, Abraham Hogenberg and Eberhard Welper. He engraved an armillary sphere drawn by Welper, and it is entirely plausible that the present sundial was engraved after him. Welper published a treatise on sundials in 1625, the same year in which Heyden printed a small pamphlet, 'Die Gestirnte Himmels Kugel', on celestial spheres, which contained a plate of globe gores.

The latitude and longitude coordinates marked upon the dial (30 degrees E, and 47-49 degrees N) correspond to the surrounds of Strasbourg. The dial is finely engraved with the sun flanked by personifications of autumn and spring. A gnomon would be fixed to a position marked "a", just below the sun. Hour lines radiate out from this point, with signs of the zodiac and vignettes of the months to the right and left borders; below is a compass flanked by personifications of summer and winter. Surrounding the work is a brief description upon the sundial, in Latin and German. The text to the lower right and left corners states that the dial is to be mounted onto a small wooden block with the four wings of explanatory text pasted to the four sides of the block.

We are unable to trace any institutional examples.

Der faden a. d. nach des pols höhe aufgericht, zeiget die gemeine stunden. Welche auß dem Centro a. gezoge seind. Der Spitz c. aber weiset die zeichen sampt den übrigen stunden.

Filum a. d. ad poli elevationem directum, vsitatas horas monstrat, ex centro a. delineatas: apex autem Styli c. signa zodiaci, cum reliquis horis explanat: cuius longitudo est perpendiculum b. c.

PRÆTERIT HICCE DIES, NESCITUR ORIGO SECUNDI, AN LABOR, AN REQUIES: SIC TRANSIT FABULA MUNDI.

Bericht über diese Ligende Sonnen uhr.

Die linien so auß dem puncten herkomen und durch auß lauffen, zeigen die gemeinen übliche Stunden an, von Mittag gezehlet.

Die klein rund gepunctierte linien weisen die stunde nach aufgang der Sonnen.

Die mit langen Strichlein bezeichnete linien erklärē die stunde nach dem nidergang der Sonnē, nach Italianischē brauch.

Spatiū intermediū inæquale Zodiacū repræsentat: lineæ transversæ duplicatæ signa utrinq, picturis et characterib. expressa: additis planetis quib. dominatū præbent: mensib. iidem, et dierum noctiūq longitudinib. Quæ singula umbra apicis extrema, à Sole projecta, sciotericō rite locato, docet.

Quæ vero trigonatis punctis adparent lineæ, horas planetarias, æquales, seu Judaicas notant.

Oblongis ductibus lineatæ, horas post occasū Solis, more Italico, indigitant.

Die mit dreyeckichten punctlin getüpfelte liniē bedeüten die Planeten oder Jüdische stunden.

Die uber zwenhe gedoppelte aber seind an statt des zeichentragers weisen die 12 zeichen wie auch die Planetē und monat deñen sie zugehörē sampt Dag und nacht länge.

Brevis Explanatio hujus horologii horizontalis.

Lineæ ex centro ductæ undiquaq, excurrentes, horas usitatas nostrates indicant, horologii scilicet minoris, à meridie numeratas.

Lineolæ rotundis punctulis insignitæ, horas à Solis ortu numerant.

diese Vier angehenckte Flügel, sollen nebens auf die dicke des bredts geleimet werden.

Quatuor hæ appendices crassitiem asseculæ monstrant, cui comodè agglutinari possunt.

The first atlas on Mercator's projection from the library of Imperial geographer Wolfgang Engelbert, Earl of Auersperg

17 DUDLEY, Robert

Dell'arcano del mare, di D. Roberto Dudleo duca di Nortumbria, e conte di VVarvich, libri sei ...

Publication
Florence, Francesco Onofri, 1646.

Description
First edition. Six parts in three volumes. Folio, complete with all the maps, plates and moveable parts as follows:

Volume I (348 by 237mm). Part I: 56pp., 30 plates (24 folding, 20 with volvelles), [3] ll. tables (ephemerides); Part II: 76, [2]pp., 12 plates (7 folding, 5 with volvelles), 15 folding maps; Part III: [4], 1-48, [4], 49-55, 8 plates (5 folding), 4 engravings on half-page, the first after plates 2, the second after plate 4, the other two between p. 16 and 17; Part IV: 39, [3]pp., 18 plates (15 folding).

Volume II (461 by 334mm). Part V: 36, [2] pp., 98 plates (with 150 illustrations), 24 folding plates (15 with volvelles), 67 plates (with 100 illustrations only on recto; 9 with volvelles), 7 plates (with 25 illustrations on recto and verso).

Volume III (460 by 333mm). Part VI: [2], 60, [2]pp., 132 folding maps (59 for Europe, 17 for Africa, 23 for Asia and 33 for America), of which 80 are double-page.

References
Phillips, Atlases 457; cf. Shirley, BL, M.DUD-1a–1e; Burden 266-267; Nordenskiöld 7; Bircher, M., 'The "Splendid Library" of the Counts of Auersperg in Ljubljana, in The German Book, 1450-1750', ed. by J. Flood and W.A. Kelly, London, 1995, pp. 285-98.

First edition of Dudley's magnificent and very scarce sea atlas 'Dell'Arcano del Mare' ('Secrets of the Sea'). The 'Arcano del Mare' is one the "greatest atlases of the world" (Wardington).

This sumptuous atlas, first published in 1646 when its author, Robert Dudley, was 73, was not only the first sea atlas of the world, but also the first to use Mercator's projection; the earliest to show magnetic deviation; the first to show currents and prevailing winds; the first to expound the advantages of 'Great Circle Sailing' (the shortest distance between two points on a globe); and "perhaps less importantly the first sea-atlas to be compiled by an Englishman, all be it abroad in Italy" (Wardington). It was, as argued by Burden, "the only exception to the total dominance of Dutch sea atlas production [in the seventeenth century]".

Robert Dudley (1573 – 1649) was the son of the Earl of Leicester (the one time favourite of Elizabeth I) and Lady Douglas Sheffield, the widow of Lord Sheffield. Although born out of wedlock, Robert received the education and privileges of a Tudor nobleman. He seems to have been interested in naval matters from an early age and, in 1594 at the age of 21, he led an expedition to the Orinoco River and Guiana. He would later, like all good Tudor seamen, sack Cadiz, an achievement for which he was knighted.

His success upon the high seas was not matched, unfortunately, by his luck at court, and at the beginning of the seventeenth century he was forced to flee, along with his cousin Elizabeth Southwell, to Europe. Eventually he ended up in Florence at the court of Grand Duke Ferdinand I of Tuscany, where he not only married his cousin and converted to Catholicism, but also helped Ferdinand wage war against the Mediterranean pirates. In his spare time he set about his great life's work: the 'Arcano del Mare'.

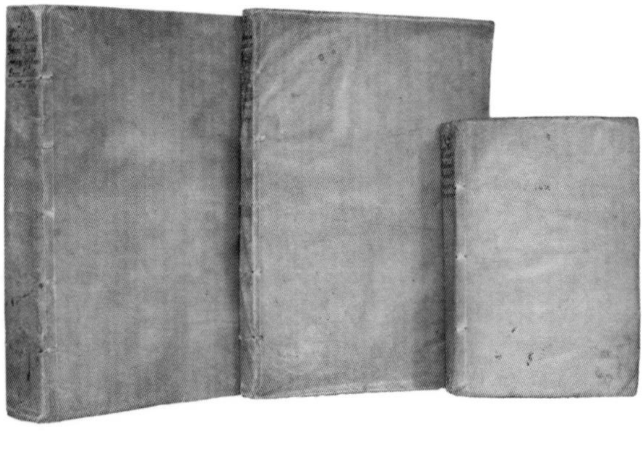

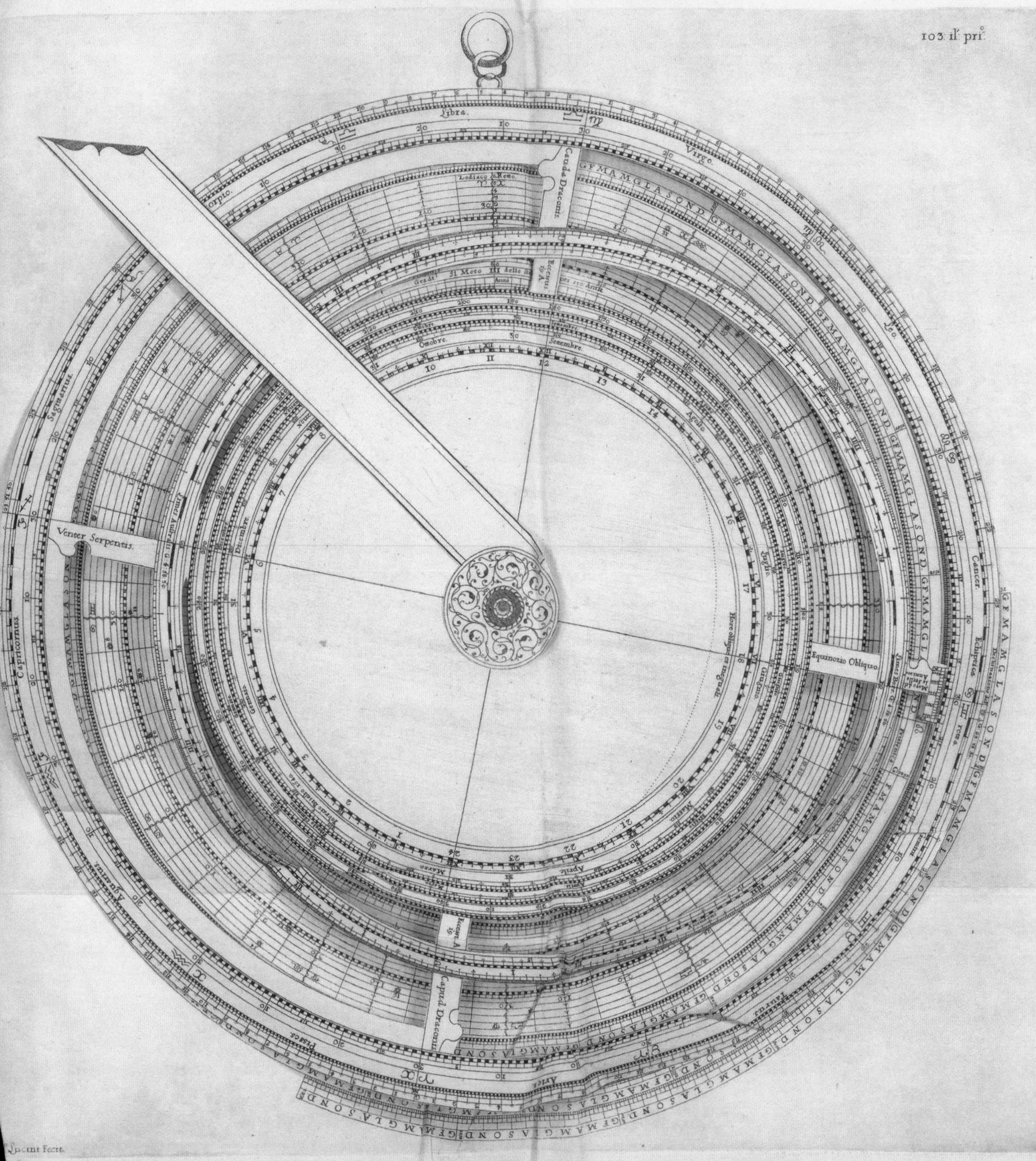

Lucini Fecit.

The atlas is divided into six books, or sections: Book One deals with longitude; Book Two covers errors in the then-existing sea charts, and includes the portolano for the Mediterranean and 15 general maps; Book Three deals with naval and military discipline, notably the former, and there is a long section on naval tactics, especially remarkable for a plan of the construction of a navy in five grades of vessel; Book Four describes the method of designing and building ships of the "Galerato" and "Galizaba" types and is concerned with naval architecture, giving the lines and dimensions of ships; Book Five is devoted entirely to navigation and methods of measuring the sun's declination and the relative positions of the stars, including numerous instruments, many with moving parts and volvelles, and at least four of which are of Dudley's own design; Book Six contains the sea atlas.

For the beautifully engraved charts, Dudley employed the services of Antonio Francesco Lucini. In a note on the example in the British Library, Lucini states in the atlases that the work took him 12 years to complete and required 5,000 pounds of copper. The charts are by English and other pilots, and it is generally accepted that the work was both scientific and accurate for the time. Dudley's sources included the original charts of Henry Hudson, and for the Pacific coast he used the observations of Henry Cavendish, the third circumnavigator of the globe and Dudley's brother-in-law. It is also possible that Dudley had access to Henry Hudson's notes and Sir Francis Drake's papers, although it is more likely that the important 'Carta prima Generale d'America' was based on the maps of John Daniell, who at the time also resided in Florence.

The 15 maps included in Book Two consist of large-scale maps of the four continents; five relate to the Americas, including the 'Carta prima Generale d'America' of Central America and Peru with a detailed inset showing the Californian coast – the first printed sea map to depict the West coast of North America (Burden 266) – and the 'Carta seconda Generale del' America', the first printed depiction made by an Englishman of the Eastern North American coast, as well as the first to record soundings methodically. The soundings in Chesapeake Bay are recorded only here: they are "curiously lacking in the more detailed chart published in the sixth part ... The most interesting area is that of New York where any indication of the Dutch presence is removed" (Burden 267). The Hudson River is named in deference to its discoverer, rather than the Dutch 'Noort River'.

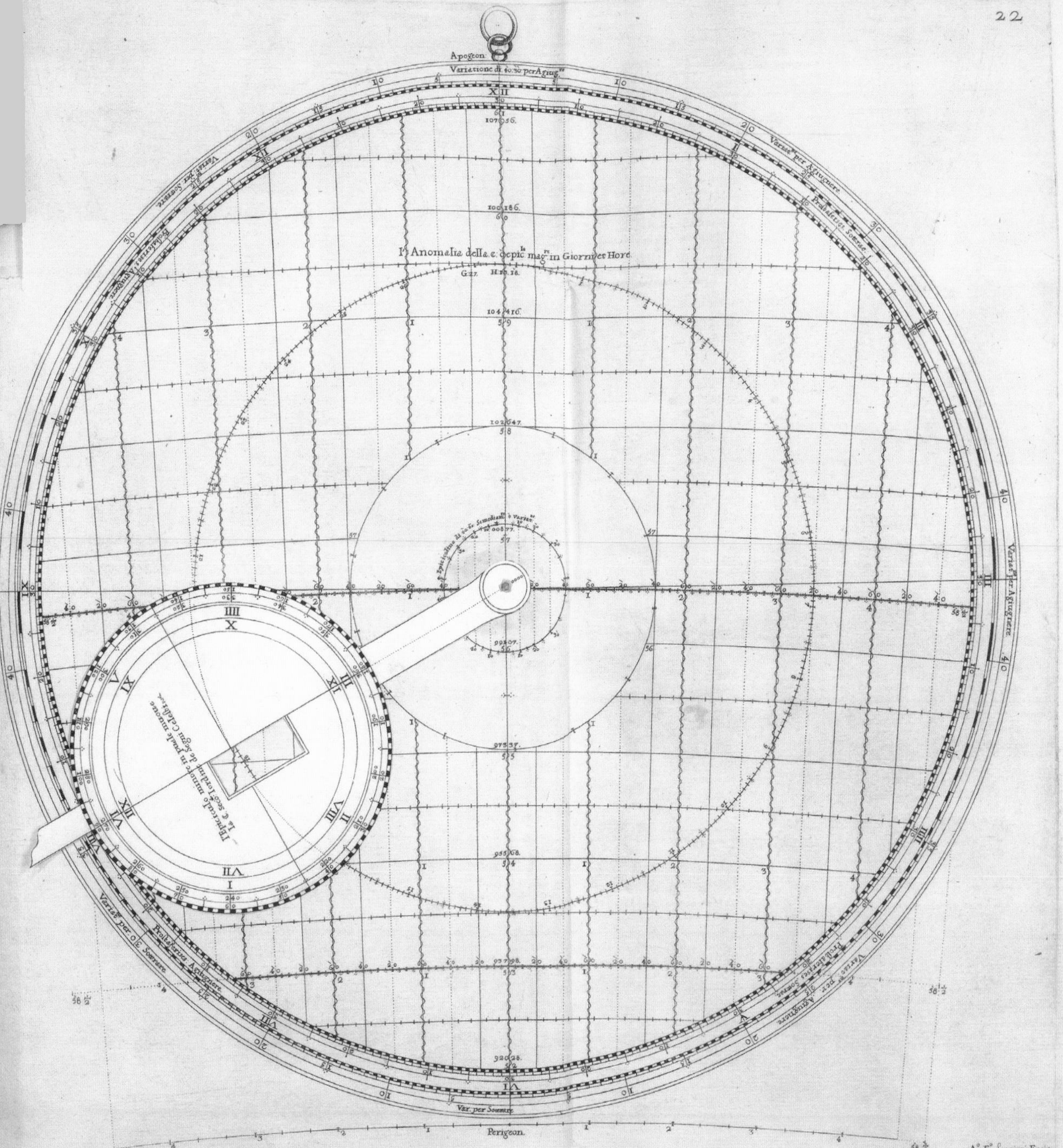

A° F° Lucini Fecit

Provenance:
Wolfgang Engelbert von Auersperg, his ownership inscription on title page of each volume (I: Wolff. Engelb. S.R.I. Com. ab Aursp. Sup. Cap. Carniae; II-III: 'Wolffg. Engelbertj S.R.I. Comitis ab Aursperg Sup. Cap. Carniae') and 'Cat. Inscriptus Anno 1656'. On the inside front cover armorial bookplate 'Fuerstlich Auerspergsche Fideicommisbibliothek zu Laybach' with manuscript shelf mark.

The present example belonged to the Imperial geographer Wolfgang Engelbert (1610-1673), Earl of Auersperg and, between 1649-1673, ruler of the Duchy of Carniola (Slovenia). Author of the 'Orbis lusus pars prima, seu Lusus geographicus' (Graz 1659), Engelbert collected in his palace in Ljubljana a splendid library, highly esteemed by his contemporaries. The library, which contained about 7,000 volumes, was rearranged and catalogued in the mid-nineteenth century by the historian Peter von Radics, who states that the collection "is unique in representing the well arranged and well chosen collection, to which no additions have been made, of an Austrian aristocrat of the seventeenth century" (quoted by M. Bircher, 'The Splendid Library of the Counts of Auersperg'). In 1895 a severe earthquake led to the loss of the Ljubljana castle, but the books were undamaged and transferred along with the family's archives to Losensteinleithen Castle in Austria. The library eventually descended to family members in Uruguay who sold it by auction in 1982-83.

A fine wide-margined copy, complete with books five and six which are often missing, as they were published later because the European maps needed updating.

Rare. The last example to come on the market, albeit a second edition, sold for $824,000 in the Frank Streeter sale (Christie's New York, 16 May 2007).

ASIA
IMPERIO DELLA CHINA
CHINCHEO
CANSAN
Quansai
IL Tropico di Cancer
Canton
I. Lamo
I. Branca
I. dos Viados
Pulo Baby
I. Coina
C. Canchi
MARE DELLA CHINA
I. Prata ò Wales
I. Choa
Var. Nulla
PARTE PIU AUSTRALE DELLA CHINA ò CINA
I. Omander ò Ouandero
Pulo Tio
Pulo Gro
Isoletta
I. Tincous
Quest Isola li Chinesi chiamano Haina come parte piu Australe della China
Corrente per Austro
Seccagna
Var. 1. Gr. Maestrale
Li Venti Cattivi Sono Becciati
Li Buoni Sono Monsoni
Var. Insensibile
G. di Cocincina
Var. 2. Gr. Maestrale
La Seccagna di Bollinao
I. di Prasel
C. Bollinao del I. Lucon
I. Campileo
Seccagna pericolosa
Mare delle Filippine
Pulo Cataon ò Cattam
Var. Insensibile
Pulo Cambir
ISIOPA
Var. 1. Gr. ½. Maestrale
C. di Auarella
C. Comarin
Carta particolare del mare di Cocincina con la parte Australe della China
La longi.^{ne} Comin.^{ca} da l'Isola di Pico d'Asores
d'Asia Carta VII.
Æ. Lucini
138
139
140
141
142
143
144
145
146
147
148

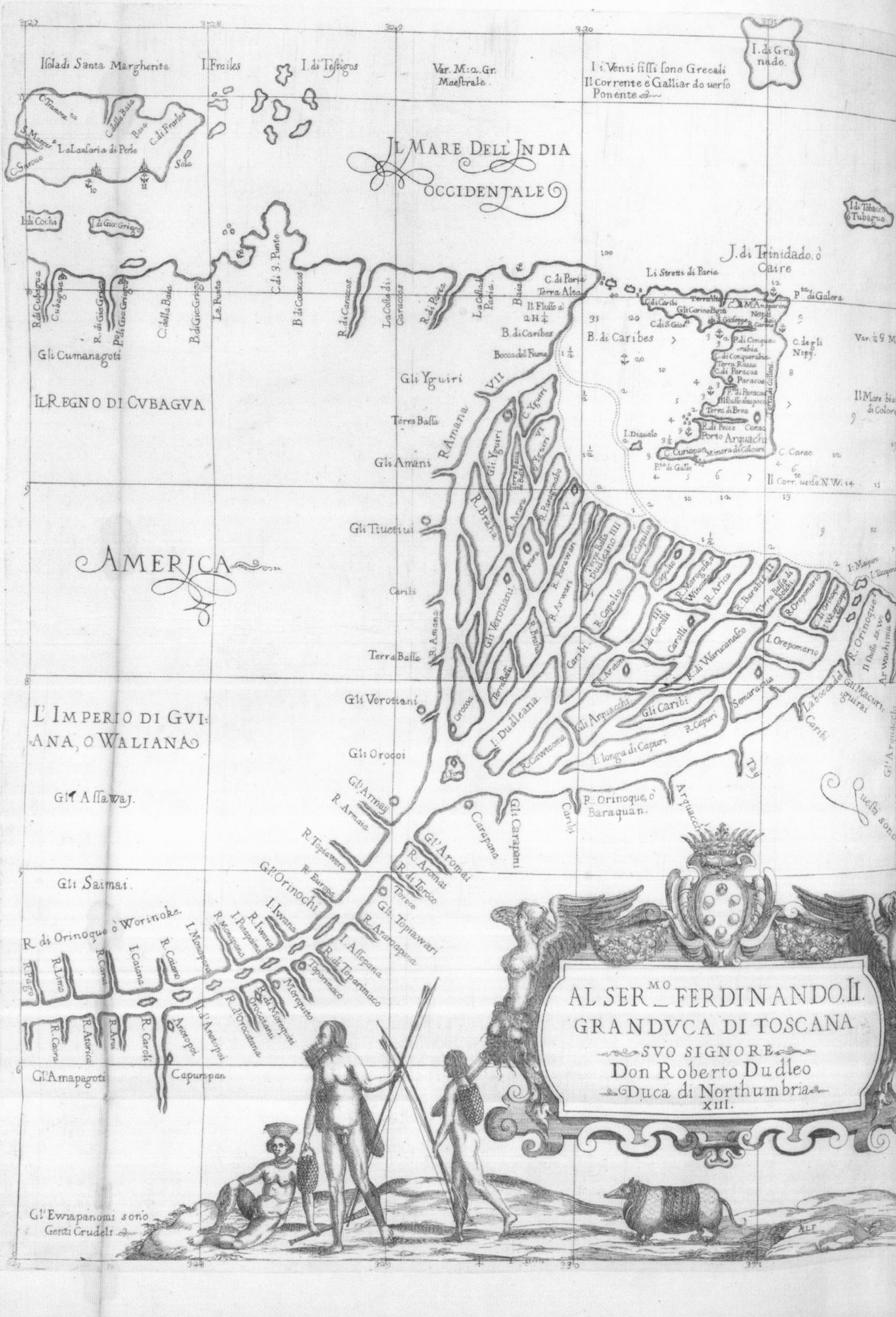

AL SER.MO FERDINANDO II.
GRANDUCA DI TOSCANA
SUO SIGNORE
Don Roberto Dudleo
Duca di Northumbria
XIII.
IL MARE DELL' INDIA OCCIDENTALE
AMERICA
IL REGNO DI CUBAGUA
L' IMPERIO DI GUIANA, O WALIANA
Isola di Santa Margherita
I. Frailes
I. di Testigos
Var. M: 2. Gr. Maestrale
I i Venti fissi sono Grecali
Il Corrente e Galliar do uerso Ponente
I. di Granado.
I. di Tobacco ò Tubaguo.
I. di Cocha
I. di Gio: Griego
J. di Trinidado, ò Caire
Li Stretti di Paria
C. di Paria
Terra Alta
B. di Caribes
Bocca del Fiume
Porto Arquachi
I. Diauolo
Il Corr. uerso N.W.
Gli Cumanagoti
Gli Yguiri
Terra Bassa
Gli Amani
R. Amana
Gli Tiuctiui
Cariti
Gli Veroriani
Gli Orocoi
Gli Assawaj
Gli Saimai
Gli Arwaj
R. Armaia
R. Topiawero
R. Europa
Gli Orinochi
R. di Orinoque ò Worinoke.
Gli Aromai
Carapana
Gli Carapani
R. Orinoque, ò Baraquan.
Arquacchi
Gli Topiawari
I. Assepana
R. di Toparimaco
Gli Amapagoti
Capurupan
Gli Ewiapanomi sono Genti Crudeli
I. Dudleana
Gli Arquacchi
Gli Caribi
I. longa di Capuri
I. Orepomarto
La bocca del
Questi sono

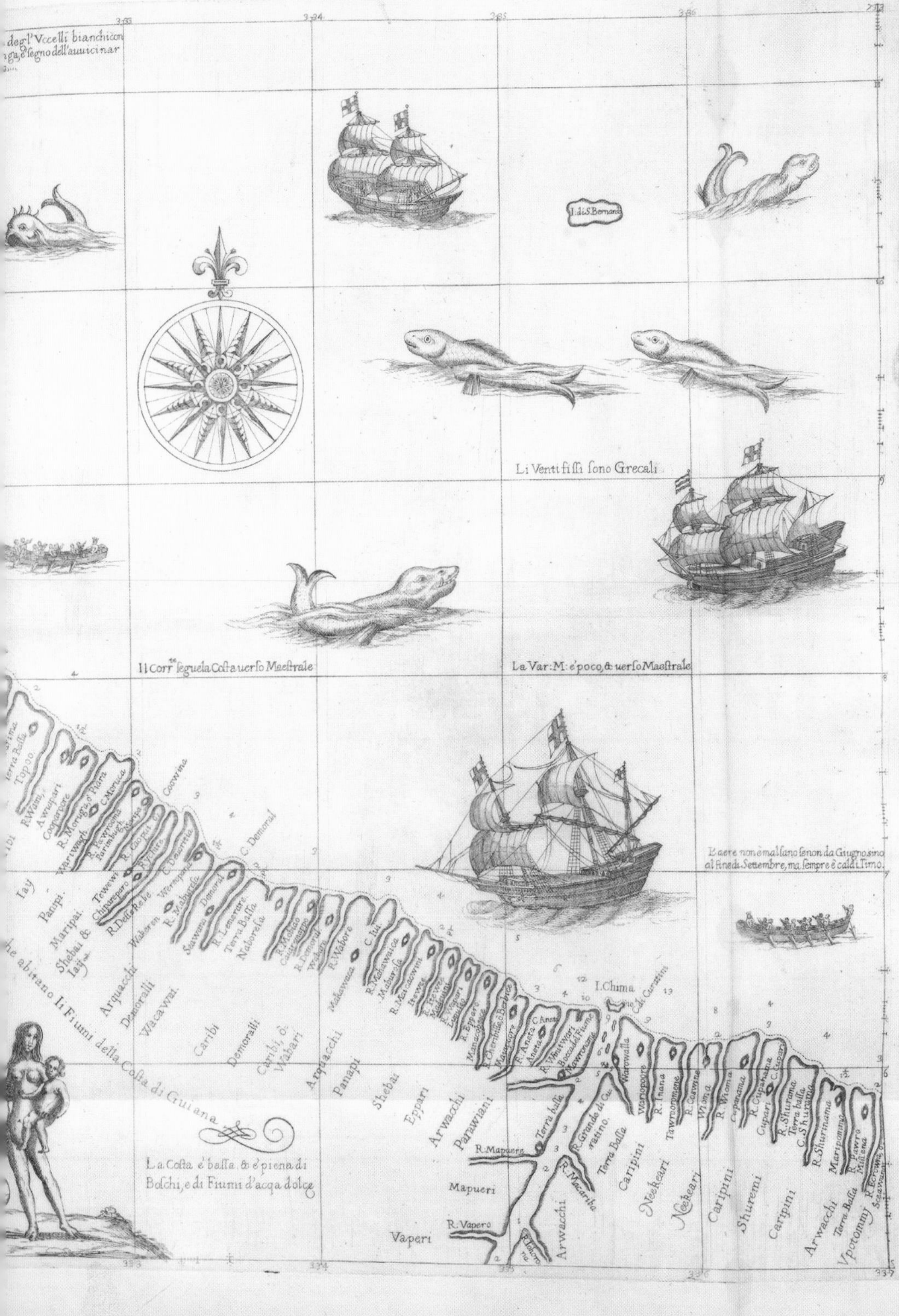

degl' Vccelli bianchi con
nga, è segno dell'auuicinar
I. di S. Bernard
Li Venti fissi sono Grecali
Il Corr.te segue la Costa uerso Maestrale
La Var: M: e' poco, & uerso Maestrale
L'aere non è mal sano se non da Giugno sino
al fine di Settembre, ma sempre è caldi. Timo.
che abitano li Fiumi della Costa di Guiana
La Costa è bassa & è piena di
Boschi, e di Fiumi d'acqua dolce
I. Chima
C. Demoral
Terra Balla
Iay
Panpi
Maripai
Arquacchi
Demoralli
Wacawai
Caribi
Arquacchi
Panapi
Shebai
Eppari
Arwacchi
Parawiani
R. Mapuere
Mapueri
R. Vapero
Vaperi
R. Macariba
Arwacchi
Caripini
Neekeari
Shureni
Caripini
Arwacchi
Terra Balla
333
334
335
336
337

Rare treatise on sundials

18 **SEITZ, David**

Gnomonica Das ist: Gründtliche Underrichtung und Beschreiburg wie man die Inclinierte Sonnen Uhren machen solle: welche zwar biß hero nit klar und deutlich sonder etwas dunckels an Tag gegeben und demnach für gut angesehen worden hierinnen allerhand Gattungen Inclinierte oder zu ruckhangende und eingebogne Sonnen Uhren zu beschreiben.

Publication
Augsburg, 1649.

Description
Octavo (195 by 160mm), title, [36]pp., 17 engraved plates tipped in throughout the work, original red marbled paper covers.

References
Zinner 534, cites only 2 plates; Arnold, 'Augsburger Drucke' 117 [without plate P]; VD17 12:163930L.

A rare and only edition of David Seitz's work on sundials.

Little is known about the author; presumably a talented amateur. The work itself gives a detailed guide to the theory and practical applications of sundials, with the work being illustrated by 17 engraved plates. Nuremberg had been a major centre for the production of sundials from the early 1500s, and Seitz's work reflects 150 years of accumulated knowledge.

Eine Sonnen Vhr die just gegen Mittag stehet/vnd erhebt sich vom Horinzont 60. grat.

1. Es soll eine Creutz Lini gemachet werden/mit A B C D das mittel ist E.
2. Der Zirckelfuß soll in E gesetzt werden/der ander Fuß soll auffthan werden/ wie man will/doch nit zu weit/es wurde sonst ein groß fundament abgeben/ vnd auff die Lini A B setzen/gibt F.
3. Die weite E F soll mit einem Zirckel genommen werden/der Fuß soll im F stehen

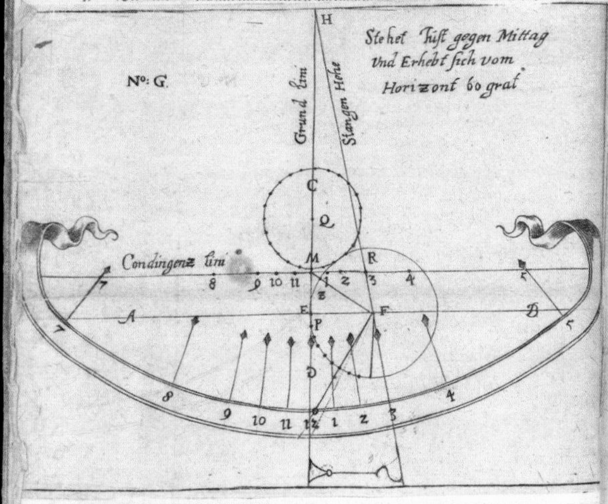

13. Der eine Quatrant gegen der r... an zu zehlen von oben herab vom ...

14. Das

14. Das Lineal soll in Centro deß runden Zirckelriß vnd zugleich auff die Equinoctial höhe der 41. grat gelegt werden/auß dem Centro/durch die 41. grat eine Lini gezogen/also ist der Quatrant W gemacht.
15. Jetzt kan ich in der Beschreibung / vnd in der Sonnen Vhr wider fortfahren/ weil der Quatrant W gemacht ist.
16. Der Zirckelfuß soll in Quatranten in W gesetzt werden / der ander Fuß soll herab in die 41. grat gewendt werden/der Zirckel soll vnverruckt bleiben.
17. Solliche weite soll in der Sonnen Vhr getragen werden/der Fuß soll in Z gesetzt werden/der ander Fuß soll herab gewendt werden / vnd wo der Fuß den runden Zirckelriß beriert/ ist P.
18. Ein Winckelhacken soll vom P vnd F gelegt werden / daß das Eck deß Winckelhacken am F anlige / an dem Winckelhacken soll eine Lini hinauff gezogen werden/ vnd wo dise Lini die Lini C D durchschneit/ist H. da wird die Stang eingemacht/ist auch die Stangen höhe.
19. Wann es sich begibt/das die Stang herabwartz stehet/ so kompt es dahero/wann das P vnder der Lini A B kompt / weil die grat vber der Polus sich erhebt/ so kompt das P vnder der Lini A B vnd wird das H oben kommen/vnd die Stang wird herabwartz stehen/vnd der Zetel vnden gemacht werden.
20. Dann soll das Lineal an F vnd H gelegt werden/eine Lini herab gezogen/gibt die Stangen höhe/vnd wo die Stangen höhe den runden Zirckelriß durchschneit/ist R.
21. Die weite M vnd R soll mit dem Zirckel genommen werden / der Fuß deß Zirckels soll in M stehen bleiben / den einen Fuß soll vbersich in die Lini C D geschlagen werden/gibt Q.
22. Auß dem Q wird gemacht der runde Zirckelriß/welchen ich den Sonnen Zirckel nennen thu/vnd wo sich der runde Zirckelriß im M durchschneit/da soll man anfangen zu thailen in 24. thail.
23. Das Lineal soll auffs Q vnd auff zwen gegen einander stehende Punckten in dem runden Zirckelriß/vnd zugleich auff die Condingenz Lini gelegt werden/darauff die Stund Punckten sollen verzaichnet werden.
24. Dann soll das Lineal auffs H vnd zugleich auff die Condingenz Lini gelegt werden/die Stunden auß dem H in den Zetel gezogen werden/die Stang soll in das H eingemacht werden.

N°: G.

Dise Sonnen Vhr soll auffgericht werden/nach der Lini C D.

Wie eine Maur zuerfahren/ob dieselbige gegen Mittag stehe.

25. Nembe das declinatorium, hebe es an die Maur/ daß die 90. grat an die Maur gehebt wird.
26. Nembe das Mangnet Kästlen/drehe das hin vnd her / biß daß der Mangnet einschlage/vnd der Zaiger/der die grat weißt/ in der Mittag Lini einschlecht/ so stehet die Maur gegen Mittag.

Wie

deß Winckelhacken am A anlige / an dem Winckelhacken soll eine Lini gezogen werden/ gibt die Stangen höhe.

30. Die weite A B soll mit dem Zirckel genommen werden/der Fuß soll im A stehen bleiben/der ander Fuß soll herumb geschlagen werden/gegen der rechten Hand / in die Lini die an dem Winckelhacken ist gezogen worden/gibt T, das Lineal soll auffs S vnd T gelegt werden/an dem Lineal soll eine Lini gezogen werden/ist die Stangen höhe.
31. Das Lineal soll auffs N vnd K gelegt werden/zeuch an dem Lineal eine Lini hinauß/ ist die Condingenz Lini.
32. Mit dem Zirckel soll man nemmen die weite N vnd L, der Fuß soll im N stehen bleiben/der ander Fuß soll herab geschlagen werden auff die grund Lini / gibt P, auß dem P ein runder Zirckelriß gemacht werden/wird genandt Sonen Zirckel/der soll in 24. thail gethailt werden/so groß man will.
33. Das Lineal soll auffs P vnd N gelegt werden / an dem Lineal soll eine Lini gezogen werden/vnd wo dise Lini den runden Zirckelriß durchschneit / da muß man anfangen zu thailen/ist Lini W. N°: O.
34. Lege ein Lineal auffs P vnd auff die Condingenz Lini /vnd auff zwen gegen einander stehende Punckten /die in dem runden Zirckelriß seyn gemacht worden / gelegt werden/ vnd wo sich das Lineal auff die Condingenz Lini legen laßt/ oder wo das Lineal die Condingenz Lini berieren kan / darauff sollen die Stund Punckten/ auff der Condingenz Lini/gemacht werden.
35. Es ist in acht zu nemmen/so offt man das Lineal auff die Condingenz Lini legen kan/ so vil Stunden werden in der Sonnen Vhr bescheint werden.
36. Wann aber das Lineal / die Condingenz Lini nimmer berieren will / oder auff die Condingenz Lini nit mehr legen laßt/so bescheint die Sonn die Stunden nit.
37. Das Lineal soll auffs S vnd auff alle Stund Punckten/die auff der Condingenz Lini seyn gemacht worden / gelegt werden / auß dem S sollen alle Stunden von der Condingenz Lini in den Zetel gezogen werden/der Zetel kan gemacht werden/wie man will.

Dise Sonnen Vhr soll auffgericht werdeu/nach der Lini C D.

Wie eine Maur zu erfahren ist/ob sie von Mittag gegen der Sonnen Nidergang stehe.

38. Nembe das declinatorium, hebe es an die Maur/daß die 90. grat an die Maur kommen / Nembe das Mangnet Kästlen / drehe dasselbige hin vnd her / biß so lang/ das der Mangnet im Mangnet Kästlen just einschlage / besihe wo der Zaiger der am Mangnet Kästlen ist/ in was für ein feldt auff dem declinatorium einschlecht.
39. Schlecht der Zaiger im feldt gegen der rechten Hand ein / so weich die Maur gegen Nidergang ab/ Ich will setzen/dise Maur weicht 40. grat gegen Nidergang ab/vnd der Zaiger der am Mangnet Kästlẽ ist/habe in die 40. grat gegen der Rechten eingeschlagẽ.

Wie die 30. grat/die sie vom Horinzont/oder zu ruck hangen/von der Maur sollen genommen werden.

40. Nembe das declinatorium, hebe es an die Maur mit der seyten / das darauff stehet Meridies, so fällt das Mangnet Kästlen sampt dem Zaiger herab/ wie ein perpendiculum.

lum, vnd besihe auff was für ein grat der Zaiger fällt / vmb so vil grat hangt die Maur zu ruck.

Volgt wie die 40. grat der M...

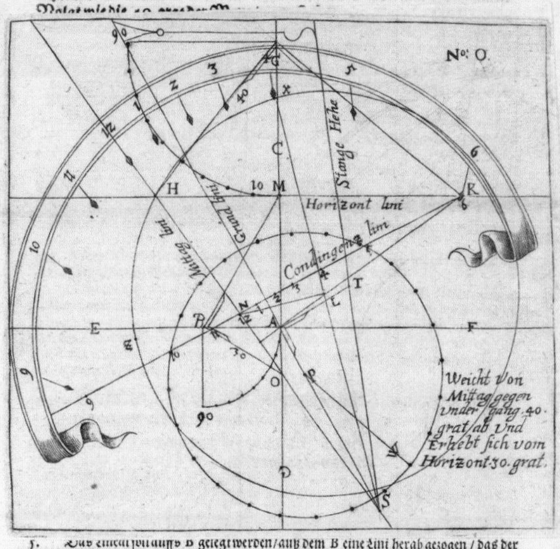

5. Das Lineal soll auffs B gelegt werden/auß dem B eine Lini herab gezogen / das der Lini C D gleich ist.
6. Der Zirckelfuß soll in B gesetzt werden/ der Fuß soll in B stehen bleiben/ auß dem B zum A einen Quatranten machen/diser Quatrant soll in 90. thail gethailt werden/anfangen zu thailen vom A herab/diser Quatrnat wird gebraucht zu dem grat/die sie vom Horinzont sich erheben/oder die grat die zu ruck hangen.
7. Das Lineal soll auffs B vnd 80. grat gelegt werden / an dem Lineal soll eine Lini gezogen werden/die die Lini C D durchschneit/ist O.

The only celestial atlas published during the Golden Age of Dutch cartography

19 **CELLARIUS, Andreas.**

Harmonia Macrocosmia sev atlas universalis et novus, totius universi creati cosmographiam generalem, et novam exhibens.

Publication
Amsterdam, Johannes Janssonius, 1661.

Description
First edition, second issue. Folio (508 by 330 mm), [14], 125, [1b.] pp.; 219 pp., engraved allegorical frontispiece by F.H. van Hoven and 29 double-page astronomical maps, all finely coloured by a contemporary hand, original publisher's Dutch vellum, gilt-panelled with large central arabesque, smooth spine in eight compartments, yapp board-edges, gilt edges.

References
Biblioteca Civica Bertoliana, Vicenza, 'Teatro del cielo e della terra', pp. 33-34, & 36. Brown, 'Astronomical atlases', pp. 40-42; Honeyman Coll. II, 658; Lalande, p. 248; Lister, p. 48; Poggendorff I, 409; Koeman IV, Cel I.

First edition, second issue (the first being dated 1660) of the only celestial atlas published during the Golden Age of Dutch cartography, and probably the finest celestial atlas ever realized.

The first 21 sumptuous Baroque style charts beautifully represent the three competing astronomical models of the day: the Ptolemaic, Tychonic and the Copernican. The Ptolemaic, named after the second century A.D. astronomer Ptolemy, was the oldest of the celestial theories and, until the beginning of the sixteenth century, was the accepted doctrine on planetary motion. Ptolemy proposed a geocentric solar system with the sun, planets and fixed stars borne on concentric spherical shells orbiting a stationary earth. The theory was endorsed by the church, which saw it as reinforcing Man's position at the centre of God's universe, and its emphasis on the dichotomy between the ever-changing sinful earth and the immutable motion of the heavens. The theory was given some scientific credence by the church's reference to the 'father of physics', Aristotle. By the turn of the sixteenth century and the dawn of the Age of Discovery, the model was beginning to show signs of age. The star charts and tables used for navigation on the high seas by the likes of Columbus and da Gama were soon found wanting. This led men to seek new and more accurate observations of the heavens. One such man was Nicholas Copernicus (1473-1543), whose observations led him to publish 'De Revolutionibus Orbium Coelestium' ('On the Revolutions of the Celestial Orbs') in Nuremberg in 1543. In it he placed the sun at the centre of the solar system with the planets orbiting in perfect circular motion. It would, however, take a century and a half for a new physics to be devised, by the likes of Galileo Galilei, to underpin Copernicus's heliocentric astronomy. Tycho Brahe (1546-1601) offered a rather inelegant third theory, which attempted to keep faith with the old Ptolemaic model, whilst embracing aspects of the new Copernican system. His theory kept the Earth in the centre of the universe, so as to retain Aristotelian physics. The Moon and Sun revolved about the Earth, and the shell of the fixed stars was centred on the Earth. But Mercury, Venus, Mars, Jupiter, and Saturn revolved around the Sun. This Tychonic world system became popular early in the seventeenth century among those who felt forced to reject the Ptolemaic arrangement of the planets (in which the Earth was the centre of all motions) but who, for reasons of faith, could not accept the Copernican alternative.

ATLAS COELESTIS;
seu
HARMONIA
MACROCOSMICA.

The last eight plates represent celestial hemispheres and planispheres depicting the constellations; they are the most ornate of all, and their level of artistic detail has made these plates very popular.

Andreas Cellarius was born in Neuhausen, a small town near Worms in Germany. From 1625 to 1637 he worked as a schoolmaster in Amsterdam and later The Hague, and in 1637 moved to Hoorn, where Cellarius was appointed to be the rector of the Latin School.

The coloured maps of the present copy are particularly attractive, with the pastiness and the opulence of the colours lending the maps pictorial significance.

Of the various engravers and authors who worked on the plates of the atlas, only two have signed their work: Frederik Hendrik van den Hove, author of the frontispiece, and Johannes van Loon, who engraved ten plates. Moreover, all the designs of the classical constellations were taken from those created by Jan Pieterszoon Saenredam.

Provenance: Ex libris 'Bibliotecae Domini De Sade' (Donatien Alfonse de Sade).

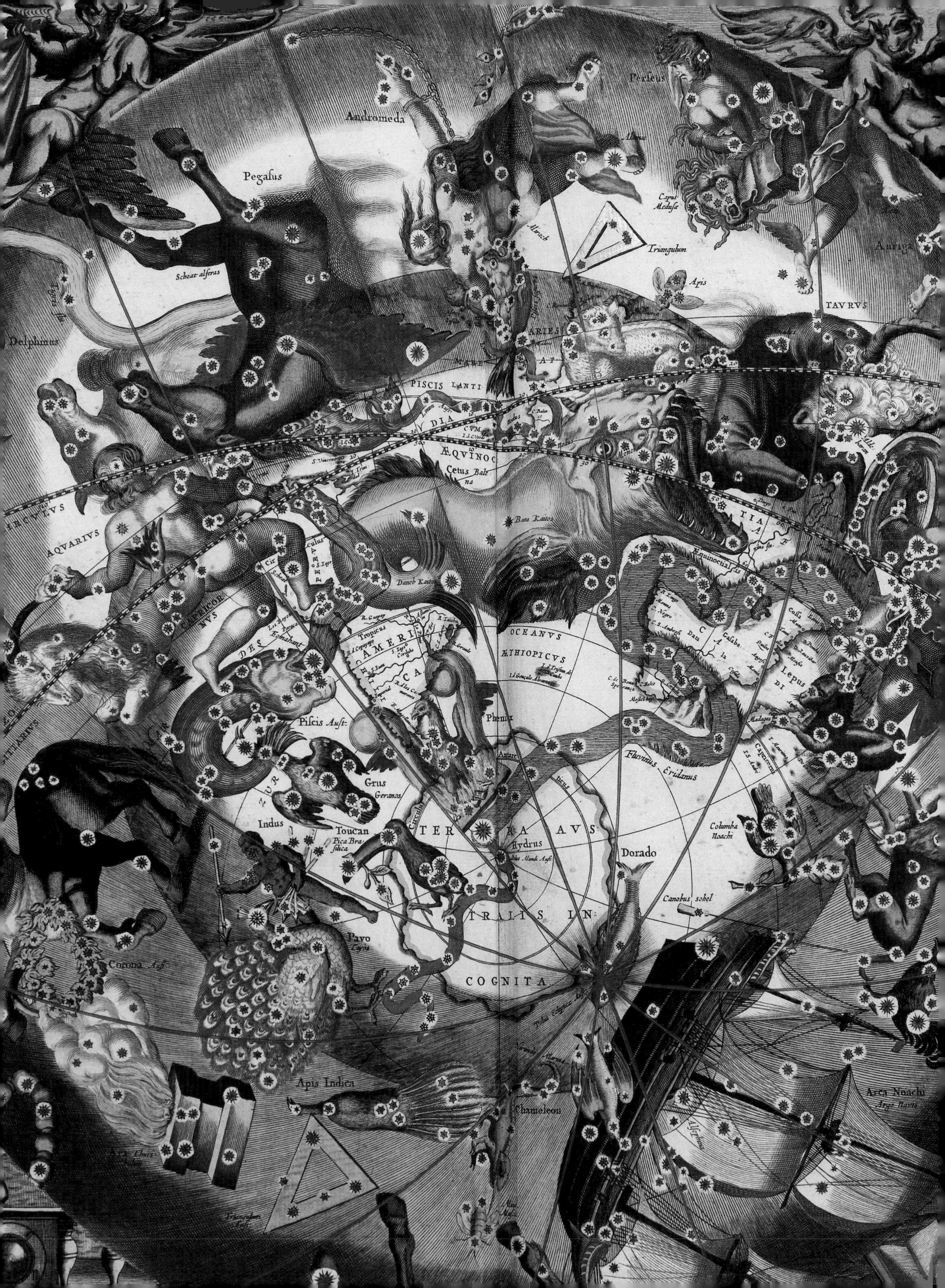

Andromeda
Perseus
Pegasus
Caput Medusæ
Triangulum
Auriga
Apis
TAVRVS
Delphinus
ARIES
PISCIS
Cetus Balæna
AQVARIVS
CAPRICORNVS
OCEANVS ÆTHIOPICVS
Fluvius Eridanus
Lepus
Piscis Aust.
Phenix
Grus Geranos
Indus
Toucan
Hydrus
Dorado
Columba Noachi
Canobus
Pavo
Corona Aust.
TERRA AVSTRALIS INCOGNITA
Apis Indica
Chameleon
Arca Noachi Argo Navis

PLANISPHÆRIVM
Sive
ORBIVM MVNDI
PTOLEMA-
NODI-
SEV CAPRICORNVS
AQVARIVS
TICA
ECLIP PISCES
ARIES
TAVRVS
GEMINI
VIA
SEPT
ORBITA IOVIS
CIRCVLVS
PLA NE
CVRRICVLVM
VENERIS
ITER MER
ORBI
SATVRNI
MVNDVS SVBLVNARIS QVATVOR EL

Nona addi-ta.

Motus ... artu in Oc-casum.

Alius.

Sphæra De-ima.

SCENO
SYSTE
COPER
ZODIACVS. ET SPHÆRA STELLARVM
CAN-
CER
IVPITER
ÆQVINOCTIVM
VERNVM
SAGIT
TARIVS

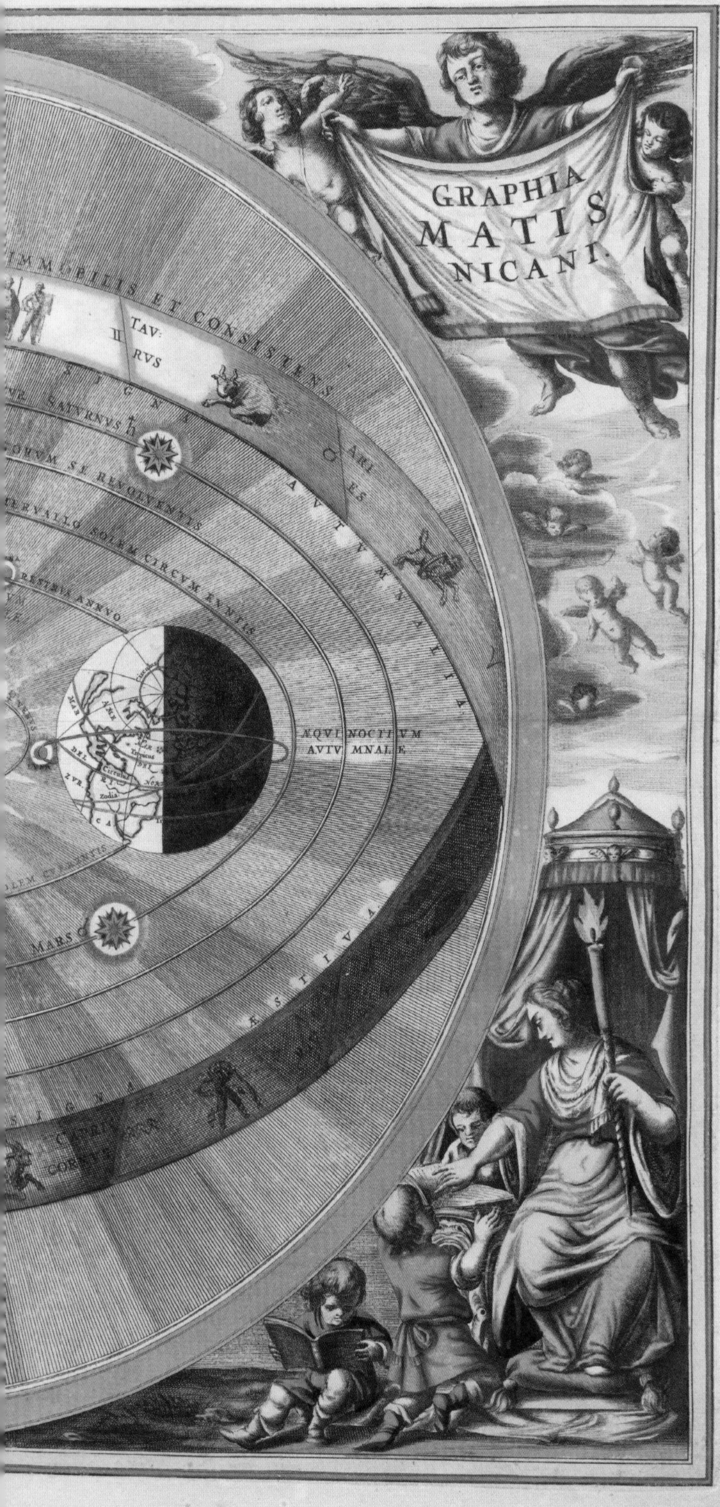
GRAPHIA
MATIS
NICANI.
IMMOBILIS ET CONSISTENS
TAV:
RVS
SIGNA
SATVRNVS
ARI
ES
AVTVMNALIA
ORVM SE REVOLVENTES
TERVALLO SOLEM CIRCVMEVNTIS
RESTRIS ANNVO
ÆQVINOCTIVM
AVTVMNALE
MARS
ÆSTIVA

The only known examples of instruments made for an unpublished quarto edition of 'Dell' Arcano del Mare'

20 **LUCINI, Antonio Francesco**

Zodiac Obliquo [with:] Diferae di Minuti in 100 Anni per causa della Stella Polar.

Publication
[?Florence, c. 1665].

Description
Two engraved paper dials with volvelles, both with moveable pointers.

Dimensions
285 by 290mm (11.25 by 11.5 inches).

References
Wardington, Lord, "Sir Robert Dudley", 'The Book Collector', 52, pp. 199-211 and 53, pp. 317-355, 2003.

An engraved instrument for the hours and minutes of the ebb and flow of the tides, and an instrument for measuring axial precession for the years 1600-1700.

Antonio Francesco Lucini (1610-after 1661) was responsible for the engraving of the greatest marine atlas of the seventeenth century: Robert Dudley's 'Dell'arcano del mare' (see item 17).

Lucini was born in Florence c. 1610. He was a pupil of Callot and a friend of Stefano della Bella. Before being employed by Sir Robert Dudley, he had already published engraved views of Florence and scenes of the Turkish Wars. Lucini put the stamp of his personality on the finished work, as did the author; the delicacy and strength of the engraving, as well as the embellishments of the lettering "alla cancellaresca", make it a true example of Italian Baroque art. In a printed introductory leaf found in one copy of the 'Arcano Del Mare' in the British Library, Lucini states that he worked on the plates in seclusion for 12 years in an obscure Tuscan village, using no less than 5,000 pounds (2,268 kg) of copper. According to the engraver, the book took 40 years to prepare and 12 to execute.

Following Dudley's death in 1649, a subsequent edition was published in 1661 by Lucini and Jacopo Bagnoni. The evident success of the second edition led to Lucini's decision to publish the work in a more manageable format, and he began on the great task of engraving new plates for the work. However, he was, for whatever reason, unable to complete the project, and only a few charts are now extant. In fact, they are so rare that when a group of the charts and two volvelles appeared on the market in the late 1980s, many were skeptical of their authenticity. It was not until three similar charts were discovered in the British Library, catalogued under Lucini, that the majority of people were convinced of the charts' veracity. Lord Wardington, in his article on the 'Arcano del Mare' in 'The Book Collector', incorrectly cites these two instruments as being "small dial without pointer" and "Zodiac Obliquo. No volvelles or pointer". They are, in fact, complete with both rotating discs and pointers and were sold as such in Sotheby's on 27 June 1991 as part of lot 202 (£28,600).

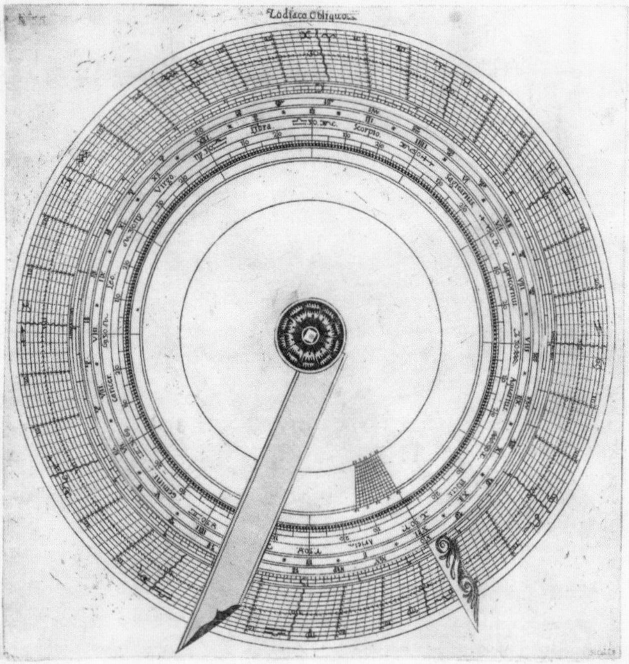
Zodiaco Obliquo
Libra
Scorpio
Virgo
Sagittarius
Capricornus
Leo

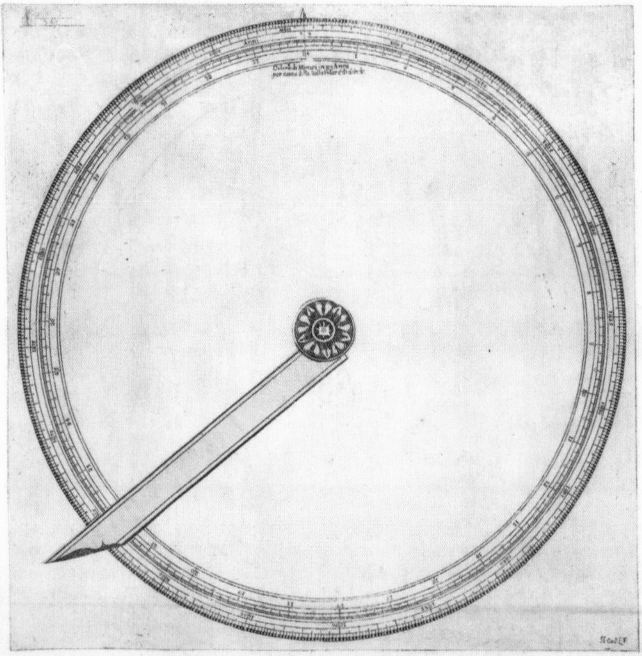

A possibly unique survival of a complete working paper instrument by John Seller

21 **SELLER, John**

[A Perpetual Calendar].

Publication
[London], John Seller, [c. 1680].

Description
Copper line engraving on paper, mounted on card and fitted with a wooden back and two wooden "rundles" with revolving dials, the whole framed in softwood and glazed, with an eyelet for hanging. Frame a little rubbed, the engraved surface with some minor discolouration and some minimal wear, but the whole in perfect working order.

Dimensions
(engraved surface) 200 by 125mm (approximately 7.75 by 5 inches).

An engraved perpetual calendar, fitted with two wooden volvelles (or "rundles", as Seller seems to have called them) each with its own engraved dial to adjust month and date, the whole framed in softwood and glazed in almost certainly its contemporary frame.

The engraving, seemingly of Seller's own design as he adds his initials at the lower corners as well as his imprint, is a fine example of seventeenth century English work, with figures representing the ruling planets, as well as conventional figures for death and escaping time, cornucopia, and a winged heart pierced by a sword, which here appears to be used as a symbol of the possibility of repentance. The days of the week are furnished with their planetary symbols, with Wednesday lacking Mercury's hat-wings at the top (without which it is identical to that for Venus). A later attempt has been made to correct this in pencil, but unfortunately the wrong symbol (that for Venus) has been corrected.

Seller's published pamphlets and almanacs (c.f. B.L. 532.a.6) describe the uses of the "perpetual almanacks of several contrivances", for which he advertised and furnished such additional aids as tables of sunrise and sunset, the length of days, significant anniversaries, new moons, tide tables and so forth, as well as "a table shewing what planets rule every hour of the day and night ... by this table you may perceive that ye sun governs ye first hour after sun rising on Sund [Mars] ye second ...". Of a similar device to the present one he notes "the uppermost of which rundles after it is once set must be moved every week and it will shew you the day of the month through the uppermost hole ...".

Seller led a remarkable life, not least in having survived being found guilty of high treason at the Old Bailey in 1662. He was eventually pardoned and went on to become one of the leading mapmakers of his day, the first (as Pepys pointed out) to break the Dutch monopoly in the provision of sea charts, attempting a national survey, and founding the Merchant Taylors' school of mapmakers. He was also the author of 'Practical Navigation' (1669). He had originally been an instrument-maker and to the end of his days continued to manufacture and provide a complete range of compasses, cross-staves, scales, quadrants, astrolabes, dials, calipers, circumferentors, theodolites, protractors, survey chains, rods, gauges, dividers, sectors, telescopes, prisms, spectacles, and much else besides (advertisement in BL Maps 8.c.5). It would appear that, apart from a fragment of a marine compass in the Museum of the History of Science, Oxford (noted by Webster), and a brass dial in our catalogue IV (item 13) no examples of his work in this field are known to survive. The present example, although among the least technically demanding of all his output, would appear to be a unique complete and working survival of the scientific and cartographic work of a figure of the first importance in seventeenth century London.

Io: Seller
Excudit
SUN — DAY
MUN — DAY
TUES — DAY
WEDNES-DAY
THURS — DAY
FRY — DAY
SATER — DAY
2
3
4
5
6
7
8
30
Apr
I
S

The first state of a rare separately-published star chart in contemporary colour

22 **VOOGHT, Claes Jansz after Jan Jansz Stampioen, the Younger**

Onderwysing van't Gebruyk des Hemels Pleyn Waar op de starren des hemels na 't oogh in 't plat gestelt zyn[.] Tot nut en vermaak van alle liefhebbers der wiskonsten.

Publication
Amsterdam, Johannis van Keulen, [c. 1680-1696].

Description
Large engraved celestial chart with a rotating printed paper ring on an off-centre axis to indicate the part of the sky visible at any date and time and to make a variety of celestial calculations, all for a latitude of 52 degrees (the Netherlands). A string with two beads serves as a pointer for aligning the scales in the stationary and rotating parts, with engraved instructions also by Vooght, the whole coloured by a contemporary hand and mounted on contemporary boards covered with marbled paper, apparently by the publisher, so that it can be folded in half for carrying.

Dimensions
566 by 665mm (22 by 26 inches); chart 325mm (13 inches) in diameter.

References
Bierens de Haan 5117?; Bom, Bijdragen ... Van Keulen, appendix B, p. 21?; Cat. NHSM, p. 640; E.O. van Keulen et al., 'In de Gekroonde Lootsman', item 4 & illustration between pp. 64 & 65 (NHSM copy); Koeman IV, Keu 28, map 6, p. 5 & p. 370, item 272 (without volvelle); Tiele, Land- en Volkenkunde 593 note; De Vries, et al., 'Van Keulen Cartography', p. 207, item 240; Warner, p. 260, items 1 & 1a; Adler Planetarium on-line database A-286; cf. v.d. Krogt, 'Advertenties' 130 (1696 ed., pub. by Loots); not in BMC Printed Maps; Cat. Nat. Mar. Mus.; Nordenskiöld; Zinner, Astron. Instrumente; NCC/Picarta; OCLC WorldCat.

Vooght's rare star chart and astronomical calculator, here separately issued in portfolio form and in its first state.

The chart shows the stars visible from 52 degrees latitude in a polar equidistant projection, with a rotating volvelle or rete to indicate the part of the sky visible at a particular moment. The circular border around the sky image and the outer part of the volvelle include scales with several kinds of data so that the chart can be used for various purposes. One can use the string to align the time in the volvelle with the date in the border of the chart, so that the part of the sky visible at that moment appears inside the volvelle. The chart with its volvelle, scales and string can also be used to calculate times for the rising and setting of constellations at various dates (or to calculate the present time based on the position of the stars). Fifty-three constellations are numbered quarter by quarter (15, 9, 14, 15), with a Dutch key identifying them in each corner and a French and an English translation in strips of panels at the head and foot. The instructional text, describing six "proposals" (the first explaining the different scales, etc., and the others giving examples of the use of the chart), stands to the right of the chart itself, and with the text were printed together from a single plate. If the ring is turned with 12 midnight to the right, the boards can be folded to each other like a portfolio, protecting the chart and making it easier to carry. It appears to have been published in this form, for the copy at the Dutch Maritime Museum in Amsterdam is similarly coloured and mounted to make a similar marbled portfolio.

The only other complete copies we have located, at the Boerhaave Museum in Leiden and the Adler Planetarium in Chicago, are also in portfolio form. Though designed for use at a latitude of 52 degrees, the text suggests it remains accurate from 49 to 55 degrees, which would allow its use through much of northern Europe.

Although astrolabes had long used a rotating off-centre ring to denote the part of the sky visible at a given time, such a ring combined with a planispherical star chart (like the cardboard or plastic star finders still popular today) often is supposed to be a nineteenth-century invention. Jan Jansz. Stampioen's 1664 chart seems to be the earliest well-documented chart of this kind, though some suppose his father's 'Coelestum Planum', mentioned in a 1619 patent and documented in 1621, was such an instrument, and Kepler's son-in-law, Jakob Bartsch, is also said to have made something similar. Vooght clearly based his chart on Stampioen's 1664 edition, published by Hendrik Doncker with text by Dirk Rembrandtsz. van Nierop. Neither it nor the 1684 version (also apparently published by Doncker) is known to survive (unless the latter was the chart alone, without volvelle or instructive text), so that Vooght's version in its present first state is the earliest known example. Comparison with a c. 1722 edition printed from Doncker's original

DECEMBER.
JANUARIUS
NOVEMBER.
SCORPIO
CAPRICORNUS
SAGITTARIUS
AQUARIUS
MAJUS.
JUNIUS.
JULIUS.
AUGUST
Noorden
Zuyden

DECEMBER.
JANUARIUS.
FEBRUARIUS.
MARTIUS.
APRILLIS.
MAJUS.
JUNIUS.
SAGITTARIUS ♃
CAPRICORNUS ♄
AQUARIUS ♄
PISCES ♃
ARIES ♂
TAURUS
t'Amsterdam by Johannis van Keulen. Met Privilegie
Auct: A. Vooght.
the great Dog.
2. Canis Minor, Procyon or the little Dog, or the dogs of the great Hunter.
3. Gemini, the Twinnes, the Northermost is Castor, the Southermost is Pollux
4. Cancer, the Grevice.
5. Hidra, the Watersnake, the clearest is the Hart, is named Alphard
6. Crater, or Drinking-Cup of Apollo
7. Leo, the Lyon, the clearest is named the Hart or Regulus, Basilicus.
8. Ursa Major, or the great Urse, the foure starres upon the body with the three in the Taile is the Wagon.
9. Argus Navis, or the Ship, on the outtermost Circle of this doth men see the cumming up and the setting of the Sunne (every day) the first cyphring letter is the cumming up, and the second next there Sheweth the setting of the sunne; where that stand two small points is the halfe houre, and where stands one pointe are the quarters of the houre.
En ce premier Quartier Signe avec le Lettre A. est
1. Cassiopea, la Mere de la triste Andromeda.
2. La triste Andromeda garotté
3. Triangulum, Deltoton.
4. Perseus, le delivreur d'Andromeda
5. Caput Medusa, le Bouclier de Perseus
6. Musca, ou le Mouche.
7. Plejades, les Sept estoiles.
8. Aries, le Belin ou le Ram.
9. Cetus, Balena, la grande Baleine.
10. Fluvius Eridanus, le riviere Eridanus
11. Auriga ou Erichtonius, le chartier, le claire Estoile Hircus le Bouc le Saute Sur le corps.
12. Taurus, le Taureau.
13. Orion, le Geant ou le grand chasseur, lequel s'oppose contre le Taureau, a qui Suivent ses chiens en l'autre quartier, la ceinture Sont les trois rois.
14. Lepus, ou le Lievre.
15. Columba Noé, la Colombe de Noé.
In this first quarter Signed with the Letter A. is
1. Cassiopea, the Mother of the dolorouls Andromeda.
2. the greevously tyed Andromeda.
3. Triangulum, Deltoton.
4. Perseus, the deliverer of Andromeda
5. Caput Medusa, the shield of Perseus
6. Musca, or the Flie
7. Plejades, the seven Starres.
8. Aries, or the Ramme
9. Cetus, Balena, the great Whale
10. Fluvius Eridanus, the River Eridanus.
11. Auriga or Erichtonius, the waggoner, the Cleare Starre Hircus, the He-goat leaping him upon his body
12. Taurus, the Bull,
13. Orion, the Gyant, or the great Hunter which opposeth him against the Bull (whose dogs are following in the other quarter) the Girdle are the three Kings.
14. Lepus, or the Hare.
15. Columba Noé, the Pigeon of Noe.

Onderwysing van't Gebruyk des

HEMELS PLEYN

PLANI CÆLESTIS

Waar op de Starren des Hemels na't oogh in't Plat gestelt zyn
Tot nut en vermaak van alle Liefhebbers der Wiskonsten

't Eerste VOORSTEL

Verthoonende de verdeelingh van dit Werktuygh

'T Eerste en buytenste rond zyn de dagen en maanden des geheelen Iaars na de Nieuwestyl, daar na volght een rond, verdeelt in 360 gelyke trappen (Gradus) verthoonende de rechte klimming) ascentionem rectam) na 't Even-nachts rond (Æquinoctialem.) Oock is dit rond verdeelt in 12 teykens. en elke teyken in 30 trappen (Gradus) elke trap overeenkomende met den dagh des Iaars. op dewelke de Zon in die trap (Gradu) is. 't Laatste en binnenste rond thoont de zons afwykingh (Declinationem) 't geheele Iaar door.

Binnen in dit werktuygh zyn 13 evenwydige ronden, waar van de negende en grofste van't midstip 't Evennachts rond is. Noch is hier 't Taan-rond ingetrokken, verthoonende de Zons wegh. als ook alle voornaamste vaste. starren na haar waare stand en rangh afgebeeld. zynde geschikt na 't Iaar 1700 na de geboorte Christi. welkers benamingen met zyfer-getaalen aan de kant gemerkt zyn

Voorts is hier toe gemaakt een bewegende kimmen) Horizon (wiens buytenste rond in 24 uuren, en elke uur in 15 trappen (Gradus), en wiens binnenste rond in 32 streken des kompas verdeelt is. en binnen deselve vier top-boogen. afbeelden de vier Hoofstreeken, met noch een rond. aanwysende de hoogte van 45 trappen (Gradibus) dewelke t'samen loopen in't top. Zynde ook in de middaghstreep van 52 trappen Aard-bols breete 't Keerstip (Polus) des werktuyghs vastgebegt. warom dese kimmen beweeght word. als ook draad aan 't selve vastgemaakt.

Tweede VOORSTEL

Te vinden Wanneer eenige Starren in't Zuyde komt

Als ik begeer te weeten op den 26 Mey. wanneer Böotes in't Zuyden komt. soo dray ik den kimmen (Horison) tot dat Böotes recht onder de Zuydstreep van 12 uuren komt en dan span ik de draat op den 26 Mey. die wyst my op de bewegelyke Kimmen ontrent 9¾ uuren na de middagh aan. dat Böotes dan in't Zuyd komt

't Derde VOORSTEL

Uyt een Waargenoome hoogte des Zons of van een Star des selfs streek en 't uur van den dagh te vinden

De Zon staat voormiddaghs den 16 Mey 42 trappen (Graduum) boven de Kimmen ik dray d'Oostkant van de Kimmen soo langh. tot de 42ste trap in de topboog de 25 trap in ♉ daar de Zon dan is. aanraakt. en dan span ik de draat op den 16 May. deselve valt regt op de 9 uuren voormiddaghs

Den Zon staat den 6 Augusti voormiddaghs op 47 trappen boven de kimmen. ik dray de kimmen, tot dat de 47ste trap in de topboogh de 15de trap van ♌ daar de Zon dan in is. aanraakt. die topboogh sie ik dan dat recht de Zuyd-ooster topboogh is.

Böotes staat den 25 Maart 42 trappen aan d'oostkant boven de Kimmen. ik dray de Kimmen, tot Böotes aan d'ooskant een topboogh net op 42 trappen ontmoet. de draad dan spannende over den 25 Maart, sie ik datse recht op de 11 uuren 's nachts valt. wesende de topboogh. die Böotes ontmoet. tusschen 't Zuydoost ten oosten. en Oost zuydoost. te kennen gevende dat Böotes dan 's nachts te 11 uuren tusschen 't Zuydoost ten oosten en oost zuydoost staat.

't Vierde VOORSTEL

Te vinden Wanneer en op wat streek de Zon of eenige Star ryst of daalt

Aan de Zon den 23 Augusti. ik beweegh de Kimmen aan't begin van ♍. daar de Zon dan is, en de draad spannende op den 23 Augusti. wyst aan 's morgens te 5 uuren ontrent in't oostnoordoost de Zon te rysen. en 's avonts te 7 uuren ontrent westnoortwest onder te gaan.

Aan de Koorn-air des Maagds den 30 January. ik beweegh d'oostkant des Kimmens aan de Star, en span de draad op den 30 January. deselve gevalt 's nachts tusschen elven en twaalven heen, en neffens de Star sie ik datse een weynigh beoosten't oost ten Zuyden ryst

't Vyfde VOORSTEL

Te Vinden Wanneer de Scheemeringh begint en Eyndight

Dat stelt men te geschieden als de Zon ontrent 18 trappen onder de Kimmen is. Den 5 November dray ik de Oostkant van de Kimmen. dat de 18de trap in de topboogh onder de Kimmen aantreft de 13de trap van ♏. daar de Zon dan is, de draad spannende op den 5 November sie ik dat den dageraat ontspringt ontrent te 5¼ uur na middernacht ontrent in't oost ten noorden soo de Kimmen aanwyst.

't Zeste VOORSTEL

Te Vinden de Gestalte des Hemels

Ik begeer den 6 January 's avonts te 9 uuren de gestalte des Hemels te weten. Spannende den draad over den 6 January, en bewegende de Kimmen. tot dat de 9 uuren aan de westkant van de Kimmen geteykent recht onder de draad komt, soo verthoont de gansche Hemelsche gestalte sodanigh. als binnen dese Kimmen verthoont wort: want men siet dan de Leeuwsstaart tusschen O.N.O en N.O. ten O. rysen, de Groote Hond ontrent 12 trappen hoogh ontrent Z.O. ten Z. de middelste der 3 Kooningen ontrent 30 trappen hoogh in't Z.Z.O. de Geyte ontrent 80 graden trappen hoogh in't Z.O. ten O. De Mond van de Walvisch ontrent 40 trappen hoogh bewesten 't Z.Z.W. 't Hooft van Medusa ontrent 68 trappen hoogh in't Z.W. ten W. De schoft van 't Paardt ontrent 15 trappen hoog in't west, de Swaansstaart ontrent 15 trappen hoogh in't N.W. 't Voorste Paart van de groote Waage ontrent 13 trappen hoogh tusschen N.N.O. en N.O. ten N. en de Lyer tusschen N.N.W. en N.W. ten N. tegen 't ondergaan.

Voorts, alhoewel dit Werktuygh gestelt is op d'Aardbols breete van 52 tr. (gr.) noordelyk overeenkomende met de hooghte van de Maase. soo kan 't nochtans sonder merkelyk misslagh te begaan 't zelve tot op de 49 en 50 trappen. als ook op de 54 en 55 trappen noorder breete, te weeten in't Canaal op de Noord-kust van Vrankryk. de Zuyd- en Oost-Kusten van Engeland. op de Kusten van de Nederlanden tot op de Elve toe. gebruykt worden om de kleyne veranderingh. die in dit Werktuygh op die hooghte voorvalt. wenschende dat de Liefhebbers door dit gebruyk ingewikkelt worden in de kennisse der Hemelse lichten, terwyl dat ik blyf uw dienstwillige.

C. I. Voogt Geometra

't Amsterdam by IOHANNIS Van KEULEN. Boekverkooper aan de Nieuw-brugh in de Gekroonde Lootsman. Met Privilegie

plate suggests that Vooght followed Stampioen closely, with the same 53 constellations (the latest introduced by Mercator and Plancius in the sixteenth and early seventeenth centuries) and the text in the corners describing them copied word for word and line for line.

In 1678/79 Van Keulen (1653/54-1715) set up at the address in the present chart (at the sign of the Crowned Pilot, opposite the New Bridge) and in 1680 he and Vooght (c. 1637?-1696) began to publish their charts with the privilege granted then, and re-granted to cover the years 1695 to 1710. The chart in its present first state must date between 1680 (since it notes the fifteen-year privilege) and 28 August 1696 (four months after Vooght's death), when Johannes Loots described Vooght's chart as new in an advertisement for his edition, also separately issued. His instructional text (by Simon van de Moolen, not mentioned in the advertisement) appears on a separate slip pasted over the engraved text, so his edition must be later than Van Keulen's. The present chart, moreover, makes no reference to Vooght's 1696 death. The chart is also mentioned in a list of Van Keulen publications in the 'Zee-Fakkel' (Bom, not specifying the edition), though supposedly including Spanish text, presumably for the constellations (Bierens de Haan probably based his description on the same advertisement). The instructional text notes that the stars are depicted in accordance with the year 1700 ("na haar waare stand en rangh afgebeeld, zijnde geschikt na 't Jaar 1700"), but such charts were often calculated for a round-numbered year a few years in advance. The chart later appeared in some copies of Van Keulen's atlases, though without volvelle in the only example we have located: his 1708/09 'Zee-Atlas' (part I) at the Dutch Maritime Museum in Amsterdam (Koeman IV, Keu 28, map 6: De Vries appears to err in citing a copy in Koeman IV, Keu 110B, the 1709 'Zee-Fakkel' at the Amsterdam University Library; and the Cat. NHSM , p. 50, errs in citing a copy in a 1684 edition of the 'Zee-Atlas'). Thiele reports a copy in a 1681/1686 atlas, not now located. In numerous Van Keulen atlases from 1682 to 1695, Koeman reports two versions of a different celestial chart, but not this one.

FEBRUARIUS
MARTIUS
APRILLIS
MAJU
AQUARIUS
PISCES
ARIES
TAURU
CAPRICORNUS
t'Amsterdam by Iohannis van Keulen
Noorden

Astronomy and astrology

23 **OURSEL, Jean**

Le grand Guidon et Tresor Journalier des Astres pour le cours des temps et diverses saisons de l'annee.

Publication
Rouen, Jean Oursel, [c. 1680].

Description
Quarto (230 by 190mm), title in red and black, 32pp., 2 volvelles, tables, and several illustrations within the text, brown paper covers.

This rare work by the mathematician Jean Oursel is a mixture of astronomy and astrology. As well as providing information on the calculation of the phases of the moon (with the use of a volvelle) and the measuring of time (by the use of a sundial), the work also covers the effect of the moon's phases upon a person's health and provides a perpetual calendar for the calculation of religious feast days.

Little is known of the mathematician and publisher Jean Oursel, although a brief view of the other works published around the time give a sense of his interests: in 1678 he published two works, one on the cures for numerous illnesses, the other an introduction to astrology; in the same year as he published the present work, he also published a book on the prophecies of Nostradamus. One should not confuse him with his son, Jean Oursel (1672-1727), who was a publisher and poet working in Rouen.

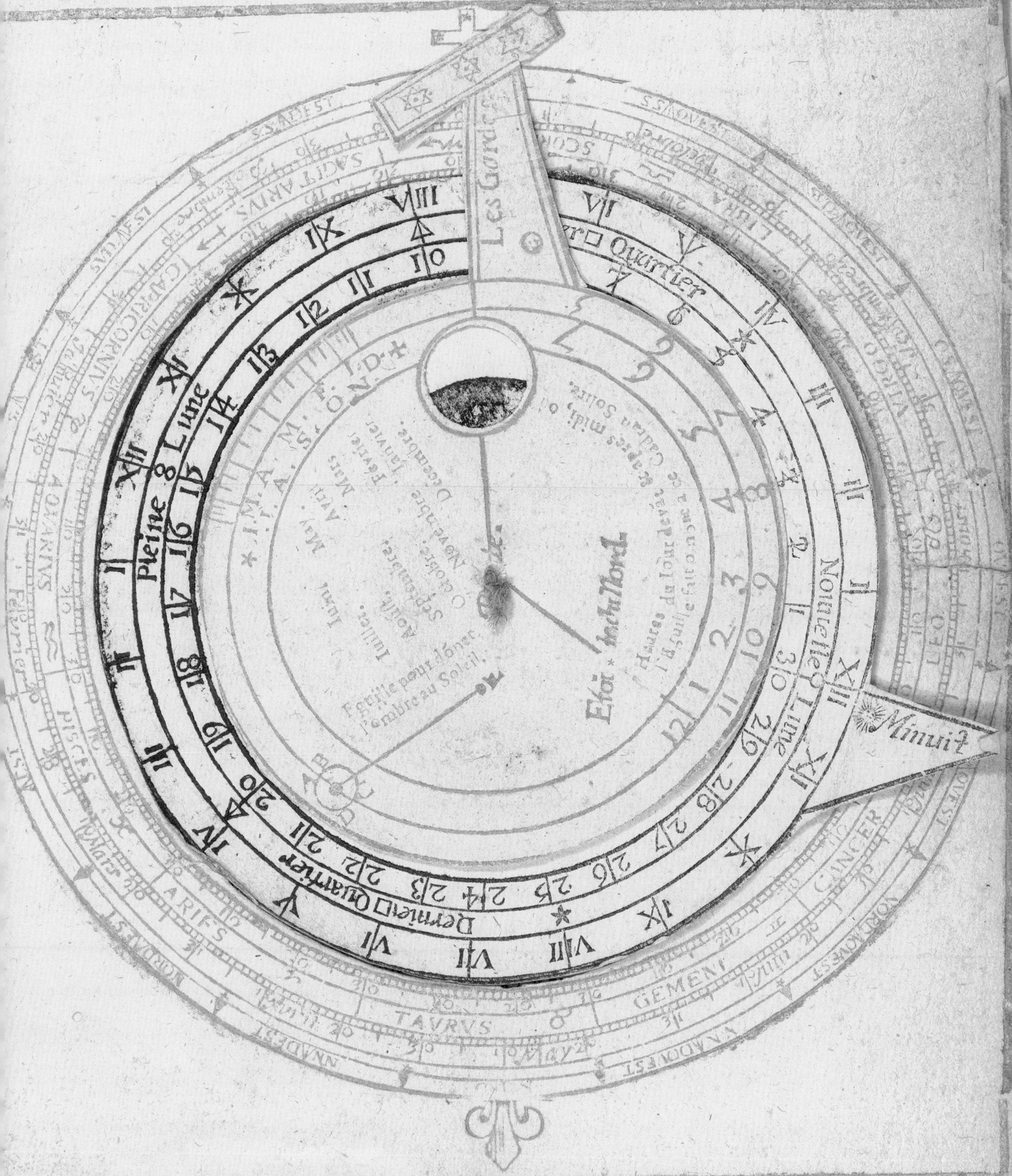
Les Gardes
Minuit
Pleine Lune
Dernier Quartier
Nouuelle Lune
Quartier
TAURUS
GEMENI
CANCER
LEO
PISCES
AQUARIUS
CAPRICORNUS
May
Feurier

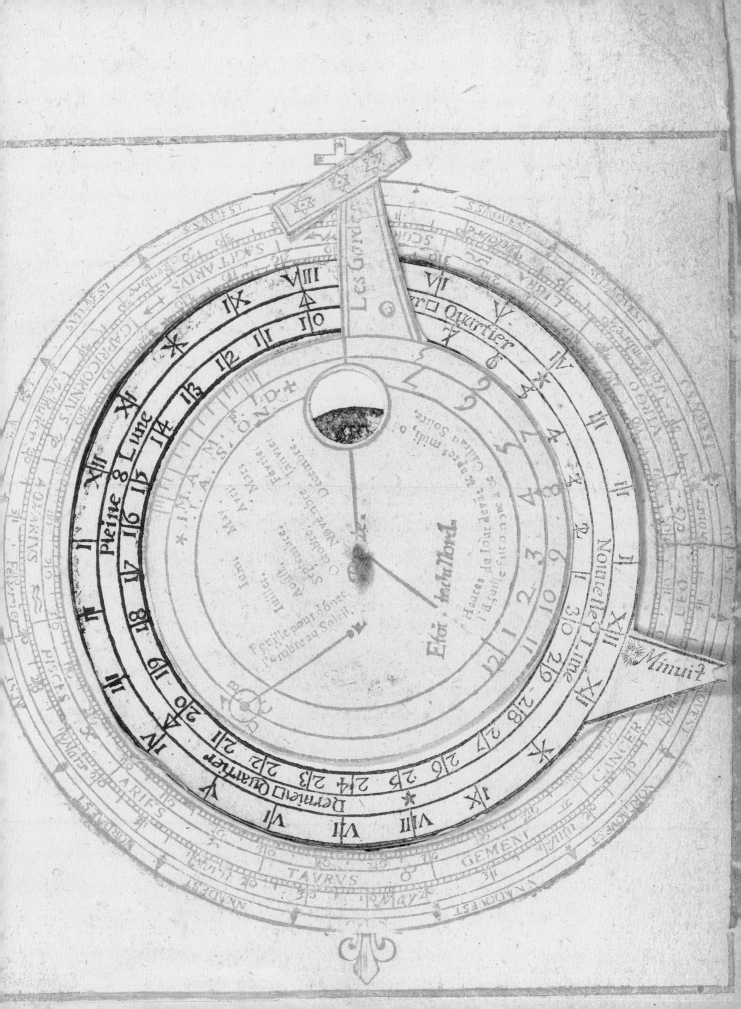

Time zones

24 **[Anonymous]**

Der Grosse Stunden-Weiser aller Länder auff der gantzen runden Erd-Kugel.

Publication
Hamburg, [c. 1680].

Description
Hand-coloured woodcut broadsheet, some minor loss to old folds, backed on Japan paper.

Dimensions
435 by 350mm (17.25 by 13.75 inches).

An early representation of global time zones.

To the centre of the broadside is a circle comprising two semicircles, one coloured yellow and marked 'Tag Stunden' (Day Hours), and the other with close engraved lines 'Nacht Stunden' (Night Hours). Surrounding the circle are two sets of Roman numerals I-XII marking out 24 hours, i.e. a whole day. The first set begins at one o'clock and ends at six o'clock, while the second begins at seven o'clock and ends at 12 o'clock. From each hour and half hour radiates several names of cities within the same time zone (or latitude). For example, midday lists Hamburg (in capital letters, as the place of publication) as well as Ulm, Genoa and Tunis. Whilst it is midday in Hamburg, it is 11am in London, 8.30pm in Peking, and 5.30am in Havana. The outer border comprises a depiction of the world. Atop the world sits Hamburg, and as we continue clockwise round the globe, we take in the Middle East and Alexandria at 2.30pm, Central Asia and Samarkand at 5pm, Nanking and China at 5.30pm; at midnight we cross the Pacific and land in the New World at 2am; we reach New Sweden (Nova-Svecia) on the Delaware River at 6am, and are safely back in London by 11am.

The last line of the text, below the engraving, suggests the broadside was accompanied by some text and was sold as a supplement to a book or, more probably, a periodical. The example in the Staatsbibliothek in Berlin was probably part of a rare magazine 'Gröste Denkwürdigkeiten der Welt Oder so genannte relationes curiosae' by E.H. Happel.

Rare. We are only able to trace two institutional examples: those in the Herzog August Bibliothek in Wolfenbüttel and in the Staatsbibliothek in Berlin.

Der grosse Stunden=Weiser/

aller Länder auff der gantzen runden Erd=Kugel.

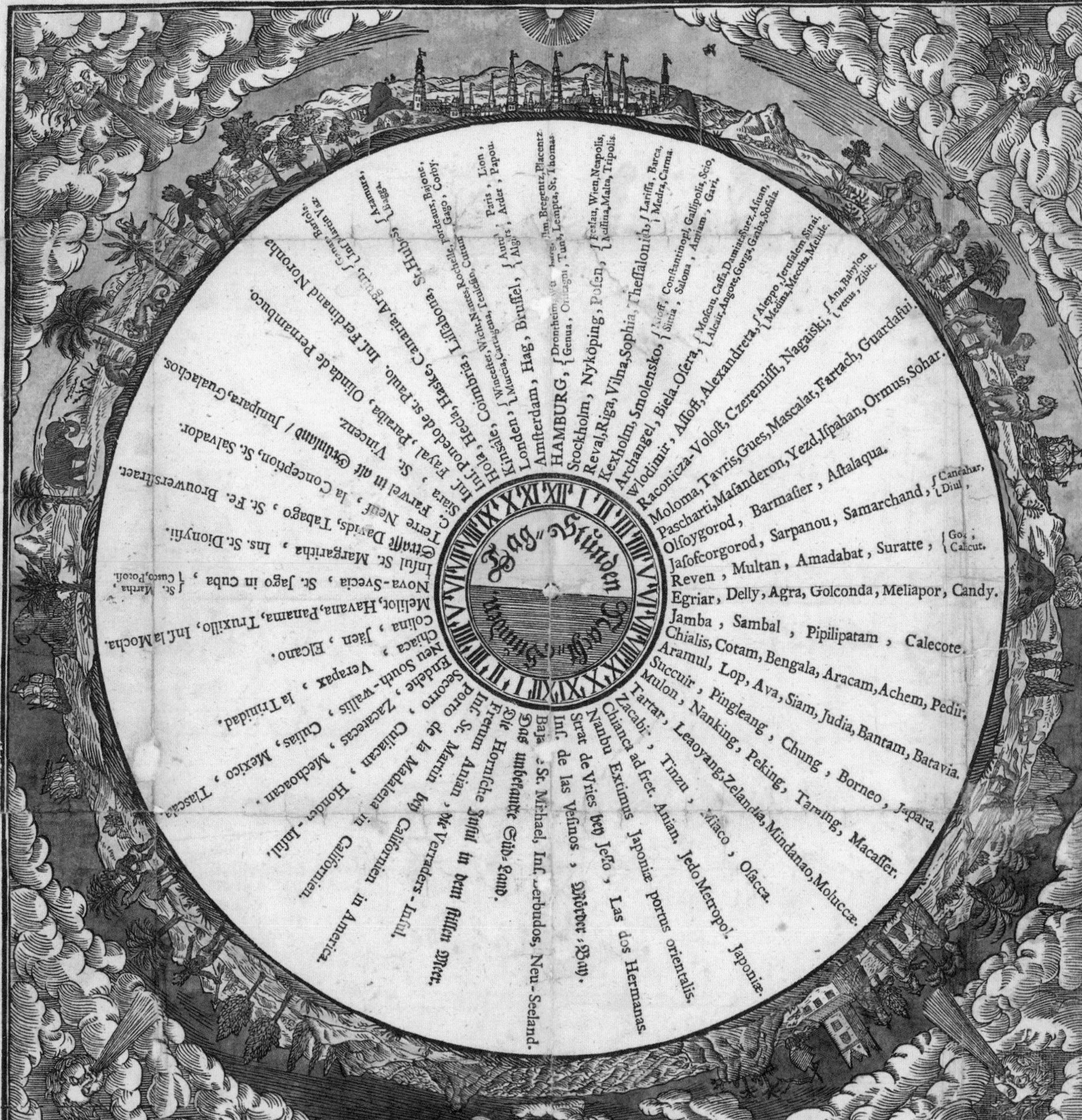

Was unterstehet sich doch nicht die frevele Kunst/ die Aeffin aller natürlichen Wunderwercke? Sie ist so vermessen/ daß sie einen Stab in die Erde pflantzet/ wohin sie will/ und denselben mit etlichen Zahlen umbsetzend/ Geboths-weise Rechenschafft fodert von der Sonnen Welt weiten Tagreisen. Der Sonnen Himmels-Wage kan nicht einen Schritt hinter sich bringen/ daß dessen Stuffen durch den Schatten-Strich nicht alsobald solten erkandt werden. Dieser Stab ist der Tags-Calender/ der Stunden-Zeiger/ ja der aller Augenblicke Lauff weiset/ und nach dem verjüngtem Maaßstab kunst-richtig abbildet. Die sonsten unbegreifliche Geschwindigkeit/ der Pfeil-schnellende Flug des glüenden Sonnen-Rads/ weiset sich durch den nichtigen und flüchtigen Schatten. Was an dem obern Himmel vorgehet/ zeiget eine niedrige Spitze auff der Erden. Gegenwärtiger Stunden-Weiser/ welcher über die gantze Erd-Kugel die Stunden aller vornehmsten Länder und Königreichen nach unserem Meridiano allhier zu Hamburg regulirt, zeiget an/ wann die Glocke hieselbst 12 oder die Mittags-Stunde ist/ was alsdann an andern Orten die Glocke/ oder Stunden/ bey Nacht und bey Tage sey. Als nehmlich/ wann es bey uns Mittag ist/ so ist es zu Golconda umb den Abend/ oder die Glocke 6/ in Berbudos umb die Glocke 12 in der Mitternacht zu St. Jago die Morgen-Stunde/ oder 6 Uhr Vormittag. Die übrigen Länder und Städte sind aus den neuesten und accuratesten Land-Karten also eingetheilet/ daß man weiß/ was an einem jeden Ort die Stunde halte. Wer Beliebung trägt/ seiner Curiosität weiter nachzuhängen/ der schneide das innwendige Runde zusambt der Stunden-Zahl loß/ mache es im Mittel-Punct auff ein untergelegtes Papier feste/ doch also/ daß es sich mitten in den angeführten Nahmen der Länder/ Insuln und Städte herumb drähen lasse/ so wird er noch mehr Lusten davon haben: dann wann man/ zum Exempel/ die Glocke 12 am Mittag auff die Stadt Jamba rücket/ so wird man sehen/ was alsdann die Stunde in solhaner veränderten Glocken-Zahl anderwerts in der gantzen Welt ist. Die äusserste umbgebende Figur ist auch nicht vergeblich/ oder nach dem Gutdüncken des Zeicheners ersonnen/ sondern man hat zufoderst dahin gesehen/ daß sich die 4 principalisten Nationes, so wie sie sich in den Stunden-Weiser geschickt/ in ihrer Kleidung præsentiret, und gleich wie die Persianer (præter propter) 3 Stunden oder einen achten Theil der Erd-Kugel/ also sind die Chinesen und Japonesen 9 Stunden oder 3 Achttheile nach Morgen zu. Die aller-östlichste Brasilianer bey Pernambuco hingegen 3 Stunden oder einen Achtentheil/ und die wilden Nord-Americaner 9 Stunden oder 3 Achttheile nach dem Westen hin von uns entfernet oder unterschieden. Ein mehrers ist auß der generalen Beschreibung/ nemblich in No. 49/ wohin diese Stunden-Uhr gehört/ zu ersehen.

A magnificent complete set of Coronelli's globe gores, including a set of counterproof images for a 42 inch concave celestial globe

25 **CORONELLI, Vincenzo**

Libro dei Globi. Globi del P. Coronelli [manuscript title within engraved border].

Publication
Venice, [Girolamo Albrizzi for Coronelli, c. 1697-1701].

Description
Folio (490 by 340mm), 160ff., two "argonauti" plates, engraved title with title in manuscript, "argonauti" plate, double-page engraved dedication to Louis XIV, two plates of globe furniture, and 152 engraved plates of terrestrial and celestial globe gores, equatorial rings, and globes (6 folding, 21 composed of two joined half-sheets), including a suite of counter-proof images for the large celestial gores, engraved portrait of Coronelli, contemporary speckled calf re-backed.

Dimensions
487 by 346mm (19.25 by 13.5 inches).

References
Wallis, H., preface to Coronelli 'Libro dei Globi', pp. xx-xxi; Armao, 'Vincenzo Coronelli', nos. 59 & 60, and p. 237; Stevenson, 'Terrestrial and Celestial Globes' II, pp. 98-120; Wallis, H., 'Coronelli Libro dei Globi', Der Globusfreund Nr. 18/20, May 1970, pp. 390-394.

Vincenzo Maria Coronelli (1650-1718), a Franciscan monk, was the official cosmographer of the Venetian Republic and founder of the first modern geographical society: 'Gli Argonauti'. He earned his great reputation by the exactitude and the beauty of his maps and globes. In his celestial globes, he designed 83 constellations and a catalogue of 1,902 stars. Of his terrestrial globes, Stevenson says that he omitted nothing of interest to geographers, navigators and explorers:

"He added a rather unusual number of legends, explanatory and informative in character, but never seemed to crowd the space which he had at his disposal. So exquisitely engraved were his maps that he was able to avoid the appearance of confusion noticeable on other globes of the century".

The 'Libro dei Globi' forms Part Ten of Coronelli's geographical opus that he published under the general title 'Atlante Veneto'. Of this book of globes Armao knew one edition of the 1697 and one of 1705, each recorded in only two examples. More recent work by Wallis has revealed intermediate stages between those listed by Armao, comprising variations in dedicatory texts, or the inclusion of new peripheral material added to each copy more or less at random in the large stock of plates from Coronelli's inventory.

Only ten institutional copies of the 'Libro dei Globi' are recorded, each representing a bespoke selection of plates available when each was made up, with versions published with between 135-169 plates and no two examples exactly the same. The gores often overlap and duplicate large areas of engraved surface (a device presumably deployed to make the globe-maker's life easier), and so it was not always necessary for an example to have every sheet. The present work has 152 leaves and, if joined, would form nine complete globes (two, four, 18, and 42 inches in diameter in both terrestrial and celestial hemispheres, including polar calottes, and a concave 42 inch celestial globe composed of counterproof gores).

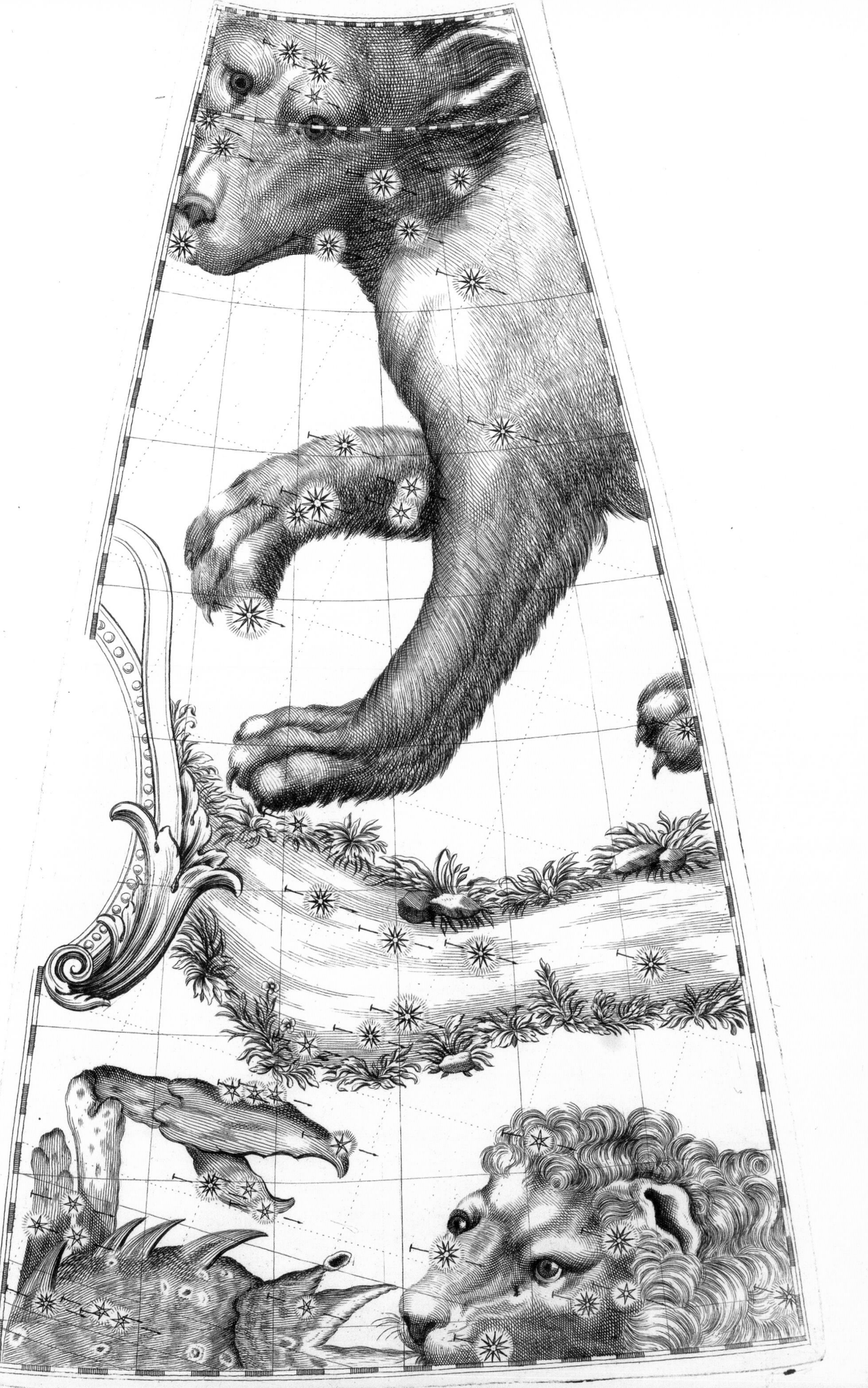

The concave celestial globe is of particular interest, and only appears in a few examples of the first edition. The first mention of Coronelli's concave globes is recorded in a speech by Sr. Carlo Malavista, given to the Accademia Fisico-Matematica in 1692, who commented on the difficulty of using a celestial globe: "as we stand on the earth the sky is above us and we observe it concave and not convex". Yet it was accepted convention to depict the heavens on a celestial globe as they would appear to an observer beyond the heavens. In order to combat this, Malavista went on to say that the Accademie had fitted Coronelli's celestial globe gores in a concave form. Coronelli had produced his new concave globe by "counter-proof printing", that is by pressing an additional sheet of paper against a freshly made print to create a reverse image.

Rare. There are seven known institutional examples of the first edition, which have been dated between 1697 and 1701. The majority of examples differentiate from the second edition of 1705 (of which there are three institutional copies) in two distinct ways: first, the 1697 edition has the title in manuscript, which is replaced by a printed title in the later edition; and second, in the way the large terrestrial gores are treated. The gores themselves were far too large for the size of the book, a problem Coronelli overcame by splitting the plates at the Tropics. In the first edition this was done by masking part of the plate he did not wish to print with paper. Hence on the present example, on only three sides of the gore is the plate mark visible. The plates for the second edition were cut at the Tropic, thus rendering a complete plate mark.

NEW NORTH WALES, ò Nuoua Galle Septent:
Ponta auanzata
C. Southampton
C. Pembrock
C. Nesdrake
C. Charles
Mill I.
STRETTO
I. Salisberi
MARE
D HUDSON, ò
Capo Filippo
Ponta Chock
BAIA DE BUTTONS Scoperta dagl Inglesi.
CHRISTIANO
Scoperto dagli Danesi
I. Sleepers
C. Smith
ESTO
THE NE
TIERRA
da Antonio
prima
Ponta delli Delfini
Porto Nelson
Nuoua Sauerna
NEW SOUTH WALES, ò la Nuoua Galle Meridionale Scoperta dagl Inglesi.
BAIA
D HUDSON
Scoperta nel 1612
Gran Baia
BAIA DE IAMES
C. Iones
Lago di Nadouessans
I
C
Lago Buade ò d'Issati
ISSATIS POPULI
XILISTINONS POPULI
ASSINIPOUALAES POPULI
NADOUESSI POPULI
GENS DES TERRES
LAGO TRACY, ò SUPERIORE
I. Minong
L. HURONS
FRONTENAC
NANTOUNAGANS POP.
LAGO ILINOIS, ò MICHIGAMI
LAGO ERIE
LE CINQUE NAZIONI
PAESI DEGL ILINOIS
TRIO
NADA
CANADA
CAROLINA
LA FLORIDA
COSTE DE LA FLORIDA
CHIKACHA POP.
TOUNICA POP.
TEGESTA PROVINCIA
LAS ISLAS
CANAL DE BAHAMA
EL PRACEL DE GROOTE VLA
IL MARE
GOLFO DEL MEXICO
ISOLA CUBA, ò CUBA, et HAUANA
Baia Carlos
Los Martyres
E

A L'AUGUSTE MAIESTÉ
DE LOVIS LE GRAND
L'INVINCIBLE, L'HEVREVX, LE SAGE
LE CONQVERANT.
CESAR CARDINAL D'ESTRÉES
A CONSACRÉ CE GLOBE CELESTE,
OU TOVTES LES ESTOILLES DU FIRMAMENT
ET LES PLANETES,
SONT PLACÉES AU LIEU MESME, OU ELLES ESTOIE
A LA NAISSANCE DE CE GLORIEUX MONARQV
AFIN DE CÕSERVER A L'ETERNITÉ UNE IMAGE FIXE
DE CETTE HEUREUSE DISPOSITION,
SOUS LAQVELLE
LA FRANCE A RECEU LE PLUS GRAND PRESENT
QVE LE CIEL AIT IAMAIS FAIT A LA TERRE
M.DC.LXXXIII.
Cet Ouvrage a été inv
acheué par le Pere
Coronelli Venitien
Illu
Gran Contestabil
Degnò prescieglermi ad
nissima, l'Eminentissimo
V. hò ristrette nella pres
nella manifattura del
uso, di quelli, c'hò publica
Se il Tipo di questo Mode
qualche simetria col mer
cui m'inchino.
D.V.E.
Venetia, 20 Genaro, 16
FICTUS, ALOYSI, TIBI SISTITUR ORBI

Eccellentissimo Sig:
Re, d'Arragona, di Napoli, etc.
in Globi per la Maestà Cristia:
D'Estrees, e per servir all' Eccellenza
proportioni matematiche
ridurre colla scala minore accio
ia Cosmografica degli Argonauti all'
, essendo pero cosa di Re, haurà
E; e colla deuotione profonda, con
Humilissimo, et Obbligatissimo Ser.
F.V. Coronelli, Cosmografo Pub.
A L'AUGUSTE MAIESTE
DE LOVIS LE GRAND
L'INVINCIBLE, L'HEUREUX, LE SAGE
LE CONQUERANT.
CESAR CARDINAL D'ESTRÉES
A CONSACRÉ CE GLOBE TERRESTRE,
POUR RENDRE UN CŌTINVEL HOMMAGE
A SA GLOIRE, ET A SES HEROIQUES VERTUS
EN MONSTRANT LES PAYS,
OU MILLE GRANDES ACTIONS ONT ESTÉ EXECUTÉES
ET PAR LUY MESME, ET PAR SES ODRES
A L'ESTONNEMENT DE TANT DE NATIONS
QU'IL AUROIT PU SOUMETTRE A SON EMPIRE,
SI SA MODERATION N'EUST ARRESTÉ LE COURS DE SES
CONQUESTES,
ET PRESCRIT DES BORNES A SA VALEUR,
PLUS GRANDE ENCORE QUE SA FORTUNE.
M.DC.LXXXIII.
Cet Ouvrage a été
achevé par le Père
Coronelli Vénitien
S AT ANTE PEDES, MARTE, IUBENTE, CADET.

Lusvergh's sales catalogue of artists' drawing and optical instruments, including Galileo's Sector

26 **LUSVERGH, Domenico and LUSVERG [LUSVERGH], Jacobus [Giacomo]**

Notta delli Stromenti Piu Generali.

Publication
[?Rome, c. 1698].

Description
Two small folio-sized engraved broadsheets each composed of two engravings measuring approximately 245 by 180mm, lightly foxed with broader faded stains on text plate, slight tears to edge and folds, not affecting text or images, ink residue and a diagram on the verso of the compass plate.

Dimensions
320 by 445mm (12.5 by 17.5 inches).

References
Not in ICCU, DigiBib, Bedini, Daumas, Gunther, or Boffito. For information on the Lusvergh family of craftsmen see: Tabarroni, Giorgio, "Una Sfera Armillare di Domenico Lusverg nella Specola di Bologna," Coelum, vol. XXII, (1954); and Todesco, P., "La famiglia Lusverg dal '600 all'800," "Memorie della Società Astronomica Italiana" 66 (1995), pp. 895-901; cf: www.mhs.ox.ac.uk/geometry/cat18.htm.

An extremely rare survival of an illustrated and priced broadside sales catalogue advertising the diverse scientific and drawing instruments manufactured by Domenico Lusvergh in Rome. Lusvergh, who inherited the family instrument-making business in 1689 from Giacomo (his uncle or grandfather), offers complete sets of astronomical, perspective, drawing and surveying tools, telescopes of various sizes, an adaptation of Galileo's proportional compass and, on a separate sheet, a quadrant and a set of decorative brass fittings available for the instruments. This ephemeral document, of which no other copy with the quadrant sheet has been traced, provides important contemporary evidence of the pricing, marketing and use of a wide range of instruments used by artists, surveyors and scientists.

Among a large assortment of artists' drawing instruments, the advertisement prominently illustrates Giacomo Lusvergh's innovative adaptation of Galileo's proportional compass, which was the subject of a pocket-sized "user's guide" produced by Domenico in 1698, 'Di Galileo Galilei Il compasso adulto per opera di Giacomo Lusvergh' (Rome, Domenico Antonio Ercole, 1698). One of several seventeenth-century versions of Galileo's useful tool, Giacomo had modified the design of the instrument to follow the general trend of the late 1600s, significantly reducing its size and eliminating the quadrant so that it could fit into the pocket case of a variety of drawing instruments. This facilitated portability, an important requirement as the market for the instrument increased and diversified, becoming "standard issue" for surveyors, engineers and artists with the need to perform quick calculations. The large image on the broadsheet, depicting the front and back of an instrument signed by Domenico in 1698, may have been originally engraved for the "user's guide." The little-known quadrant plate was engraved even earlier; the instrument is signed by Giacomo Lusvergh and dated 1668, exactly as seen in the price list. The broadside, while undated, presumably was produced either as an insert for the small-format guide or as a promotional leaflet in the first decades of the eighteenth century. Traces of a cancel slip are evident on the leftmost compass, appearing to cover existing text on the original copper plate prior to printing.

The engraved text on the broadside comprehensively lists Domenico's merchandise, including the prices in scudi. The quadrant plate is the first item listed for sale, the compass is the second. In the lower corner of the broadsheet, a smaller compass, made by Giacomo in 1686, is offered with a set of silver instruments. These are the only instruments illustrated, and the first two plates are explicitly mentioned in the main list: "la carta stampata." Domenico offers a variety of drawing instruments either singly or in packages. Included among them is a parallelogram, described by Christopher Scheiner in 1631, for

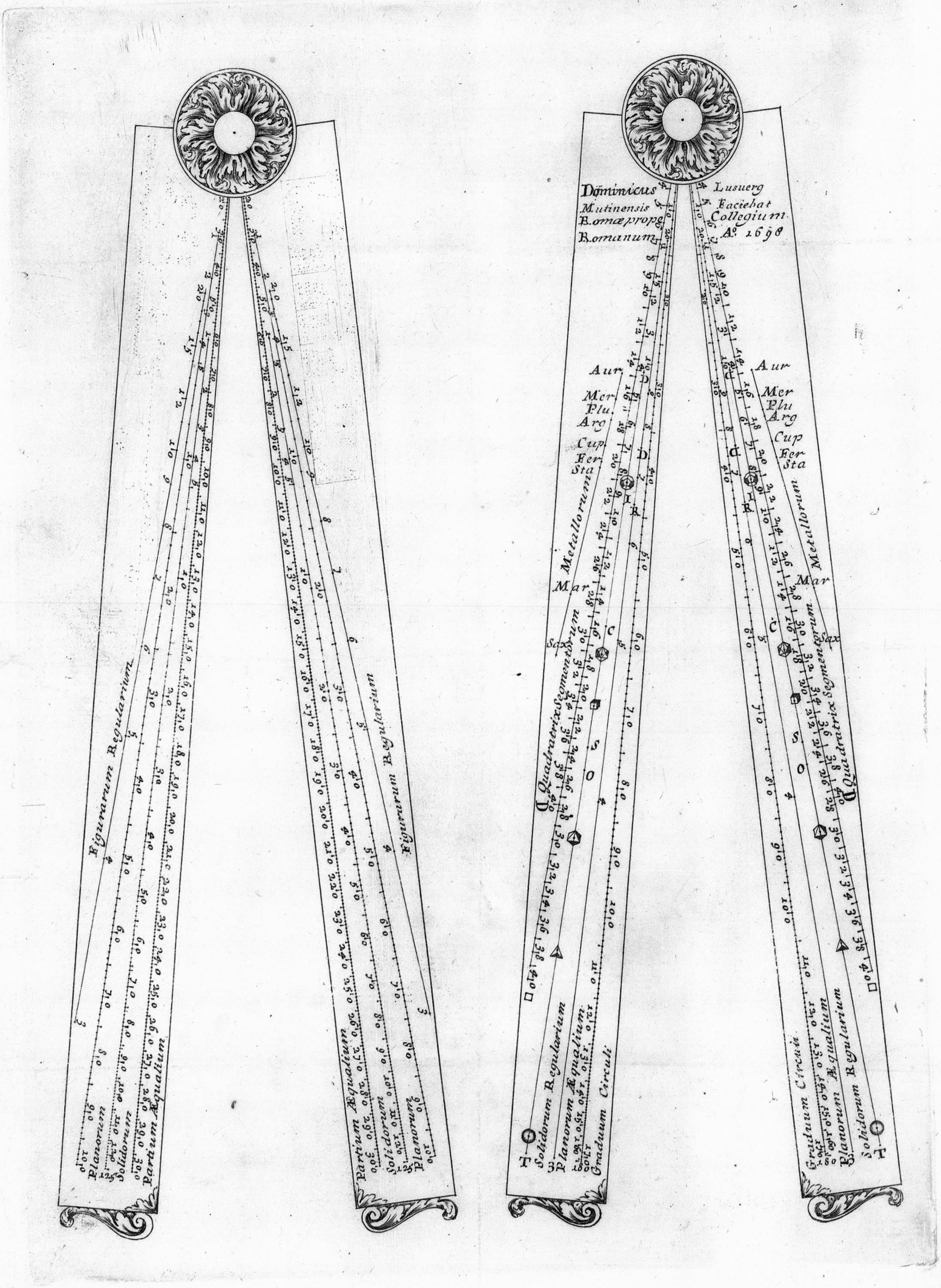
Dominicus Lusverg
Mutinensis Faciebat
Romæ prope Collegium
Romanum A° 1698
Figurarum Regularium
Planorum
Solidorum
Partium Æqualium
Metallorum
Aur
Mer
Plu
Arg
Cup
Fer
Sta
Mar
Sax
Quadratrix Segmentorum
Solidorum Regularium
Planorum Æqualium
Graduum Circuli

making copies of drawings or manipulating proportions in drawings. A list of 21 different instruments, all priced individually, are offered as a group in a "stuccio di segrino", a case costing 6 scudi, for a total of 198.50. Several sets of brass instruments by the Lusverghs, comprising anywhere from eight to several dozen instruments, survive in their original cases in the Medici collection of scientific instruments (now the Istituto e Museo di Storia della Scienza, Florence). The Museum of the History of Science, University of Oxford, possesses an example of the quadrant fitted with the ball and socket joint and brass bosses as advertised on the broadsheet.

Domenico Lusverg(h) [or Lusuerg] (1669-1744) was either the grandson or nephew of the renowned Modenese instrument maker Giacomo/Jacopo Lusverg(h) (c. 1636-1689). Giacomo had an active workshop in the Piazza of the Collegio Romano between 1672 and his death in 1689, at which point, Domenico took over the business.

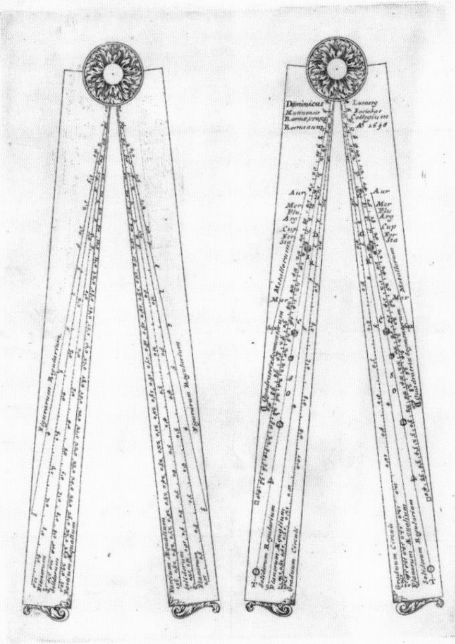

NOTTA DELLI STROMENTI PIU GENERALI

Vn quadrante per leuar le piante, con quattro stromenti, cioè gradi, minuti, primi e secondi di noua inuentione, con il quadrato geometrico, ò scala altimetra, e rete, e si uede l'operatione di tutti quattro gl'instromenti nel medemmo tempo, e quello della rete mostra immediatamente quello, che si cerca senza operatione d'Aritmetica conforme la carta stampata, l'anno 1668 importa scudi cinquanta — 50

Vn compasso di proportione con dieci linee conforme la carta stampata, importa — 21

Vna squadra zoppa con la bussola, e diuisione delli gradi, per leuar gli angoli interiori, et esteriori per l'architettura ciuile, e militare, e dall'altra parte ui è la diuisione per l'eleuatione delle bombarde, e scala — 12

Vn declinatorio per l'architettura, per l'orologij a sole con la bussola — 15

Vn archipendolo modato con la diuisione de gradi per liuellare, e mettere in piano — 8

Vna riga, et una squadra modata, con la diuisione del palmo, e piede romano — 7

Vn semicircolo con la diuisione delli gradi, e poligoni — 2

Vn parallelogramo per l'architettura — 36

Vn passetto con la diuisione del palmo e piede geometri. — 4

Vn compasso grande — 5

Vn compasso con una molla, per pigliare minutamente le diuisioni del compasso di proportione — 5

Vn compasso con una cassetta da leuare, e mettere quattro punte, una per diuidere, una per scriuere, un'altra per il lapis, e la quarta con la rotina per fare i circoli ponteggiati, et anco serue per tirare le linee rette ponteggiate come tiralinee — 6

Duoi compassi picioli, uno per diuidere, e l'altro per scriuere — 3

Vn compasso picolo di acciaro con le uite a molle per diuidere — 2

Vn compasso curuo per li corpi sferici — 4

Vn compasso fedele per tagliar sfere, e ogni altra cosa che occorre a disegnare in qualsiuoglia modo, con due cassette per leuare e mettere sette punte, e serue ancora per far l'ouato più acuto, e ottuso conforme si desidera, et anco fà la figura dell'uouo differente dell'ouato, tanto per disegnarlo, come per tagliare cartone, ottone, o rame, e le dette punte seruono per l'uno, e l'altro seruitio — 18

Vn compasso per trasportare li triangoli per le piante — 5

Vn compasso per la nauigatione — 5

Dui tiralinee, uno per la fortificatione, e l'altro per l'architettura, con un toccalapis — 3

Vna cassetta con l'Aritmetica di neuperio per hauere qualsiuoglia gran multiplicatione, diuisione, radice quadra, e cuba — 2

Vn orologgio uniuersale astronomico, che mostra l'hore, che battono l'orologgi a rota, e l'hore astronomiche nell'istesso — 12

Questi sono gli stromenti ordinarij, che si mettono dentro ad un stuccio di segrino, quale importa — 6

198-50

Vna sfera armillare, se ne fanno di diuerse grandezze, come anco nelle diuisioni maggiori, e minori, e così uariano i prezzi di ciascheduna, e la più ordinaria importa — 30

Vn radio latino — 30

Vn bussola agrimensoria ordinaria — 15

Vn planisferio — 36

Vna squadra per li bombardieri, con la diuisione del calibro di tutte le palle di ferro, pietra, e sasso — 6

Vn'astrolabio con dieci tauole — 60

Vn parallelogramo per copiare le figure di grande in piccola, e di piccola in grande come si uuole — 15

Vn sestante per le osseruatione celesti — 60

Duoi compassi uno, che dà la mota, e l'altro il terzo per l'architetti — 10

Vna sfera compendiata uniuersale, che mostra l'hore astronomiche, babiloniche, e italiane, e serue ancora per fare orologgi tutti — 30

Tre compassi mezzani, uno con la penna da scriuere, uno con il toccalapis, e l'altro per diuidere — 6

Vn compasso astronomico, che si mette dentro il cannocchiale per misurare, e leuare di piante, cinque, ò sei miglia lontano, e per misurare li corpi celesti — 12

Vna bussola grande con la diuisione delli gradi, e minuti primi, à uno per uno, e scala altimetra per leuare le piante, con la bussola, e tutti li uenti, e serue anco per declinatorio — 50

Vn semicircolo grande con li gradi, e mezi gradi, con li traguardi e nodo per leuar le piante — 35

Vn horologio grande uniuersale e mostra le hore astronomiche, e italiane nel medemo tempo, con la bussola gradi, e tutti li uenti, per la nauigatione, e serue anche per declinatorio — 36

Vna squadra grande agrimensoria, e sopra la bussola con la diuisione delli gradi, e quadrato geometrico, con la diottra e traguardi, per leuare le piante — 18

Cannochiali di quattro uetri di palmi dieci, e dodeci	30
Di palmi 15	45
Di palmi 20	60
Di palmi 25	80
Di palmi 30	100
Di palmi 40	150
Di palmi 50	200
Di palmi 80	400
Di palmi 100	600

E desiderandosi di maggior grandezza, si faranno, come saranno richiesti.

E i detti cannochiali m'obligo darli alla proua, e paragone di qualsiuoglia, così di tutti li altri stromenti, e per chi uuol spender meno sene fanno delli più ordinarij.

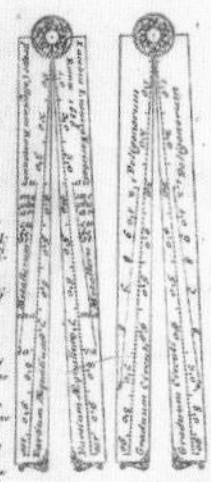

Stromenti per fare un stucchio piccolo di argento, Vn compasso di proportione con le quattro linee presente

Vn compasso della cassetta con tutte le punte sudette, e uno due compassi, uno da scriuere, e l'altro per diuidere, un tiralinee doppio, un porta lapis, un temperino, un semicircolo con l'angolo retto, et un paro di forbicine, con il stuccio di segrino guarnito di bollette di argento, tutto importa quaranta scudi, e si uaria come uolete ordinate

4128

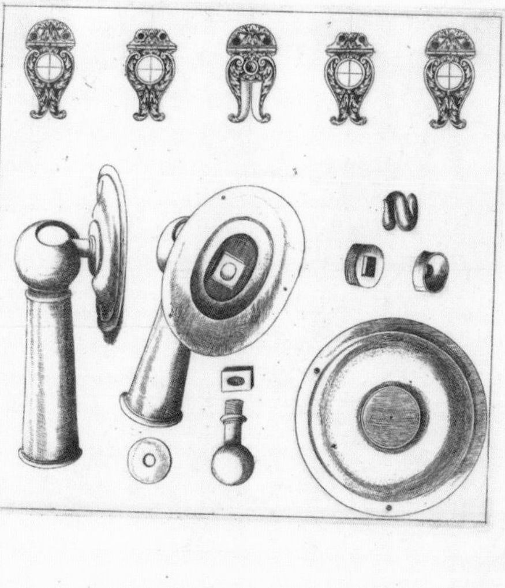

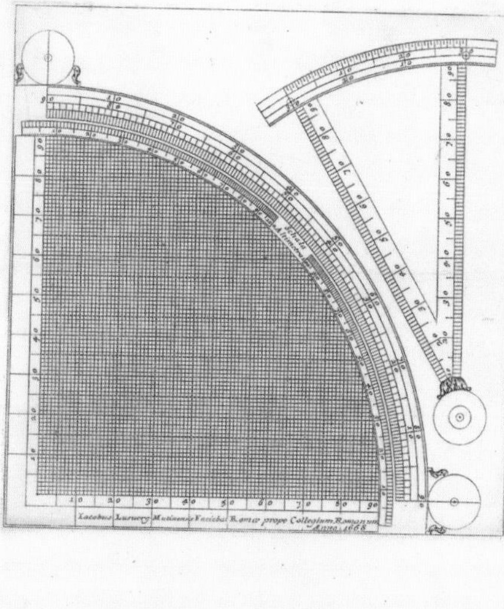

One of the earliest illustrated trade catalogues and a fascinating glimpse into the use of scientific instruments at the beginning of the eighteenth century

27 **[TUTTELL, Thomas]**

Mathematical Cards.

Publication
[London, John Lenthall, c. 1700-1718].

Description
Second issue. A set of 52 engraved playing cards, each with a cartouche surrounded by tools specific to a particular mathematical instrument above a view of the tool as used in practice, and an explanation of the card's subject.

Dimensions
90 by 58mm (3.5 by 2.25 inches).

References
Crom, Theodore, 'Trade Catalogues 1542-1842', Melrose, Florida, 1989, p. 53; Wayland, V. & H., 'Playing Card Society Journal', vol 2, number 3, item VII, 1973; Wilshire E177.

Tuttell based his cards on three educational sets of playing cards produced by Joseph and James Moxon during the latter years of the seventeenth century. James Moxon, recognizing Tuttell's expertise in practical mathematics, asked him to help with the revisions of his father's very popular book 'Mathematics Made Easie' which was republished in 1701.

The first issue of the present set included an advertisement engraved on the king of clubs but here in the second issue it has been re-engraved to form a card on 'Building'. The ace of spades, however, still retains Tuttell's name in a list 'Bookes & Instrumts. for Navigation' in an almanac of 1701.

The cards are more detailed than similar examples from this period in that the mathematical instruments and their uses can be identified easily. The set thus constitutes a remarkable pictorial trade catalogue of the period.

According to Wilshire, Chatto, writing in 1848, states "the pack of mathematical cards by Thomas Tuttell ... [was] designed by Boitard and engraved by J. Savage".

Rare. Of the first series, only one complete set, the Ortiz Patino set, is known. Two sets (both incomplete) are held at the British Library (31 cards E177) and UCLA (44 cards); complete sets of the second series are held at the New York Public Library and British Library (E67) with five further cards at the British Library. We are also aware of a further complete set in a private collection in Edinburgh.

An Instrum.^t for take=ing a large Mannor, County, or Lordspp. or where tis requisite to have y^e Bearing. Well approved, & much used, by our **Surveyors;**

An Instrum.^t use'd at **Sea** *to find y^e Altitude or the Depression of y^e North Starr in respect of y^e* **Pole** *it selfe in order to find y^e* **Latitude** *and nearly y^e* **Hour** *of y^e Night.*

Our Glory, safety, trade, & Navigation. wholly depends on our **Ships**, *they depend upon* **Art**, *which not only inrich, but affords y^e greatest defence:*

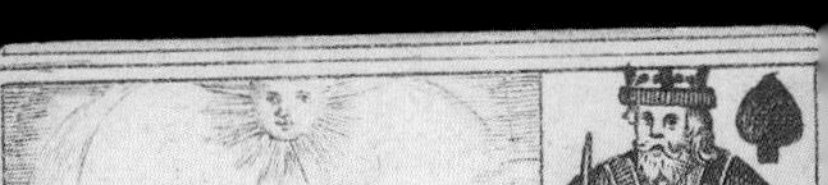

the General Use of **Spheres** *is to shew y^e progress of the Wandring Starrs, or Planets, both as to their Dyurnal and Anual Motions.*

Mathematical Instruments
Curiously fram'd, very exactly and minutely divided, by the Contrivance of our modern Artists, both for Observation & Operation to the great improvement of Arts & Sciences
Imperial or Plain Table
Are Instrum.ts contrived to contain all other Surveying Instrum.ts very ready to take Enclosures, & gives a very good demonstration of the practical part of Surveying;
Gauger
The 4 foot Gaugeing Rod & Semicircle, ye long Slideing Callipers, & the various Sorts of Slideing Rules in Canes and for the Pocket, are ingeniously applyd.
Almanacke
Years
Sundays
To find what day of the Month if the first Monday in Jan: 1701
Over ye Year you find E, against Jan over E, you find ye first Sunday the 5th & counting on ye next Collumn, monday the 6th &c.
Architect
Drawing Tables, T's or double Squares Sectors, Scales, Compasses, and drawing penns, ought to bemost accurately made for these uses,
Circumferentor
An Instrum.t for takeing a large Mannor, County, or Lordsp or where tis requisite to have ye Bearing, Well approved, & much used, by our Surveyors;
Dyaling Globe
An Instrum.t wth a moveing Horizon & Index, wth gives ye true Idea or Nature of Dyaling & Shews readily to draw the Furniture & Ornaments on Dyals.
Theodolet & Semi Circle
The Theodolet is a Whole Circle divided into 360 deg. The Semicircle into 180 deg. both very excellent Instruments in Surveying, to take Heights & distances.
Protractor
An Instrum.t that readily makes & measures any Angle on Mapps or draughts, Used in Surveying to make the Plott, after the Angles are taken.
Sinical Quadrant
An Instrument that Solves by inspection all right angle'd plain tryangles, & Usd by Mariners to Answer all Questions in plain Sailing.
Thermometre
An Instrum.t that measures ye unperceiveable alterations of ye Weather, as to heat & Cold, also fit for Bagnio's, Greenhouses, & many usefull Experiments.
Barometre
An Instrument shewing the gravitation of ye Air (invented by Torrecellus) being altered by the different compressions of ye Atmosphere it foretells ye rising Fair or Frost, ye falling Rain Snow, wind or Stormes:
Mathematicks
By the assistance of a Master are made so delightfull & pleasant, & of Such general use, that they aggrandize a Man for all Conversation & make him Capable of any Employ.
Croß-staffe
An Instrument much use'd at Sea for takeing ye Altitude of ye Sun, or Starrs, in order to find ye Latitude.
Plows & Bows
These Instruments if well made, are yet in esteem amongst many Navigators their description & Use may be found in Guntor, Sr Jonas Moor, &c.
Sea Quadrant
An Instrument containing ye 4th part of a Circle, or 90 deg: well contrived for ye Mariners use, ye great Arch plac't at a Convenient distance for ye Eye, ye lesser for ye Shadows
Cone
Admits of 5 Sections, viz: Parabola, Hyperbola, Elipsis, Tryangle & Circle, of many Uses in Mathematicks, perticularly drawing ye furniture on Sun dials
Miner
Generally Uses a good Leavell to bring home his Soughs for dreining Mines, a Compass box and Needle to take his bearings & a Universal Dyal
Bookes & Instrum.ts for Navigation
Quadrant
Fore & back staffe
Double Guntor
Plain Scale
Nocturnall
Slideing Guntor
Sinical Quadrant
Universal Equinoctial Dyal
2 pr of Compasses
2 pr of draught Comp.
2 pr of dividers
2 pr of Globes
Azimuth Compass
Navigation Sector
Sr Jon. Moors Works
Newhouse's Pr Naviga
Sturmy's Magazine
Seaman Practice
Mariner Kalendar
Norwoods Systeme Epitome Trygonometr.
Atkinsons Epitome
Tuttells Use of the Universal Equinoctial Dyal
Journal Bookes
Sea Charts & Platts
Slate & penns
Use of ye Globes
Tellescope
Charts
The plain Chart, has the degrees of Latitude & Longitude Equal, Mercator ye deg of Longitude Equal, but those of Latitude unequal, both usefull in Navigation.
Tryangular Quadrant
An Instrument capable of many improvements, well contrived to hold much usefull Worke & very portable.
Quadrant
An Instrument Several ways contrived, to find ye Hour & Azimuth, & for Solveing most propositions of ye Globe, & for takeing the height of Trees, Steples, Towers, &.
Platonicke Bodys
Are 5 regular Solids Usefull to informe all Students to a right conception of their Nature and being furnished wth Dyals (that Set them selves) are of great Use
Carpentor
Chiefly uses the two foot and 18 Inch Rules with Squares, Bevels, Levels, and a Case of Instrum.ts wth Sector Scales, Compasses &c for Draughts.

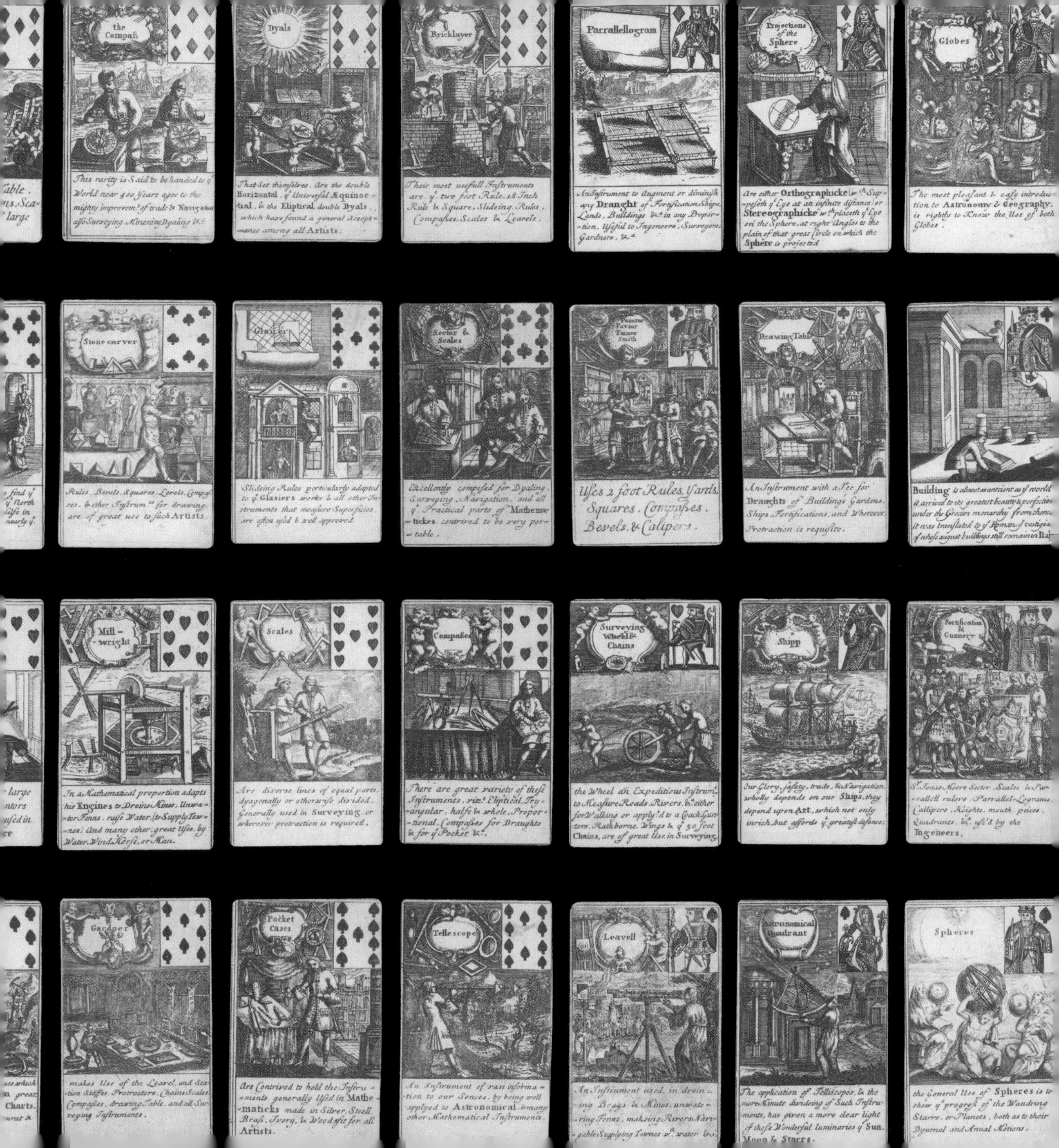
the Compass
This rarity is Said to be handed to ye World near 400 Years agoe to the mighty improvemt. of trade & Navigation also Surveying Mineing Dyaling &c.
Dyals
That See themselves. Are the double Horizontal, ye Universal Æquinoctial, & the Eliptical double Dyals which have found a general Acceptance among all Artists.
Bricklayer
Their most usefull Instruments are ye two foot Rule. 18 Inch Rule & Square, Slideing Rules, Compasses, Scales & Leavels.
Parrallellogram
An Instrument to Augment or diminish any Draught of Fortification Ships, Lands, Buildings &c. in any Proportion. Usefull to Ingeneers, Surveyors, Gardners, &c.
Projections of the Sphere
Are either Orthographicke wch. Supposeth ye Eye at an infinite distance or Stereographicke wch. placeth ye Eye on the Sphere at right Angles to the plain of that great Circle on which the Sphere is projected
Globes
The most pleasant & easy introduction to Astronomy & Geography is rightly to Know the Use of both Globes.
Stone carver
Rules, Bevels, Squares, Levels, Compasses, & other Instrumts. for drawing, are of great use to such Artists.
Glasier
Slideing Rules particularly adapted to ye Glasiers worke & all other Instruments that measure Superficies are often used & well approved.
Sector & Scales
Excellently composed for Dyaling, Surveying, Navigation, and all ye Practical parts of Mathematicks contrived to be very portable.
Painter Paver Turner Smith
Uses 2 foot Rules, Yards, Squares, Compasses, Bevels, & Calipers.
Drawing Table
An Instrument with a Tee for Draughts of Buildings Gardens, Ships Fortifications, and Wherever Protraction is requisite.
Building is almost as antient as ye world it arrived to its greatest beauty & perfection under the Grecian monarchy from thence it was translated to ye Romans vestigia of whose august buildings still remain in Ital
Mill-wright
In a Mathematical proportion adapts his Engines to Dreine Mines, Unwater Fenns, raise Water, (to Supply Towns) And many other great Uses, by Water, Wind, Horse, or Man.
Scales
Are diverse lines of equal parts, dyagonally or otherwise divided, Generally used in Surveying or wherever protraction is required.
Compasses
There are great variety of these Instruments, viz. Elliptical, Tryangular, halfe & whole, Proportional, Compasses for Draughts & for ye Pocket &c.
Surveying Wheel & Chains
the Wheel an Expeditious Instrumt. to Measure Roads Rivers &c. either for Walking or apply'd to a Coach. Gunters, Rathborne, Wings & ye 50 foot Chains, are of great Use in Surveying.
Shipp
Our Glory, safety, trade, & Navigation wholly depends on our Ships, they depend upon Art, which not only inrich, but affords ye greatest defence.
Fortification & Gunnery
Sr. Jonas Moers Sector, Scales & Parallell rulers, Parallel-lograms, Callipers, Heights, mouth peices, Quadrants, &c. us'd by the Ingeneers.
Gardner
makes Use of the Leavel, and Station Staffes, Protractors, Chains, Scales, Compasses, drawing Table, and all Surveying Instruments.
Pocket Cases
Are Contrived to hold the Instruments generally Used in Mathematicks made in Silver, Steell, Brass, Ivory, & Wood fit for all Artists.
Tellescope
An Instrument of vast information to our Sences, by being well applyed to Astronomical & many other Mathematical Instruments.
Leavell
An Instrument used in dreining Boggs & Mines, unwatering Fenns, makeing Rivers Navigable, Supplying Townes wth. water &c.
Astronomical Quadrant
The application of Tellicopes, & the more Minute divideing of Such Instruments, has given a more clear light of those Wonderful luminaries ye Sun, Moon & Starrs.
Spheres
the General Use of Spheres is to shew ye progress of the Wandring Starrs, or Planets, both as to their Dyurnal and Annual Motions.

A perpetual calendar fit for a king …

28 [Anonymous]

[Perpetual Calendar] Cadran Annuel de Cabinet.

Publication
Paris, se vend à Paris chez l'Auteur rue de Grenelle quartier St Honoré. Et chez Limosin rue de Gesvre au grand Coeur Avec Privilege du Roi, 1710.

Description
Engraving in fine original hand-colouring heightened with gold and silver, mounted on cardboard as issued, three moveable volvelles.

Dimensions
410 by 280mm (16.25 by 11 inches).

A calendar for the years 1710-1736.

The presentation copy of this perpetual calendar was made for King Louis XIV and kept in his personal cabinet, "Presenté au Roi le 13 Janvier 1710 et se conserve dans le Cabinet de sa Majesté". The present example is dedicated to Louis Nicolas Le Tonnelier de Breteuil, Baron de Breteuil et de Preuilly, the Introducer of Ambassadors and foreign Princes to the King. The circular calendar is surrounded by figures of the Four Seasons, and shows the phases of the moon, new moons, age of the moon and dates of the month. The two smaller dials add information on years, solar cycles, months, zodiac signs, feast days, length of the day, etc.

AN DE GRACE
Nombre d'Or
Cycle Solaire
Indiction Romaine
Lettres Dominicales
Festes du Mois
Nom du Mois
Signe du Mois
Lever du Soleil
Longueur du
Heures. Minutes.
CADRAN ANNUEL DE CABINET.
Dimanche
Lundy
Mardy
Mercredy
Ieudy
Vendredy
Samedy
Dimanche
Années du Seigneur
Iours des Cendres
Pasques
Ascension
Pentecoste
Feste Dieu
Avent
Age de la Lune
TEMPUS EDAX RERUM
Pour trouver lage de la lune on calcule lépacte de lannée le quantieme du mois et le nombre des mois à comencer par Mars Jusqu'a Fevrier led. Calcul fera lage de la Lune, sil ne va pas jusqua trente sil va a trente il ni a point de Lune et si le dit calcul excede trente lexedant fera lage de la Lune.
Fevrier qui a 28. jour en aura 29. en Bisexte et la Lune toujours egalle au contraire des autres Mois ou elle a toujours un jo. de moins
Les 4. tems arivent les Mercredys qui suivent les Cendres la Pentecoste Ste. Croix en Sept. et Ste. Luce en Decembre.
Dedié a Monsieur le Baron de Breteuil et de Preuilly, Premier Baron de Tourraine, Introducteur des Ambassadeurs et Princes Etrangers auprés du Roy.
Par son tres Humble et tres obeissant Serviteur le BOUTEUX.

Fine broadside illustrating the so-called "Leiden Sphere" — the first mechanical model of a Copernican solar system

29 **AA, Pieter Van der**

Sphaera Armillaris Copernicana ...

Publication
Amsterdam, 1711.

Description
Hand-coloured engraved broadsheet.

Dimensions
500 by 380mm (19.75 by 15 inches).

A fine broadside illustrating the so-called "Leiden Sphere," engraved by Pieter Van der Aa.

The Leiden Sphere, a mechanical armillary sphere or orrery, was built around 1670 by the clockmaker Steven Tracy, for the mayor of Rotterdam, Adriaen Vroesen. It is among the earliest and most elaborate mechanical planetaria to be operated by a clockwork mechanism. The device depicts the Copernican solar system, in which the Earth and the other planets revolve around a stationary sun. In order of distance from the sun, the sphere includes Mercury, Venus, the Earth (with its moon), Mars, Jupiter with the four Galilean satellites, and Saturn. The mechanism in the base of the sphere regulates an accurate representation of the orbital periods of each of the planets and their inclined orbits around the sun.

In 1710, this magnificent piece was given to the University of Leiden, where it could be seen in operation for more than a century. Tracy incorporated two vertical brass rings (1.5 meters in diameter), which support a wide ecliptic (28.6 cm) composed of embossed constellation figures cut from sheet brass and mounted in rectangular frames. The sphere sits on a wooden cube (84 cm high). A 13 centimetres clock-face at the top of the pedestal displays the time and slot apertures indicate the day, month and year.

The sphere was the first such device to incorporate a geared model of Jupiter's system. The basic design is similar to that of the Rømer-Horrebow ceiling planetarium, but with a number of important additions, including the incorporation of offset cams to give the model planets a Keplerian motion similar to those on the Rittenhouse orreries. The Saturn cam is inclined, whereas for the other planets (other than Earth), the cams are horizontal.

Following receipt, the sphere was thoroughly overhauled by the Den Haag clockmaker Bernard van der Cloesen. The Leiden Sphere still resides in Leiden in the Museum Boerhaave.

The illustration provides an excellent depiction of the sphere, although it omits the eccentric collars, but adds a ring for the celestial equator and a spindle that passes upwards through the sun. There are apparently two editions of the broadside, one in French and Dutch (the present example) and one in English and Dutch. Both are exceedingly rare.

LA SPHERE AUTOMATIQUE,

Travaillée par THRASIUS,
Par les Soins de Mr. ADRIEN VROESEN, & suivant les Calculs de NICOLAS STAMPIOEN.
Elle fut donnée à l'usage du Public par la Veuve & les Heritiers de
Mr. SEBASTIEN SCHEPERS,
SENATEUR de la Ville de Rotterdam, &c.
Et augmentée & mise en un meilleur ordre par le très Ingenieux
BERNARD CLOESEN.
Messieurs les CURATEURS de l'Université & Messieurs les BOURGUEMAITRES de la Ville de LEYDE l'ont destinée aux Amateurs des beaux Arts & de l'Astronomie, en l'An MDCCXI.

SPHERA AUTOMATICA,

Bewerkt en opgemaakt door THRASIUS,
Onder 't beleydt van de Heer ADRIAAN VROESEN,
Volgens de oprekeningen van NICOLAAS STAMPIOEN.
Geschonken tot 't gebruyk van 't Gemeen door de Weduwe en Erfgenamen van
De Heer BASTIAAN SCHEPERS,
RAAD der Stad Rotterdam, &c.
Vermeerdert en in een beter order gestelt door den seer vernuftigen
BERNARD CLOESEN.
En door de Heeren CURATEUREN van de Universiteit en BURGERMEESTEREN der Stadt LEYDEN
Geschikt tot 't gebruyk van de Liefhebbers der Weetenschappen en van de Astronomie, in 't Jaar 1711.

Courte Description de la Sphere * Armillaire de Copernic.

Toute la Sphere est de Cuivre, aussi bien que les principaux Cercles, à savoir l'Equateur [1], les deux Colures [2], & l'Ecliptique [3], par le quel le Zodiaque [4] est partagé suivant la latitude en deux parties, ayant de part & d'autre dix degrés de largeur & ses douze Signes d'un ouvrage cizelé, avec leurs noms marquez sur l'Ecliptique. L'Ecliptique [3] est divisé en degrés & en demi degrés. Le Diametre de chacun de ces Cercles & par consequent de toute la Sphere est de cinq pieds de Rhinlande.

La Sphere [5] s'éleve du Piedestal de trois pieds, dans le quel est enfermée l'Horloge avec sa pendule & ses poids: cette Horloge va pendant neuf jours, & pourroit aller plus longtems si on vouloit: elle marque l'année, les mois, les jours, les heures, & les minutes: Et elle fait aller toutes les Planettes, tant du premier que du second ordre, entre les quelles la Terre est comprise, suivant le systême de Copernic, selon leurs mouvements naturels & réglés, excepté les Satellites de Saturne; le tout dans l'ordre qui suit.

Le Soleil [6] occupe le Centre de la Sphere, & quoiqu'il y soit immobile, il est aisé de s'imaginer qu'il tourne autour de son Centre.

Mercure [7] est le plus près du soleil, & par consequent le tour qu'il fait autour de lui est le plus court de tous; il l'acheve en 88 jours.

Venus [8] occupe le second rang, & comme elle est plus éloignée du Soleil, elle fait aussi un plus grand tour; elle l'acheve en 225 jours.

Au troisiéme rang est la Terre [9], qui étant emportée avec la Lune [10] fait son cercle annuel autour du Soleil, en 365 jours & près de six heures; mais de maniére qu'elle se meut autour de son propre Centre toutes les vingt quatre heures, & que son Axe est toujours paralelle à lui-même, & que ses Poles sont continuellement tournés vers les mêmes points du Firmament; lequel Paralelisme est formé, suivant le sentiment de quelques uns, par un mouvement qu'ils apellent d'inclinaison.

L'Horizon & le Méridien de la Terre sont mobiles en cette Sphere, ensorte qu'étant donné la latitude d'un lieu on en peut savoir la longueur du jour & de la nuit, de même que l'heure du jour où l'on est.

Pendant que la Terre décrit son cercle avec la Lune [10] dans l'espace d'une année autour du Soleil, la lune se meut autour de la Terre en 29 jours & 12 heures plus ou moins dans un cercle, lequel étant prolongé, coupera l'Ecliptique en deux points diamétralement opposés, les quels points sont nommés Noeuds ou jointures par les Astronomes; ce qui sert à conoitre tous les jours sa latitude Meridionale ou Septentrionale, comme aussi le temps des Eclipses tant du Soleil que de la Lune.

Au quatriéme rang est Mars [11], qui étant plus éloigné du Soleil que la Terre, acheve son Tour en 687 jours.

Au cinquiéme lieu est Jupiter [12], lequel avec ses quatre Satellites fait son tour à l'entour du Soleil en onse ans, 315 jours & 20 heures: pendant ce Tems là chacun de ses Satellites fait son tour à l'entour de Jupiter; savoir le plus proche [a] de Jupiter, en quarante deux heures & demi; le second [b] en trois jours & 13 heures & demi; le troisiéme [c] en 7 jours & 12 heures; & enfin le quatriéme [d] comme le plus éloigné de Jupiter fait le sien en 16 jours & 18 heures.

La derniere Planete & la plus éloignée du Soleil c'est Saturne, qui ne tourne point dans cette Sphere sur son centre, mais qui néanmoins fait ici son tour à l'entour du Soleil en 29 ans 166 jours, & douze heures; les cinq Satellites de Saturne sont aussi immobiles & attachés à son anneau qui est de même immobile: cela ne pouvant pas se faire autrement à cause du peu de place, & n'étant d'ailleurs pas fort necessaire.

Il faut remarquer que si on prolonge chaque cercle des Planetes, ils coupent l'Ecliptique, ensorte que par là l'on peut connoitre la latitude des lieux tant Septentrionale que Meridionale.

On peut aisement observer dans cette Sphere les directions des Planetes, leurs Stations, leurs retrogradations, & les retardements & accélérations de leurs mouvemens.

Il n'est pas necessaire que nous avertissions, que toutes les fois que de la Terre on regarde le Soleil par une ligne droite, on peut sçavoir dans quel signe du Zodiaque il est alors, & même dans quel degré de ce signe.

On peut voir aussi en remuant l'horloge, les Positions de toutes les Planetes tant pour les temps passés que pour l'avenir, sans que pour cela le mouvement ordinaire de la Machine s'arrête ni en soit interrompu en aucune maniere.

Au reste, après avoir observé les mouvemens des Planetes pendant quelques mois sur cette Sphere, on a trouvé qu'ils s'accordent parfaitement bien avec les plus nouvelles, & les plus exactes observations des Astronomes.

* c. d. Sphere à jour, qui n'est composée que de Cercles, sans représenter la solidité du Globe.

SPHÆRA ARMILLARIS COPERNICANA.

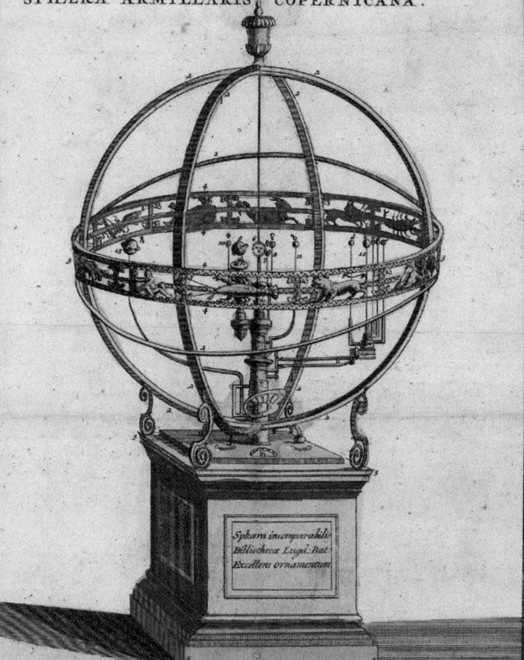

Machina ingenioso artificio extructa,
ope et industria Bernardi a Cloese restituta,
Europæ admiratio.

Korte Beschryving van de * Armillare Sphera van Copernicus.

De geheele Sphera is van koper, gelyk ook de voornaamste Cirkels, te weten, de Equator [1], de twee Coluren [2], en de Ecliptica [3], door dewelke de Zodiacus [4] in de breedte verdeelt is in twee deelen, hebbende aan weer-zyden tien graden, en des selfs twaalf teekenen van uitgesneden werk, met hunne namen recht-over op de Ecliptica geteekent. De Ecliptica [3] is in graden en halve graden verdeelt. De Diameter van ider deser Cirkelen, en by gevolg van de geheele Sphera, heeft vyf Rynlandse voeten.

De Sphera [5] staat op een Pedestaal van drie voeten, in dewelke 't Uurwerk met des selfs Penduul en Gewicht gesloten is: 't gaat negen dagen lang, en soude nog langer kunnen gaan indien men wilde: het merkt 't jaar, de maanden, de dagen, de uren, en de minuten: en door 't selve werden alle de Planeten, soo van de eerste als van de tweede order, onder dewelke de Aarde begrepen is volgens het Systema van Copernicus, bewogen volgens hunne natuurlyke en gereguleerde bewegingen, uitgesondert de Satelliten van Saturnus, en dat op deese order.

De Son [6] staat in 't middelpunt van de Sphera, en hoewel hy aldaar onbeweeglyk is, soo kan men sig gemackelyk inbeelden dat hy op syn middelpunt draayt.

Het naast aan de Son staat Mercurius [7], welkers Cirkel rond om de Son, bygevolg, de kleynste is, de selve voleindigende in de tyd van 88 dagen.

In de tweede rang staat Venus [8], dewelke verder van de Son afgelegen zynde, een grooter Cirkel rontom hem doet, de selve voleindigende in de tyd van 225 dagen.

In de derde rang staat de Aarde [9], dewelke met de Maan heenen gevoert werdende, haare Cirkel rontom de Son voleindigt in de tyd van 365 dagen en omtrent 6 uuren, maar sodanig dat sy alle vier-en-twintig uuren op haare middelpunt draayt, en dat desselfs asch altyd parallel is aan sig selve, en dat haare Poolen altyd gekeert staan na de selve punčten van 't Firmament; welke Parallelismus veroorsaakt is, volgens 't gevoelen van sommige, door een schuynselyke beweeging, so als sy die noemen.

De Horizon en de Meridiaen van de Aarde syn beweeglyk in deese Sphera, so dat, de hoogte van een plaats gegeven synde, men de lengte van de dag en nagt, en de uur van den dag waar men is, weten kan.

Terwyl de Aarde met de Maan [10] haar Cirkel beschryft rontom de Son in de tyd van een jaar, soo draayt de Maan rontom de Aarde in de tyd van 29 dagen en omtrent 12 uuren, in een Cirkel, dewelke uytgestreckt synde de Ecliptica in twee tegengestelde punčten sal snyden, die de Astronomi Knoopen of Voegselen noemen, 't welk dient om alle dag de Noordelyke of Zuydelyke hoogte van de Maan te kennen, als ook de tyden der Eclipsen soo van de Son als van de Maan.

In de vierde rang is Mars [11], die verder van de Son is afgelegen als de Aarde, en syn Cirkel rontom de selve voleindigt in de tyd van 687 dagen.

In de vyfde rang is Jupiter [12], dewelke met sijn vier Satelliten syn Cirkel rontom de Son voleindigt in de tyd van elf jaren 315 dagen en 10 uuren: terwyl de selve aldus beweegt, so doet ider Satelliet syn Cirkel rontom Iupiter; te weten, de naaste [a] aan Jupiter, in twee-en-veertig uuren en een half; de tweede [b], in drie dagen en dertien uuren en een half; de derde [c], in 7 dagen en twaalf uuren; en eindelyk de vierde [d], als de wydst afgelege van Jupiter, in 16 dagen en 18 uuren.

De laaste Planeet en de wydst afgelegene van de Son is Saturnus, dewelke in deese Sphera op zyn middelpunt niet en draeyt, maar nogtans alhier syn Cirkel rontom de Son voleindigt in de tyd van 29 jaren 166 dagen en 12 uuren; de vyf Satelliten van Saturnus syn hier ook sonder beweging, en gehegt aan desselfs ring, die ook hier onbeweeglyk is: dit niet kunnende anders geschieden van wegens de kleynte van de plaats, en ook niet seer nodig synde.

Men moet aanmerken dat ider Cirkel van de Planeten, indien men de selve verlengt en uytstrekt, de Ecliptica sodanig snyd, dat men daar door de hoogte der Plaatsen soo Noordelyke als Zuydelyke kennen kan.

In dese Sphera kan men ook ligtelyk bemerken de Directien der Planeten, hunne stilstanden, hunne agter-uitgangen, en de verminderingen en vermeerderingen hunner beweegingen. Ook is 't niet noodig te waarschouwen, dat, soo dikwils als men van de Aarde regt-draats de Son aanschouwt, men weeten kan in wat teeken van de Zodiacus hy is, en selfs in welke graad van dit teeken.

Ook kan men, als men 't Uurwerk beweegt, de Stellingen van alle de Planeten sien, 't zy voor de voorleedene, 't zy voor de toekomende tyd, sonder dat'er de minste veranderinge in de ordinare beweging van de geheele machine geschied.

Eindelyk, na dat men gedurende eenige maenden de bewegingen van de Planeten op deese Sphera heeft aangemerkt, soo heeft men bevonden dat de selve volmacktelyk overeenkomen met de niewste en naaukeurigste aanmerkingen der Astronomi.

* Sphera dewelke alleen uyt Cirkels bestaat, sonder de dikte van de Globus te vertoonen.

The Copernican solar system

30 **PIGEON D'OSANGI, Jean**

Planisphere des Planetes Selon l'Hypothese de Copernie avec leurs neuds leurs distance et leur exentricité. Presenté a son altesse Royale Monseignr. le duc Orleans. Par son très humble et très obeissant Serviteur J. Pigeon Mathematicien avec Privilege 1713.

Publication
Paris, chez l'Auteur au premier appartement du S. Filio Limonadier Place Dauphine proche le Palais, 1713.

Description
Engraved planisphere, trimmed to within neatline, with minor loss to image, varnished.

Dimensions
555 by 555mm (21.75 by 21.75 inches).

Jean Pigeon d'Osangi (1654-1739) was one of the leading scientific instrument makers in Paris during the early eighteenth century. He is known to have made instruments for Louis XIV, and dedicated this planisphere to Philip II, the Duke of Orleans (1674-1723), two years before he became Prince Regent. Pigeon was not only a celebrated master instrument-maker but also a versatile artist, whose life was written up in detail by his daughter, Marie-Anne-Victoire Le Guay in her biography of him, 'Le méchaniste philosophe' (1750). In the early eighteenth century Pigeon became famous as the inventor of the rotating armillary sphere operated by an integrated clockwork movement. His renown grew with the publication in 1714 of his treatise 'Description d'une sphère mouvante'. Pigeon had made his first rotating armillary sphere in 1706 for Louis XIV; he would dedicate his second armillary sphere to the Duke of Orleans in 1714.

The present instrument is dated 1713, and also dedicated to the Duke of Orleans. The title and dedication are surrounded by an elaborate cartouche featuring the coats-of-arms of the Duke of Orleans, several scientific instruments including an armillary sphere, a quadrant, a telescope, a pair of compasses, and two putti surveying the heavens through telescopes. As the title suggests, the instrument depicts a heliocentric universe in accordance with Copernicus. At the centre is the sun with each planet's orbit delineated, from Mercury to Saturn, together with its title and planetary symbol. Between the orbits of Jupiter and Saturn are placed the signs of the zodiac, together with the orbital period for each planet through the zodiac and their aphelion (i.e. the point in their orbit where they are furthest from the sun). There are also letters placed upon each orbital path: 'S', 'M', 'D', and 'A'; 'A' & 'D' mark the point of the planet's ascension and declination, with 'S' and 'M' marking planetary nodes.

Rare. We are only able to trace one institutional example of the work, that in the Bibliotheque Nationale de France (FRBNF42097471).

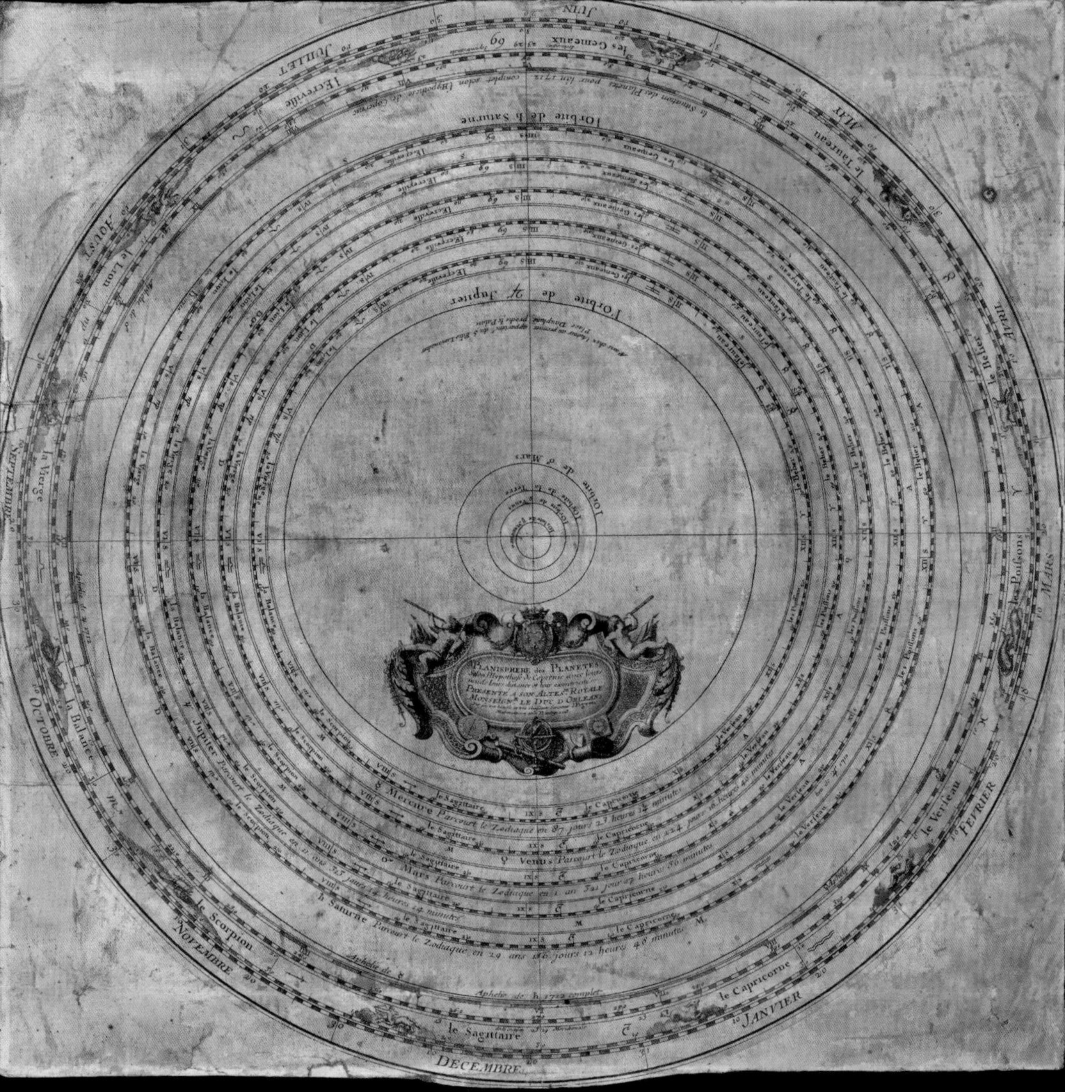
PLANISPHERE des PLANETES
PRESENTE A SON ALTESSE ROYALE
MONSEIGNR. LE DUC D'ORLEANS
Mercure Parcourt le Zodiaque en 87 jours 23 heures 14 minutes
Venus Parcourt le Zodiaque en 224 jours 16 heures 40 minutes
Mars Parcourt le Zodiaque en 1 an 321 jours 23 heures 30 minutes
Jupiter Parcourt le Zodiaque en 11 ans 315 jours 14 heures 24 minutes
Saturne Parcourt le Zodiaque en 29 ans 156 jours 12 heures 48 minutes
Orbite de Saturne
Orbite de Jupiter
Orbite de Mars
Orbite de la Terre
le Sagittaire
le Capricorne
le Verseau
les Poissons
le Belier
le Taureau
les Gemeaux
l'Ecrevisse
le Lion
la Vierge
la Balance
le Scorpion
DECEMBRE
JANVIER
FEVRIER
MARS
AVRIL
MAY
JUIN
JUILLET
AOUST
SEPTEMBRE
OCTOBRE
NOVEMBRE

The second known example of Stampioen's star chart in fine contemporary hand-colour

31 **STAMPIOEN, Jan Jansz the Younger, [and] Marten CALMAM**

Onderwys in 't Regte Gebruyk van het Hemels-Plyn strekkende tot nut en vermaak der liefhebbers.

Publication
Amsterdam, Jochem Hasebroek, [c. 1722].

Description
Large engraved celestial chart by Stampioen with a rotating printed paper ring (volvelle or rete) on an off-centre axis to indicate the part of the sky visible at any date and time and to make a variety of celestial calculations, all for the latitude of 52 degrees (the Netherlands), with letterpress instructions by Calman on a separate slip at the right. A string with a bead serves as a pointer for aligning the scales in the stationary and rotating parts, coloured by a contemporary hand and mounted on contemporary boards covered with marbled paper, apparently by the publisher, so that it can be folded in half for carrying.

Dimensions
566 by 665mm (22 by 26 inches); chart 325mm (13 inches) in diameter.

References
Koeman IV, p. 5 (no location noted; cf. p. 153); Warner, p. 260, no. 1c (no location noted; cf. p. 247); Adler Planetarium on-line database A-259; cf. Bierens de Haan 4516 (1684 ed., not seen: see his Bouwstoffen II, pp. 386 & 429 note 5); van Keulen, E.O. et al., "In de Gekroonde Lootsman," item 4 & illustration between pp. 64 & 65 (1680/1696 Vooght/Van Keulen ed.); not in BMC Printed Maps; Zinner, Astron. Instrumente; NCC/Picarta; OCLC WorldCat.

See item 22 for a discussion of Stampioen's chart.

The chart is here in its third state, but we have located no complete example of any earlier version. The Boerhaave Museum in Leiden has the chart without volvelle or instructional text, published by Doncker, but the 1664 edition described in Doncker's advertisement clearly included the volvelle and instructional text. Perhaps the surviving chart is the 1684 version mentioned but not seen by Bierens de Haan, who provides neither a detailed description nor a source for his information. They and the present version (printed from Doncker's plate c. 1722) seem to have appeared only as separate publications, hence their great rarity. The circular border around the sky image and the outer part of the volvelle include scales with several kinds of data so that the chart can be used for various purposes. One can use the string to align the time in the volvelle with the date in the border of the chart, so that the part of the sky visible at that moment appears inside the volvelle. The chart with its volvelle, scales and string can also be used to calculate times for the rising and setting of constellations at various dates (or to calculate the present time based on the position of the stars). Fifty-three constellations are numbered quarter by quarter (15, 9, 14 and 15), with a Dutch key identifying them in each corner. Calman's instructional text, printed letterpress on a separate slip (495 by 185 cm) and mounted to the right of the chart itself, describes the different scales, etc., then presents nine "proposals" (giving examples of the use of the chart). If the volvelle is turned with 12 midnight to the right, the boards can be folded to each other like a portfolio, protecting the chart and making it easier to carry. It may have been published in this form, for the only other copy located, at the Adler Planetarium in Chicago, is similarly mounted. The marbled paper covering the portfolio, similar to Wolfe 33-35, was common in the Netherlands in the late seventeenth and early eighteenth centuries.

In the plate of the star chart itself is engraved, "Auct. J. Stampioen. 't Amsterdam by Iochem Hasebroek" but Hasebroek's name is larger and in a different style than the rest of the lettering, and one can see traces of an earlier name under it. Although the older name cannot be deciphered, one can see that "Hendrick Doncker" would fit (with traces of the H and Do, and marks where the ascenders to the d, k and k would have been), making it clear that the present chart is printed from Doncker's original plate. Calman advertised his Amsterdam boarding school for calligraphy, mathematics, etc. in 1722, and Hasebroek (1682-1756) is recorded as a sea chart publisher and instrument maker from 1714 to 1743.

IUNIUS
IULIUS
MAIUS
AQVARIUS
Noorde
Nto
Nno
Notn
No
Noto
Zuyd
Zuyde
Oost
Cassiopea
Andromeda
Triangulum
Perseus

JUNIUS
JULIUS
AUGUSTUS
SEPTEMBER
OCTOBER
NOVEMBER
GEMINI
CANCER
LEO
VIRGO
LIBRA
SCORPIUS

Onderwys in 't regte gebruyk van het

HEMELS-PLYN,

Strekkende tot nut en vermaak der Liefhebbers.

VAN DE VERDELING.

HEt buytenste Rond is verdeeld in maanden en dagen, op een gemeen Jaar, naar de nieuwe Styl, en de week-letter op yder dag van 't Jaar, staande op den eersten January de letter A Het volgende Rond is in 360 graden verdeeld, zynde de *Ascensie-Recta*, of regte op-gang naar den Evenaar, is verdeeld in 12 tekens, yder teken in 30 graden, passende yder graad op den dag van 't Jaar, daar die onder staat: in yder teken is ook gestelt de Caracter van een der Planeten; naar de meening der *oude Sterrekykers*, welke oordeelde dat die in zoodanige tekens de kragtigste uytwerkinge dede. Het Rond hier binnen toond aan het gehele Jaar door de Zonne declinatie

Binnen op 't Hemels-plyn zyn 13 evenwydige Ronden getogen uyt een zelfde middelpunt dat de Noordpool is: de negende en gosste is den *Æquinoctiaal* of Evenaar: yder Rond staat 10 graden van den andere: Door het Middel-punt van 't Hemels-plyn zyn 2 middel-lynen getogen, die malkanderen regthoeks doorsnyden, eindigende in 't Rond van de *Regte ascensie*, den eene op 0 en 180 graden; dese is de Hoofd-tydkring der Evenagten, den andere eyndigt op 90 en 270 graden; welke is de Hoofd-tydkring der Keer punten als de Zon in dese komt, maakt in de eerste, de geheele wereld door dag en nagt even lang, en in de andere is de Zon op 't uyterste ten noorden en zuyden geweken: den eene Hoofd-tydkring is in gelyke delen verdeeld dat graden zyn, van de Noordpool tot den Evenaar in 90 graden, en verder van den Evenaar af daar buyten in nog 40 graden, dat is bezuyden den Evenaar. Nog is hier opgetogen een lang rond, dat door-snyd den Evenaar in de evenagts-tyden, en wykt in de Keer-punten 23½ graad benoorden en bezuyden den Evenaar; dit lang-rond is de *Ecliptia*, of Zons-weg, die in 12 tekens, en yder teken in 30 graden verdeeld is, welke altyd de Zons-graad in de Zodiac aanwyst. Nog zyn op dit Hemels-plyn de voornaamste vaste Sterren gestelt, die hier te lande konnen gezien worden, op hun regte Evenaars breete en lengte, na 't Jaar 1700. ook zyn dese Sterren in onderscheyde beelden verdeeld, en in de hoeken van yder vierendeel de namen daar van met reken-letters uytgedrukt.

Hier op werd vast gemaakt een bewegende Horisont, diens buytenste Rond in 24 uuren, en yder uur in 15 deelen is verdeeld: het binnenste Rond in 32 streeken van 't Compas, en viermaal 90 garden. Hier binnen zyn 8 *Virticalen*, of Top-bogen die de voornaamste streeken van 't Compas zyn: het punt daar die elkanderen snyden, is 't *Senit*, Top-punt, welke Top-bogen ook in 90 graden zyn verdeeld Nog is hier door getogen een *Almucantarath* of Hoogte-kring van 4 graden

De *Meridiaan* van dese *Horisont* werd op 52 graden vast gemaakt in de Noord-pool, zodanig dat die kan rondom draijen, daar ook een draad aan vast word gemaakt aan welke draad een knoopje is dat heen en weder kan schuyven.

EERSTE VOORSTEL.

Om de Sterren Evenaars breete en lengte te vinden.

ALs men begeerde te weten de Ster *Botes*, wat Evenaars breete en lengte die heeft, spand de draad over de voornoemde Ster, en ziet op hoe veel graden dat die in 't buytenste Rond komt te leggen, zult vinden, na genoeg 113 graden voor de Sters regte Ascensie: schuyft het knoopje op 't middel-punt van de Ster, en dan gespannen op de verdeelde Meridiaan, zult het knoopje zien leggen op 21 graden voor de Noorder Evenaars breete.

TWEEDE VOORSTEL.

Om de Zons Evenaars breete en lengte te vinden, en de plaats in de Zodiac.

BY voorbeeld op den 10 Augusti, spand den draat in 't buytenste Rond op den 10 Augusti, ziet op hoe veel graden den draad in 't buytenste Rond komt te leggen, zult vinden op de 138ste graad, dat is voor de Evenaars lengte of Zonne-tyd na de Lent-snee: dan zal men de draad ook zien legge op de Zons declinatie op 16½ graad, voor de Zons Evenaars breete: Ziet ook welke graad van de *Ecliptica* door dees alzoo gespannen draad word afgesneden, men vind 15 graden in *Leo* voor de Zons-plaate in den *Zodiac*.

DERDE VOORSTEL.

Wanneer een bekende Ster in 't zuyde of noorden komt.

DEn 20ste November het zeven gesternte *Pliades*, wanneer die aan 't zuyden komt: spand den draad op den 20ste November, en draayt den Horisont tot de Zuyd-streek op 't zeven gesternte legt: ziet dan hoe veel tyd den draad aan wyst op de rand van de Horisont, zult vinden 's avonds ten 11 uuren 36 min. op welke tyd *Pliades* in 't zuyden zal komen.

VIERDE VOORSTEL.

De gestalte des Hemels te vinden, dat zeer dienstig is om de Sterren te leeren kennen.

OP den 5 December, 's avonds ten 9 uuren, begeerd men te weten de gestagte des Hemels: spand den draad op den 5 December, en dan de Horisont omgedraayt tot aan de west-kant 9 uuren op den rand van den Horisont boven den draad lyd, dan zal men zien het *Hoofd van den Ram* in 't zuyden 59 graden hoog: *Hircus* den Bok een wynig benoorden het oost hoog 60 graden: *klyne Hond* in 't oosten 10 graden hoog: den *grooten Hond* in 't O. Z. O in den Horisont: het *voorste Paard* van de groote Wagen in 't noorden 10 graden hoog: den *Dolfyn* in 't west hoog 17 graden: *Pliades* in 't Z. O. hoog 55 graden: *Aldebaran* wat oostelyker als in 't Z. O. ten O. hoog 42 graden: den *vligende Arend* 2 graden boven den Horisont, en wat westelyker als west ten noorden.

NB. Nadien dit Hemels-plyn is gestelt op 52 graaden Noorder breete, dat met de Maze over een komt, evenwel zal men dit konnen gebruyken in 't Canaal, de Noord zee ontrent de kust der Nederlanden, alzo 2 á 3 graden verschil in Polus hoogte weynig hinder kan by brengen: ook zal men door de gestalte des Hemels zeer gemakkelyk door middel van dit werktuyg de sterren leeren kennen.

VYFDE VOORSTEL

Wanneer en in welke streek de Zon of Sterren op en ondergaan.

DEn 15 April begeerende de tyd der Zons op en ondergang; spant den draad op den 15 April, en draayt den Horison zodanig heen en weder, tot desselfs oost en westzyde de *Ecliptica* doorsnyd, op de zelfde laats daar die van den draat wort doorsneeden; ziet dan welk uur en streek op de draat komt te leggen inden 's morgens ten 5 uuren 8 minuten 74 graden beoosten het noorden: en 's avonds ten 6 uuren nuten 74 graden bewesten het noorden

len zelfde dagh den *groten Hond*: den draat blyft als boven leggen, en den oostkant van de Hori den *groten Hond* gedraayt, dan vint men den Horisont leggen boven den draat op 12 uuren 12 na de middag dat de *grote Hond* opgaat in 't o z. o. en draayt men de west-kant van den Horisont ster, men vint de ondergang in 't w. z w. 's avonts ten 9 uuren 40 minuten.

r zal men konnen weten hoe laat dat het is, als men de zon of eenige sterren ziet op of ondergaan.

SESDE VOORSTEL.

Zon of Sters streek bekend zynde, te vinden de tyd hoe laat, en deszelfs hoogte boven den Horisont.

Mey is voor de middag de Zon bevonden in 't Z. O.: om hier door te weten hoe laat het is: spand den draat 25 Mey, en dan de *Virticaal* van zuyd-oost gedraayt tot die de *Ecliptica* doorsnyd ter plaatse van de draad; n boven den draad op de rond van den Horisont staan 9 uuren 48 min. welke de tyd voor middag is: en de d op 53 graden van de *Ecliptica* en draad doorsneden, dat is voor de Zons hoogte.

lve tyd des nagts vind ik *Arcturus*, de Zoom van botes Rok, legt in 't Z. W.: den draat als vooren geden Horison gedraayt tot de *Virticaal* van Zuyd-west komt te leggen op *Arcturus*, dan wyst den draad voor tyd 's nagts ten 12 uuren: en staat *Arcturus* in de voornoemde zuyd-west streek hoog 49 graden.

SEVENSTE VOORSTEL.

or de hoogte der Zon of Sterren te vinden de tyd hoe laat het is, en in welke streek die zyn.

8 July 's morgens is bevonden de Zon boven den Horisont 28 graden: den draad gespaanen op den 18 July, en Horison gedraayt tot het punt van den *Ecliptica*, welke van den draad is doorsneden 28 graden boven den Hon vind men boven de draad leggen 's morgens 7 uuren 8 min., en de *Virticaal* van oost op den draat, daarom n op die tyd in 't oost.

gelyke, op dezelve dag 's avonts de klaarste in de vliegende Arend gelchoten hoog te zyn 34 graden: hier mede kt in de Zon; men vind voor de tyd, des avonts ten halftien, en de Ster in 't Z. O.

ACHTSTE VOORSTEL.

Om 't begin en eynden der Honds-dagen te vinden.

DE *Oude* hebben die tyd, wanneer de Sterre in de *grote* en *klyne Hond* met de Zon omgaan, genaamt de *Honds-dagen* welke op 't Hemels plyn aldus word gevonden: draayd den Horison zodanig, dat de uyterste Ster in de *klyne Hond* in den Horison staat, en spand den draat door dat punt, daar den Horison de *Ecliptica* doorsnyd; dan vind men den draat op den 27 July voor 't begin; van gelyke gedaan met de uyterste in de *grote Hond*, komt voor 't eynde den 18 Augstus.

NEGENDE VOORSTEL.

Om 't begin en eynden der Schemering te vinden.

DEn 10 September: spand den draad hier over de oost en west-kant van den Horisont omtrent 18 graden staat binnen het punt daar de draad den *Ecliptica* doorsnyd; ziet dan hoe laat den draad komt te leggen, zult vinden ten 3 uuren 's morgens, en 9 uuren 's avonds voor 't begin en eynde der Schemering.

Tot dus verre het vermakelykste gebruyk verklaart hebbende, verblyve onderwyle U E. toegenegene Vriend.

MARTE CALMAN,
Leermeester der Wiskonst, alhier.

t' Amsterdam, by JOACHEM HASEBROEK, Boekverkooper en Graad-boogmaker in de Nieuwebrug-Steeg, in het Stuurmans Gereetschap,

The celestial vault in paper

32 **ANDREAE, Johann Ludwig**

[Pair of celestial charts on a conical projection]. [North equatorial pole to equator WITH:] Coniglobium hoc geminu ad Catalogum Fixaru celeberrimoru accurate delineavit Astrophilisq. primu in hac forma usui dedit. M. Johannes Ludovicus Andreae. Past Wurtembergensis Ao. 1724 [South equatorial pole to equator].

Publication
Württemberg, 1724.

Description
A pair of engraved star charts of the northern and southern hemispheres on a conical projection, joined.

Dimensions
430mm diameter (each); approximately 430 by 800mm joined.

References
Warner, Andreae 1A & 1B; cf: Stevenson, E.L. 'Terrestrial and Celestial Globes', New Haven, 1921, Fig. 118a; Dekker and van der Krogt, 'Globes from the Western World', pp. 102-103.

Johann Ludwig Andreae (1667-1725), globe maker, was born in Messtetten, Württemberg, and followed his priest father into Holy Orders in Tübingen. In 1711 he moved to Esslingen where he began to make globes. His work was part of the early eighteenth-century explosion of globe-making in Germany, centred particularly around Nuremberg, and which included such makers as Eimmart, Doppelmayr and Homann. He is known to have produced globes of 5½, 10, 12 and 19 inches in diameter, having the construction carried out in the commercial centre of Nuremberg; he also appears to have been assisted in some way by the Rector of the Egidian Gymnasium there, Samuel Farber (1657-1716), whose name appears on the 19 inch globe. He was succeeded by his mathematician son, Johann Philipp (c. 1700-after 1757), who also worked from Schwabach from 1734 onwards.

Andreae is only known to have produced two celestial broadsheets: the present charts. They are centred on the equatorial poles using a polar equidistant projection with geocentric orientation. The maps are influenced by Coronelli and could be bent into cones and viewed from the inside to give an illusion of the celestial vault.

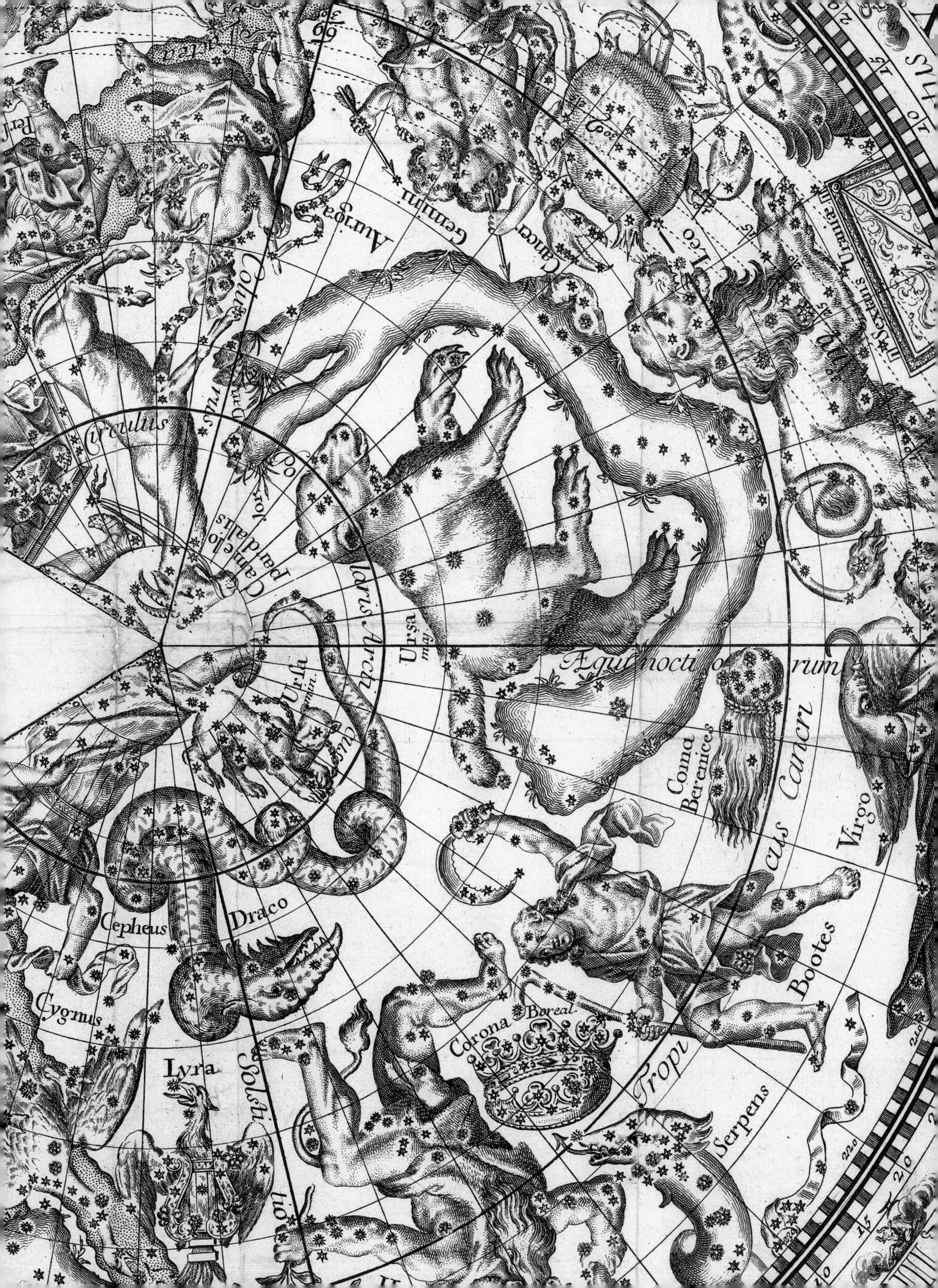
Auriga
Gemini
Leo
Camelo pardalis
Ursa maj.
Ursa min.
Coma Berenices
Virgo
Bootes
Serpens
Corona Boreal
Cepheus
Draco
Cygnus
Lyra

Monoceros
Lepus
Canis Major
Eridanus
Cetus
Columba
Argo Navis
Dorado
Hydrus
Rhombus
Crater
Corvus
Centaurus
Robur Caro-linum
Chamaeleon
Musca
Apus
Toucan
Pavo
Indus
Phoenix
Grus
Pisces Austrinus
Capricornus
Aquarius
Antinous
Lupus
Scorpio
Libra
Tropicus Capricorni
September
October
November
December
Januarius
Februarius
Martius
Aprilis
Maius
Junius
Julius
Augustus

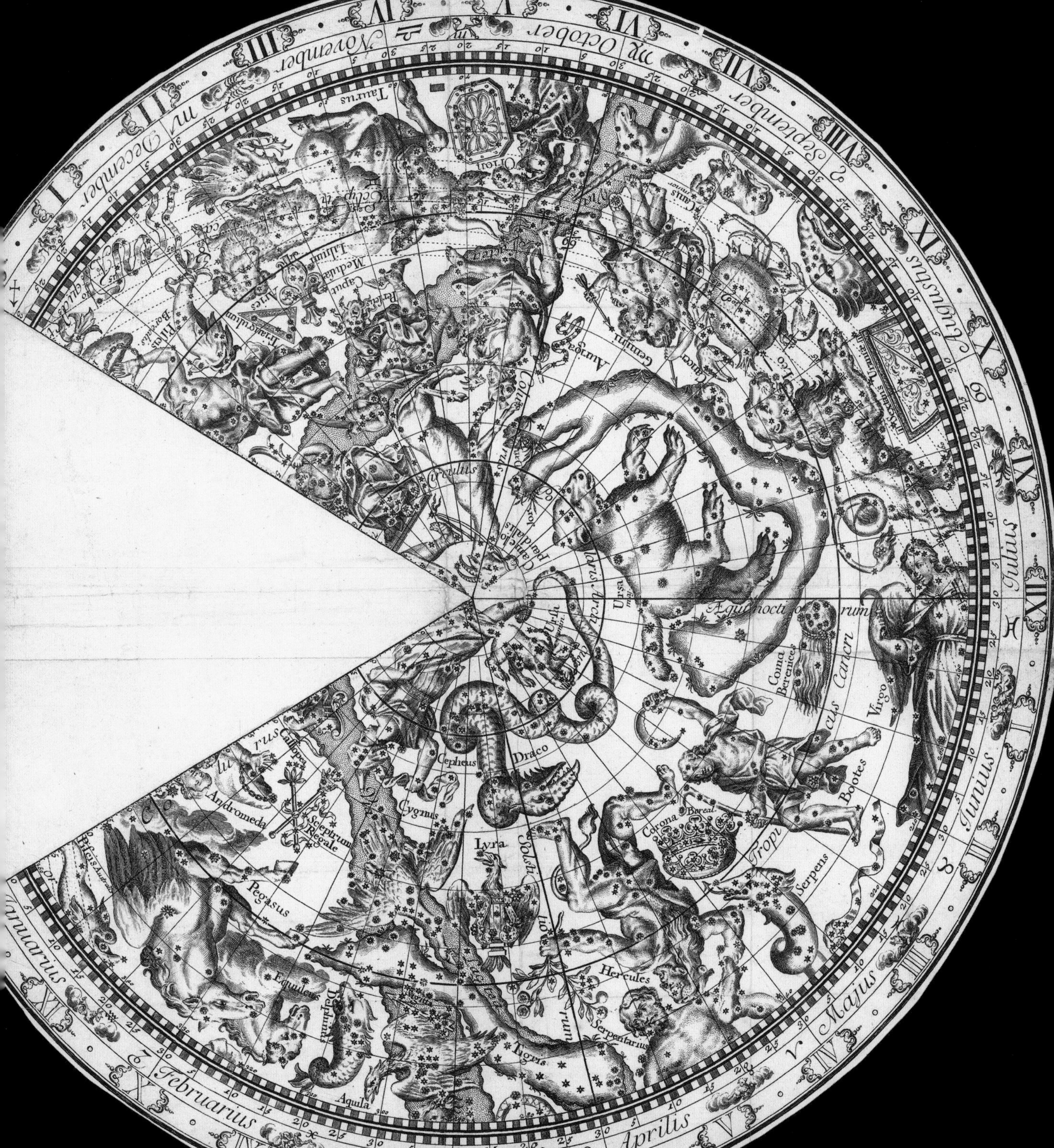

Martius
Aprilis
Majus
Junius
Julius
Augustus
September
October
November
December
Januarius
Februarius
Andromeda
Pegasus
Sceptrum Regale
Cygnus
Cepheus
Draco
Lyra
Hercules
Serpentarius
Serpens
Bootes
Corona Boreal
Virgo
Coma Berenices
Delphinus
Aquila
Taurus
Aries
Triangulum
Gemini
Auriga
Æquinoctiorum

A pair of rare advertisements with a globe gore of the East Coast of North America

33 **FRANZ, Johann Michael [and] LOWITZ, George Moritz**

Homännischer Bericht von Verfertigung grosser Welt-Kugeln. [WITH:] Description complete ou Second Avertissement sur les Grands Globes Terrestres et Celestes ...

Publication
Nuremberg, Au Bureau Geographique de Homann, 1746 and 1749.

Description
Quarto (270 by 210mm), 2f. letterpress pamphlet [together with:] 40pp. [1], diagram, and a globe gore, original paper wrappers, pamphlet loosely inserted.

A rare booklet and pamphlet advertising Georg Lowitz's never-realized pair of 36-inch globes, with a scarce gore of the east coast of North America.

The pamphlet advertising the globe, by Johann Franz, was first published in 1746 shortly after Lowitz had joined the firm of Homann's heirs. The second advertisement, the booklet, was published some three years later and gives a detailed description of the progress of work on the large pair of 36 inch globes: the style of engraving, the mathematical and geographical problems encountered, and the numerous sources that Lowitz has drawn upon, most notably Henry Popple's map of the 13 colonies, which he praises highly. Bound at the end of the text is a contract between the Cosmographical Society of Nuremberg and the Homann Heirs' firm. It states that a down payment of 36 ducats has been made by the society for a pair of globes, advertised on 1 December 1749 (i.e. the present advertisement booklet), with 120 ducats being the final price. The text goes on to state that the finished globes would be ready 30 months from the date of the contract, and shipped to the society as long as the bill has been settled in full. However, the contract is not all that it would seem, as the Cosmographical Society in question was, in fact, founded by the Homann firm in 1746 (the date of the first advertisement). The contract was, therefore, little more than an elaborate ruse to garner orders on the back of fact that a contract was already in existence between the manufacturers and a "respectable" society. A third advertisement was issued in 1753, giving reasons for the delay in the publishing of the globes. In the end, however, the contracted work was never completed, with only the small set of five and a quarter inch globes (published in 1747) being produced by the time Lowitz left the firm in 1757.

The title of the globe gore reads: 'Specimen Trigesimae sextae partis ex Globo Terrestri trium pedum Parisii' or 'A Specimen of the thirty-sixth part of a three Parisian foot globe'. The gore itself covers the North American east coast from Nova Scotia to North Carolina, the Caribbean from Cuba to the Leeward Islands and the north coast of South America. The cartography, as Lowitz states in the booklet, is based upon the work of Danville, Charlevoix, Barriere, and Cadwallader Colden, among others; however, he reserves the highest praise for Henry Popple's multi-sheet map of America: "la grande Carte de Popple merité le premiére rang".

Georg Moritz Lowitz (1722-1774) joined the Nuremberg firm of the Homann Heirs in 1746 and left in 1757 to become professor of mathematics at Göttingen University. His globes continued to be reissued by the firm, however, with editions appearing in 1779 and 1810. Lowitz moved to St Petersburg in 1767 to join the Russian service as a surveyor, and was murdered by Cossacks whilst working in the Volga region.

Rare. We are only able to trace one institutional example with both the pamphlets together: that held by Strasbourg University Library.

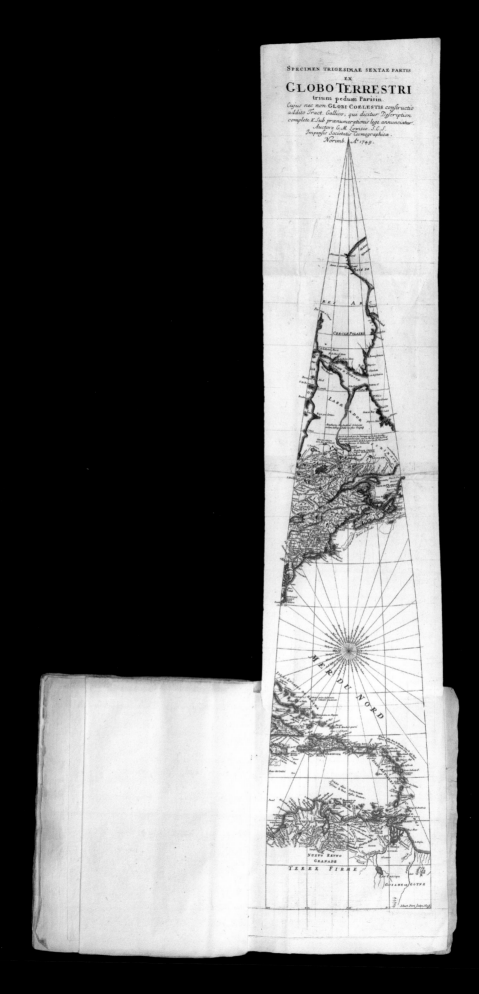

Specimen trigesimae sextae partis

ex

Globo Terrestri

trium pedum Parisin.

Cujus nec non Globi Coelestis *constructio addito Tract. Gallico, qui dicitur Description complete & Sub praenumerationis lege annunciatur.*

Auctore G. M. Lowizio. S.C.S.

Impensis Societatis Cosmographicae.

Norimb. A° 1749.

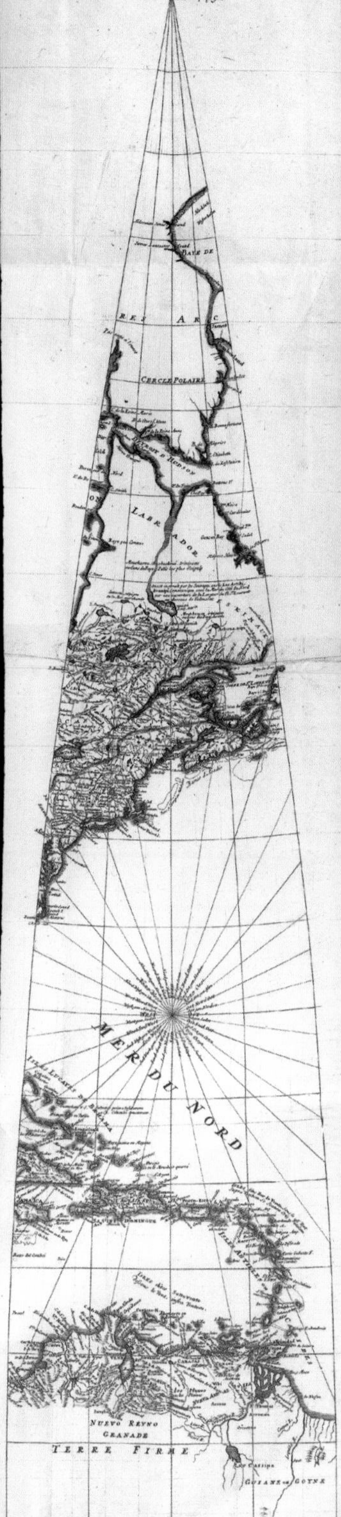

The wheelwright of the heavens

34 **FERGUSON, James**

The Astronomical Rotula Shewing the Change and Age of the Moon, the Motion of the Sun, Moon and Nodes, with all the Solar and Lunar Eclipses.

Publication
[London, c. 1750-60].

Description
Circular scale with four volvelles, engraved by J. Mynde. Second edition, re-engraved from the first from the change of stile in 1752.

Dimensions
440 by 370mm (17.25 by 14.5 inches).

References
Millburn, pp. 21, 120, and 293.

The instrument takes the form of four volvelles over a circular scale, the central volvelle with an engraved face of the sun. These volvelles are designed to show the ecliptic with its twelve signs through which the sun travels in twelve months, to the circle of twelve hours, similar to the dial plate of an early clock, the hour-hand to the sun, and the minute hand to the moon: moving in the ecliptic, the one always overtaking the other at a place farther than it did at their last conjunction. This shows the motions and places of the sun and moon in the ecliptic on each day of the year perpetually and, consequently, the days of all the new and full moons from the years 1752 until 1800.

James Ferguson, astronomer, instrument maker, lecturer, natural and experimental philosopher, was born in 1710 at Core of Mayen in the east-most corner of Banffshire. His father was a cottar and too poor to provide him with any formal education. However, his aptitude for learning soon became apparent. At seven, he learned to read by listening to his father teach the catechism to his elder brother. At ten, to earn his keep, he was sent to tend sheep for a neighbouring farmer, and what little spare time he then had was devoted to his developing interest in astronomy, making maps of the stars using beads and thread.

Undaunted by the lack of access to books in his younger years, he set about discovering the principles of mechanics for himself, making models of the machines he saw, including a weight-driven wooden clock with a broken bottle chime – the only materials he had available. The clock kept quite good time, so he attempted to make a watch – the size of a cup – but getting it to work proved beyond the limits of wooden wheel and whalebone spring technology.

This extraordinary ingenuity became known to the neighbouring gentry, who gave him some help to improve his knowledge of mathematics and drawing. For a time he was employed by Sir James Dunbar of Durn, and it was while staying at Sir James's house that he painted the two gate stones: one as a terrestrial globe and the other as a celestial map. While there he was introduced to Lady Dipple, Sir James's sister, who assisted him in going to Edinburgh, where he supported himself for some years drawing miniatures.

THE ASTRONOMICAL ROTULA, Shewing the Change and Age of the Moon, the Motions of the Sun, Moon and Nodes, with all the Solar and Lunar Eclipses.
The Dominical Letter for each Year and mean Time of New Moon in January from A.D. 1752 to 1800 inclusive
M signifies Morning A Afternoon N.B. Leap Year has two Dominical Letters the first serves for Jan. and Feb. and the last for all the rest of the Year.
Days of the Months
Janu. 31 Octob. 31
Feb. 28 Mar. 31 Nov. 30
April 30 July 31
August 31
Sept. 30 Dec. 31
May 31
June 30
SUN
MOON
Moon's Place
ASCENDING NODE.
Asc. Nod.
Def. Nod
J. FERGUSON inv. et delin.
J. Mynde Sculp.
Capricornus
Aquarius
Sagittarius
DECEMBER
FEBRUARY
MAY
JUNE
JULY
AUGUST
Cancer
Gemini
Leo
Scorpi
Taurus
Nor. 18' Lat.
Sou. 18' Lat.

After returning north to Inverness to find work, an astronomical rotula that Ferguson had produced was sent to Professor Maclaurin in Edinburgh, who immediately recognized Ferguson's ability and gave him encouragement and assistance. In 1743 Ferguson was able to go to London, where he was introduced to the Royal Society and published astronomical tables and lectures. He also gave lectures in experimental philosophy, and was heard by George III, then Prince of Wales, who afterwards gave him a pension of £50 a year.

In 1763 he was chosen a fellow of the Royal Society, without the usual fees. Ferguson's influence extended widely in his own lifetime: he was the first to form a nebular theory, Thomas Paine mentioned him in his publication 'The Age of Reason', and William Herschel studied astronomy from his books. However, it is, perhaps, as one of the first popularisers of science that his main influence was felt. Ferguson created a number of orreries and machines to illustrate his lectures, and published several books and paper instruments including: 'Astronomical Tables and Precepts' (1763); 'Introduction to Astronomy' (1769); 'Astronomy Explained' (1772); 'Lectures on Mechanics, Hydrostatics, Pneumatics, and Optics' (1772); 'Select Mechanical Exercises' (1773); 'The Art of Drawing in Perspective' (1775); and 'An Introduction to Electricity' (1775).

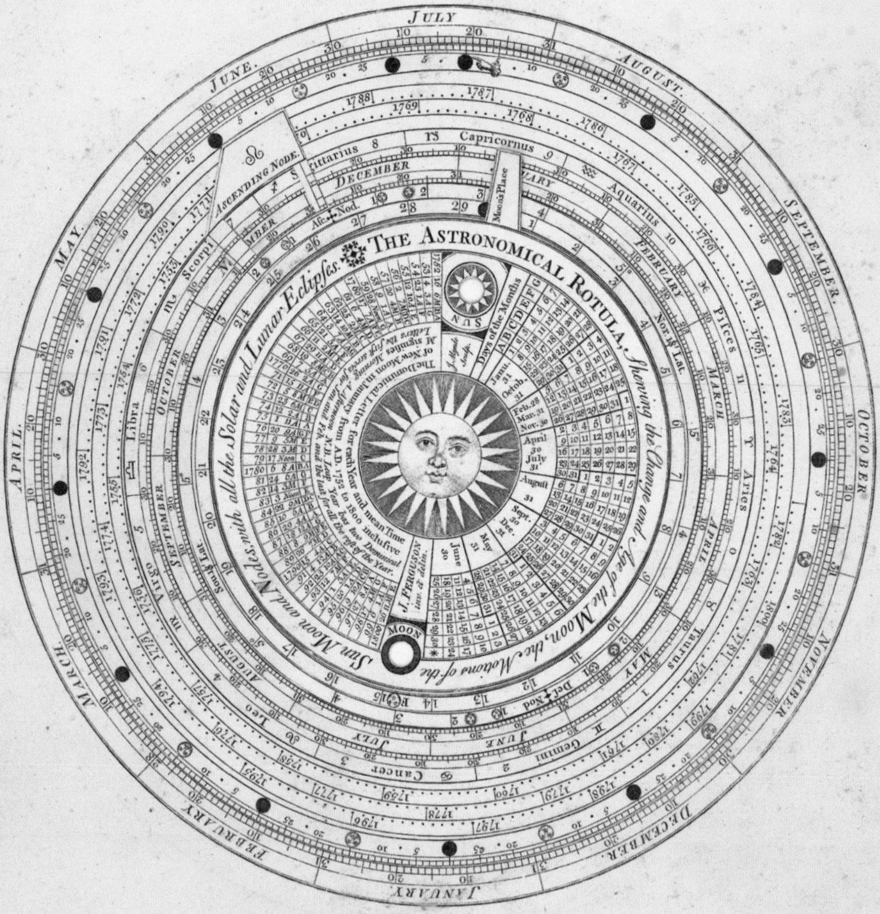
THE ASTRONOMICAL ROTULA, Shewing the Change and Age of the Moon, the Motions of the Sun Moon and Nodes, with all the Solar and Lunar Eclipses.
J. FERGUSON inv. & delin.
J. Mynde Sculp.
The Dominical Letter for each Year and mean Time of New Moon, Morning or Afternoon, from A.D. 1753 to 1800 inclusive
Days of the Months
SUN
MOON
ASCENDING NODE.
Moon's Place
JANUARY
FEBRUARY
MARCH
APRIL
MAY
JUNE
JULY
AUGUST
SEPTEMBER
OCTOBER
NOVEMBER
DECEMBER
Aries
Taurus
Gemini
Cancer
Leo
Virgo
Libra
Scorpi
Capricornus
Aquarius
Pisces

A Dutch calendar

35 **HENNING, Veit Balthasar**

Eeuwig Durenden Almanach.

Publication
[Nuremberg, Veit Balthasar Henning, c. 1750].

Description
Wall calendar, consisting of a base and two volvelles fastened with wooden spindle, hand-painted and varnished engraving with floral motives and two climbing lions at the top and the motto "Omnes continet unus" (One contains all) at the bottom, mounted on pasteboard, affixed to wooden mount, a few minor cracks to surface.

Dimensions
345 by 200mm (13.5 by 7.75 inches).

References
Thieme - Becker 16, p. 408; cf. Zinner, p. 372.

A rare perpetual wall calendar with two volvelles, produced for the Dutch market, displaying the month "Maende", days of the week "Tage", date, Zodiac signs "Loop van de Sonne", time of sunrise and sunset "De Opgaende Sonn ten ... Uren De Nedergaede Sonn te ... Uren", length of day and night in hours "Langhte van den Dage ... Langte van de Nagt", and important feast days for the month "De Heylig Daghen", in accordance with the volvelle settings.

The instrument maker, Veit Balthasar Henning (1706-1762), also published an important illustrated instrument book in Nuremberg in 1756, 'Sammlung nützlicher Machinen und Instrumenten nebst deren Erklärung aus dem Französischen, Englischen und anderen Sprachen ins Teutsche übersezt', which went through several editions, all of which are rare.

EUWIG DURENDEN ALMANACH
AUGUS
XXXI
Tage
DE OPGAENDE SON
DE NEDRGAENDE SON
HEY LIG
DAGH EN
Portiuncula
St. Laurens
Mar Hemelvart
St. Bartholome
21. 22. 23. 24. 25. 26. 27.
SONN DAGH
MAAN DAGH
DINGS DAGH
WOENS DAGH
DONDER DAGH
VRY DAGH
ZATUR DAGH

An engraved trade card for Heath and Wing

36 **MILLER, J[ohn] S[ebastian]**

Heath and Wing near Exeter Exchange in the Strand, London. Make and Sell all Sorts of Mathematical and Philosophical Instruments Accurately finished according to the best Improvements of ye most eminent Professors: Also the best Black lead Pencils and Books of the Use of Instruments.

Publication
[London, 1751-1767].

Description
Engraved trade card.

Dimensions
85 by 120mm (3.25 by 4.75 inches).

References
Whipple Museum, Wh.3546; Taub, Liba, 'Introduction: Reengaging with Instruments', History of Science Society, Isis, Vol. 102, No. 4, December 2011, pp. 689-696.

A rare trade card advertising the scientific instrument firm of Heath and Wing.

What is striking about the text upon the card is the absence of the phase "scientific instrument". The instruments that the firm made and sold are referred to as "mathematical and philosophical", i.e. for the aid of mathematical calculations and for use in experimental philosophy (what we would now understand as physics). The use of the phrase "scientific instrument" would not be coined until the mid nineteenth century. One should also note the phrase "Also the best Black lead Pencils and Books of the Use of Instruments" on the card. "Heath and Wing signaled the importance of printed literature related to instruments in the period; indeed, a number of prominent makers and sellers were engaged in producing and purveying books as well as instruments" (Taub). To the sides and below the text are images of scientific instruments, including a barometer, an armillary sphere, and a theodolite.

Thomas Heath (fl.1714-65) was one of the most notable instruments makers of the first half of the eighteenth century. He was joined in partnership in around 1740 by the younger Tycho Wing (Jnr.) (fl.1731-81), a member of the notable family of mathematical practitioners, of whom the earliest was Vincent Wing (1619-1668).

HEATH and WING
near Exeter Exchange in the Strand,
LONDON:
Make and Sell all Sorts of
Mathematical and Philosophical
Instruments
Accurately finished according to the best
Improvements of ye most eminent Professors:
ALSO
The best Black lead Pencils and
Books of the Use of Instruments.
J. S. Müller del. & Sculp

An astronomical clock depicting the Tychonic solar system

37 **FREY, I[gnaz]**

[Astronomical Clock].

Publication
Prague, 1751.

Description
Engraving, trimmed to within left neatline, minor loss to image lower to lower left.

Dimensions
500 by 360mm (19.75 by 14.25 inches).

References
Dlabacz, Gottfried Johann, 'Allgemeines historisches Künstler-Lexikon für Böhmen und zum Theil auch für Mähren und Schlesien', Prague, 1815.

An engraving of an astronomical clock depicting a Tychonic solar system by the leading Czech mathematician and instrument maker Johannes Klein.

Father Johannes Klein (1684-1762) joined the Jesuit order in 1703 and taught mathematics, astronomy, and mechanics. From 1732 until his death, he was Professor of Mathematics at the Klementinum, the leading seat of learning in Prague at the time. He is best known for the production of astronomical instruments, most notably of astronomical clocks. Among his most important works were two clocks produced in 1751 and 1752 and still housed in the Klementinum in Prague. The clocks depicted, respectively, a Tychonic (depicted in the present work) and Copernican solar system.

Ignaz Frey (1727-1790) was an engraver and artist working in Prague. Gottfried Dlabacz's work on Czech artists, published in 1815, lists only four works by the artist: an astronomical clock depicting the Tychonic solar system (presumably the present work); another depicting a Copernican solar system; an engraving of the Archbishop of Prague; and an engraving of a religious scene.

We are unable to trace any institutional examples.

I. Frey fecit Praga. 1751.

Ferguson's 'Luminarium'

38 **FERGUSON, James**

Luminarium.

Publication
[London, c. 1751].

Description
Engraved astronomical instrument on card with internal rotating disc and two pointers on verso.

Dimensions
75 by 75mm (3 by 3 inches).

References
Millburn, pp. 70, 292, & 300.

"On 18 November [Ferguson] advertised in the 'Bath Journal' that he would begin a course of five astronomical lectures at Wiltshire's Rooms on Monday 25 November, at 1p.m. Subscriptions were being taken in at Mr Leake's and Mr Frederick's bookshops, where "a Syllabus of the lectures may be seen"... In a footnote he mentioned that his "portable CARD-DIALS' were sold at a shop in Wade's Passage at a shilling each". In a further advertisement he mentioned his card dials again, and also his "LUMINARIUM (a small portable instrument) for shewing the Day of the Month, Age of the Moon, Places of the Sun and Moon in the Heavens, and Times of their Rising and Setting every day of the Year for ever"; this was priced at 2s 0d. One of these devices was enclosed in his letter to [Hugh] Rose [Esq., of Geddes]. That particular example is no longer filed with the letter (at St Andrews University Library), but another, or possibly the same one, is at the Royal Scottish Museum in Edinburgh" (Millburn).

Extremely scarce. We are only aware of one other example: that held by the Royal Scottish Museum in Edinburgh.

For a discussion of the life of James Ferguson, please see item 34.

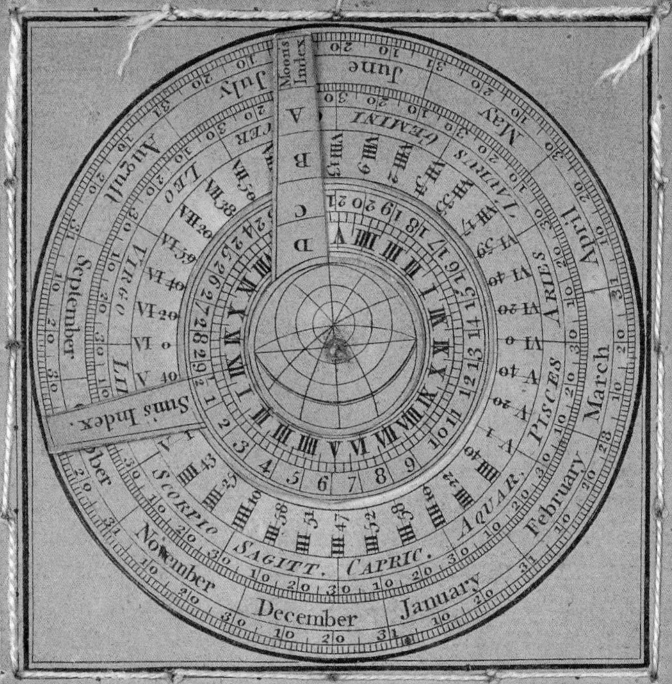

The LUMINARIUM.

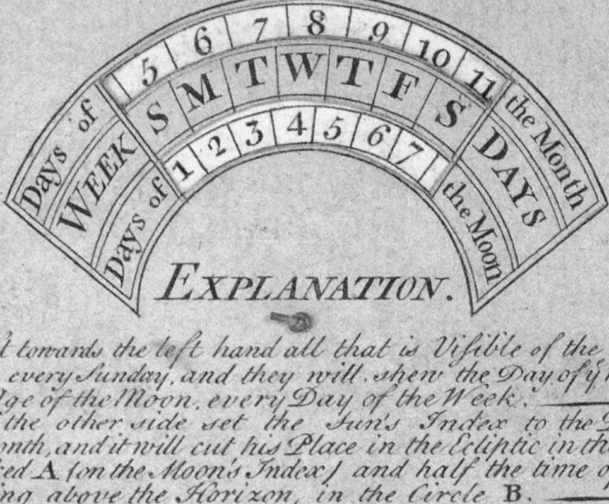

EXPLANATION.

Shift towards the left hand all that is Visible of the above Plates every Sunday, and they will shew the Day of ye Month, and Age of the Moon, every Day of the Week.

On the other side set the Sun's Index to the Day of the Month, and it will cut his Place in the Ecliptic in the Circle Marked A (on the Moon's Index) and half the time of his staying above the Horizon, in the Circle B.

Keeping the Sun's Index there, set the Moon's Index to the day of her Age in the Circle C, and it will cut the time of her coming to the Meridian in the Circle D, and the hours & minutes of her Semi-diurnal Arc in the Circle B, which Arc counted backward in ye circle D from ye time of ye Moon's coming to the Meridian, gives ye mean time of her rising; & counted forward therefrom in ye same Circle gives ye mean time of her setting.

J. Ferguson inv. *B. Cole Sculp.*

A previously unrecorded state of a rare promotional broadside for an astronomical clock

39 **NAYLOR, Joseph**

[Sheet entitled:] An Astronomicall and Chronologicall Clock, shewing all the most usefull parts of an Almanack. Io.S Naylor near Nantwich Cheshire. [Inset: Untitled Map of the Northern Hemisphere south to Cuba.]

Publication
Nantwich, Joseph Naylor, [c. 1752].

Description
Separately published broadside engraved map.

Dimensions
629 by 385mm (24.75 by 15.25 inches).

References
Cf. Cheshire Sheaf, 5th Series, 1977/78, p.85.

Locations:

The Clock:
BM, G39/dc9; Registration number: 1985,1005.1; Picture number: AN233605001. Illustrated in Thompson, 'British Museum Clocks', pp. 106-109.

The Broadsheet:
State 1: BM, G39/dc9
State 2: BM, Department of Prints & Drawings, BL, Maps *35.(1.):
State 3: The present example.

John Naylor was one of an important school of clock-makers based in Nantwich, Cheshire, active from about 1725. By about 1740 he had relocated to London, and seems to have died there in 1752.

It seems likely that, in about 1726, he designed a series of engraved metal plates that could be used to make a clock face, such as the example in the British Museum. In parallel, he must have published a second, near identical clock face, to be used as a promotional broadsheet for the clock, or as an instructional guide to the uses of the clock. While virtually identical, the promotional version has engraved hands over the face of the clock, so it could not be used to make up a working clock face, as the owner would have the mechanical, rotating hands and the engraved hands of the print.

As he was principally a clockmaker, rather than a mapmaker, it is perhaps no surprise the geography is outdated. In fact, the cartography is largely based on John Carte's astronomical clock of circa 1700; this would suggest that the engravings were first made in the early part of Naylor's career, reinforced by the Nantwich address used, but no example of the broadsheet datable to this period has been traced and, until such an example has been found, this first state must be speculative (but likely).

The British Museum has the first state of this promotional engraving, with the text at the top commencing "The Explanation March the first 1725/6 ...", which was acquired with their example of the clock.

The British Museum also has a second state of the complete promotional engraving, with the text at the top revised, with the text commencing "The Explanation March the first 1750/1 ...", evidently published to coincide with, and capitalize on, the British change-over from the Julian to Gregorian calendar. The British Library example is of the clock only, lacking the Sun God engraving and text.

This example is the third state, with the Christian name in the imprint revised from 'Jo.n' to 'Jos.p' (John Naylor's successor Joseph Naylor), apparently also in 1752, and with the hand of the various dials in the border re-aligned.

Joseph Naylor seems not to have been a clock-maker, but seems to have inherited a finished clock. In time-honoured fashion, he planned a lottery to maximise his profit on the inheritance. There is an accompanying booklet to launch the lottery entitled 'An explanation of an Astronomical Clock …' and, presumably, he re-engraved the broadsheet at the same time.

The Explanation March the first 1751
The first is a Large Plate 15 Inches square which is fixt. The next is a Large Circle which Contains the twelve Month of the Year with every day of each Month with all the Saints days, which by the help of two Indexes placed on the Left hand side of the first Plate Mark'd OS for Old Stile and NS for New Stile. Shew you the day of the Month, as against OS March the first Old Stile and against NS March the 12th New Stile this Circle Moves Round once in a Year.
At the top of the Great Circle is a little Circle which shews you the day of the Week by a hand pointing to Friday the day for the time given. The Next within the Day of the Month Circle there's a fixt Circle with the Minuts on the inner edge & the Sundays and Moveable Feasts on the outer edge Which Moveable Feasts are found by observing that Index Which moves with the Circle of Months. Which you'l find to point between the first and second Sundays in Lent. The next within the Minute Circle is the Hour Circle which Contains twice twelve Hours for the Day and Night which Circles are Joyn'd together by four Bars, those two that are Curved Represent the Eastern and Western Horizons, between these two Circles, and behind the four Bars moves a Plate which Contains that part of the Celestial Globe which lies between the Tropick of Capricorn and the Tropick of Cancer Upon this Plate You have first the Equinoctial Which is divided into 360 Degrees begining at ♈ & Numberd at every 10 Degrees. & Runs parralel to the Center, and is divided at every 30 Degrs by straight lines from the Center or Poles of the World. The next is the Ecliptick Lying oblique from the Equinoctial making an Angle of 23½ Degrees with it, the Equinoctial Cutting the Ecliptick in two equal parts, in the first point of Aries & Libra, Noted with the Characters belonging to them & is divided into 12 parts or Signs, & every Sign into 30 parts Number'd 10 20 30 at every 30 Degrees are Curv'd Lines which are the Circles of Longitude whose Center is the Poles of the Ecliptick, the two Tropicks are two Circles parralel to the Equinoctial, the Tropick of Cancer touching the Ecliptick at Cancer & the Tropick of Capricorn at Capricorn. Upon this Plate you have all the Zodiackal Constellations, by which you see at any time what Stars are either above or below the Horizon, also their Rising, Setting, & Southing, with many more Astronomical questions. this Plate having a Diurnal Motion, going one turn in a Year. Between the Hour & Minute Circles, & before the Plate moves two small Rods, that next you having a Yellow Stone at the end Representing the Sun, and the other a White Stone Representing the Moon. The Sun allways moving upon the Ecliptick shews you at any time, in what Sign & Degree the Sun is in at that time, as at the time given you'l find the Sun in 21 Degrees 36 Minutes of ♓, and the Moon not keeping her Course upon the Ecliptick, but Crossing it Shews you something near what Lattitude the Moon hath & whether North or South. So that March the first the Moon was in 2 Degrees 36 Minutes of ♍ & 4 Degrees 51 Mts South Lattitude. To know whether the Sun or the Clock goes faster, observe how much the Sun in the Clock is before or after the Hour Hand, & you'l find it about 2 Degrees 30 Min which shews that the Clock is 10 Minutes to fast.
The Sun at his Coming above the Eastern Horizon shews his Rising, and at going down below the Western Horizon shews his Setting, the same for the Moon or Stars. To know the time of high Water at London Bridge. You must first observe 6 Divisions between half an Hour past one, and & three on the outer edge of the Hour Circle, that next 3 being the Least, the next Longer & so on for the Rest, So that at the time of New or Full Moon it's high Water, when the Moon Comes to that Division next 3 a Clock, but if ye Moon be either one, or eleven Hours before, or after ye Sun it's high Water, when the Moon Comes to the Second Division from 3 a Clock, and when the Moon's either 2 or 10 Hours distant from the Sun it's high Water, when the Moon Comes to the third Division from 3, & for 3 or 9 Hours distant the 4th & so for the rest, but when its 6 Hours distant from the Sun which is at its first or last quarter, then its high Water when ye Moon Comes to the first Division thats near half an Hour past one. NB. As the Tide flows ♂ Hours & Ebbs ♇ You may by observing what Hour the Moon's at know whether the Tide Ebbs or flows. Upon the Moveing Plate near Libra there is a little Semicircle, cut through the plate wch Shows whether the Moon be in her Apogeon or Peregeon by observing when the word Apo: or Per be at the top of the Semicircle, as at the time given the Moon was in her Peregeon.
Within the Hour Circle ther's a small Mapp of that part of the Northern Hemisphere which lies within 66 Degrees of the North Pole which shews the difference of the Meridians of these Countrys. In the top Corner to the Left hand for the Year 1751 you have 24 the Cycle of the Sun, which is the same Old Stile or New Stile, & F the Dominical Letter Old Stile & C the Dominical Letter New Stile. In the top Plate to the Right hand you'l find the Golden Number is the same Old Stile or New Stile which you'l find to be 4 & the Epact Old Stile 14 and for the Epact New Stile 3. To find Easter first look for the Golden Number Old Stile in the top Plate towards the Right Hand which is 4, & then look for the Dominical Letter Old Stile in the top Plate towards the Left hand & you'l find it F. Then look in the table below, in Golden Number Old Stile for 4 then look for the next F that is either over it or after it & over that F stands the day of the Month that Easter Sunday falls on for that Year, so that over 4 stands F & over F the 7th of April for Easter, for the Year 1751.
To find Easter New Stile, the Golden Number being 4 as before, then look for the Dominical Letter in the New Stile which is C then look for 4 in the Golden Number New Stile in the lower table & for the next C that follows & you'l find it to stand under April 11th for Easter New Stile for the Year 1751.
Having at the begining of the Year shifted ye two Hands at the top for Golden Number and Dominical Letter, and by the lower Table found Easter, move the Index in the Circle of Months to the Day of the Month that Easter fall on, and it shews you all the Sundays Moveable feasts, or Terms for that Year.
The little Plate in the Week Circle haveing the seven Letters that answer the Days in the Calender. You may by help of two small holes in it move the Dominical Letter under Sunday and all the other Letters will answer for that Year.
Dominical Letter N.S.
Dominical Letter O.S.
Cycle of the Sun
Epact Old Stile
Golden Number
Epact N S
Easter March
Dominical Letter
Golden Number
Ios. NAYLOR near Namptwich Cheshire
An ASTRONOMICALL and CRONOLOGICALL CLOCK, shewing all the most usefull parts of an Almanack

Rare uncut sheets for an armillary sphere

40 **ROBERT DE VAUGONDY, Gilles and Didier**

[Uncut sheets for an armillary sphere].

Publication
Paris, chez Sr. Robert. Geographe ordinaire du Roi. Sur le Quai de l'horloge, 1754.

Description
Four sheets containing horizon and ecliptic rings, hour ring, arctic ring, four arcs for Tropic of Cancer, colure for the solstices, calendrical horizon, Antarctic ring, four arcs for Tropic of Capricorn, colures for the equinoxes, meridian ring.

Dimensions
(diameter of horizon ring) 340mm (13.5 inches).

Gilles Robert de Vaugondy (1688-1766) and his son Didier (c. 1723-1786) were among the leading cartographers working in eighteenth century Paris. The father and son team were related to the great French cartographer Nicolas Sanson, whose grandson, Pierre Moulard-Sanson, was Gilles's uncle. Upon the death of Pierre in 1730, Gilles acquired the large Sanson stock and, in 1734, was appointed Geographer to the King.

The author of the present work was most probably Gilles, as the imprint has been engraved upon the meridian ring 'A Paris chez Sr. Robert. Geographe ordinaire du Roi. Sur le Quai de l'horloge 1754'. His son Didier applied his imprint via a printed label.

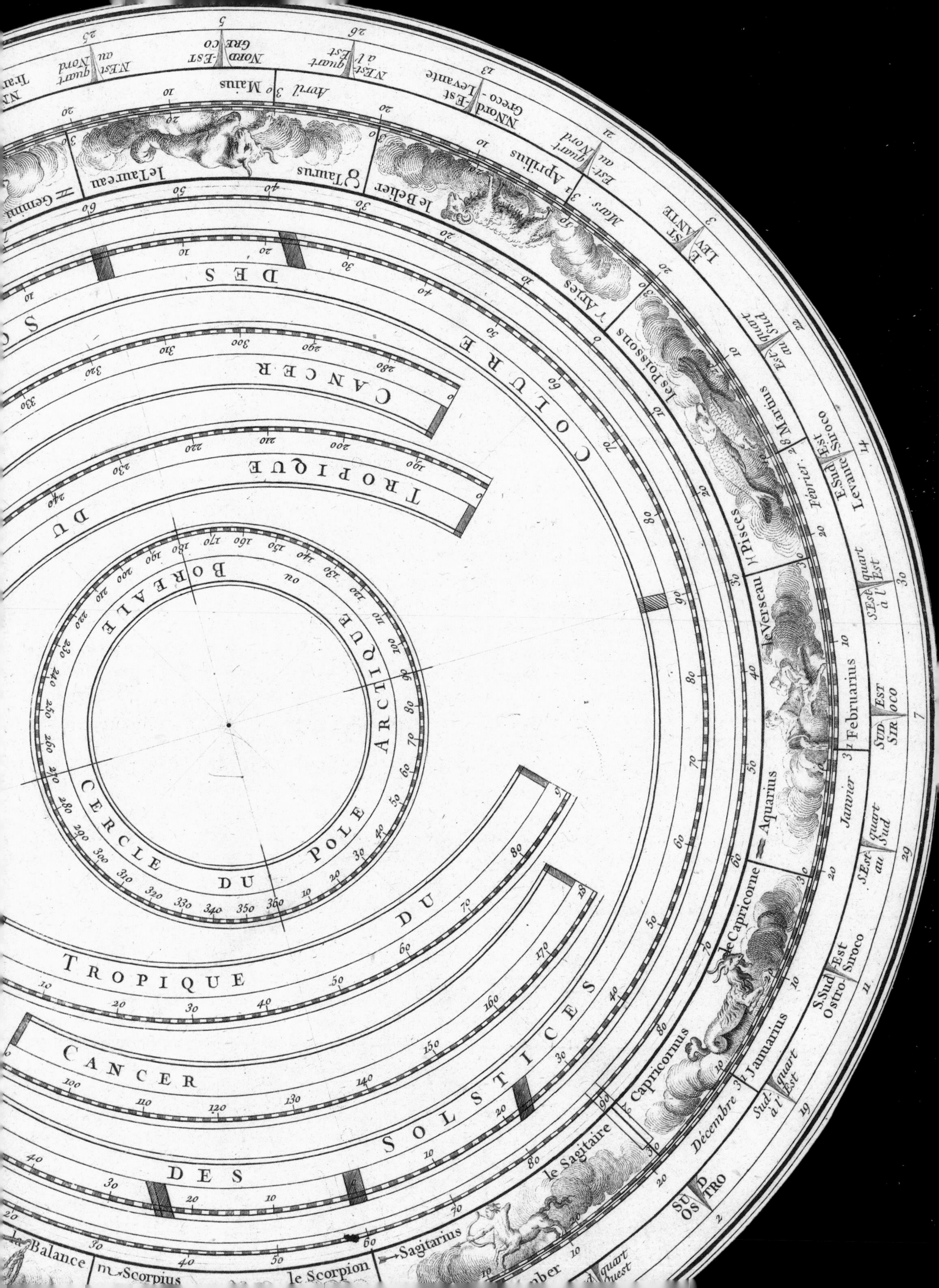

CERCLE DU POLE ARCTIQUE BOREALE
TROPIQUE DU CANCER
COLURE DES SOLSTICES
COLURE DES
le Belier
♈ Aries
♉ Taurus
le Taureau
♊ Geminis
les poissons
♓ Pisces
le Verseau
Aquarius
le Capricorne
Capricornus
le Sagitaire
Sagitarius
le Scorpion
♏ Scorpius
la Balance
Avril
Maius
Mars
Aprilius
Martius
Fevrier
Februarius
Janvier
Januarius
Decembre
NNord-Est Greco-Levante
Nord-Est GRECO
N.Est quart au Nord
N.Est quart a l'Est
Est quart au Nord
EST LEVANTE
Est quart au Sud
E.Sud Est Levante Siroco
S.Est quart a l'Est
SUD EST SIROCO
S.Est quart au Sud
S.Sud Est Ostro Siroco
Sud quart a l'Est
SUD OSTRO

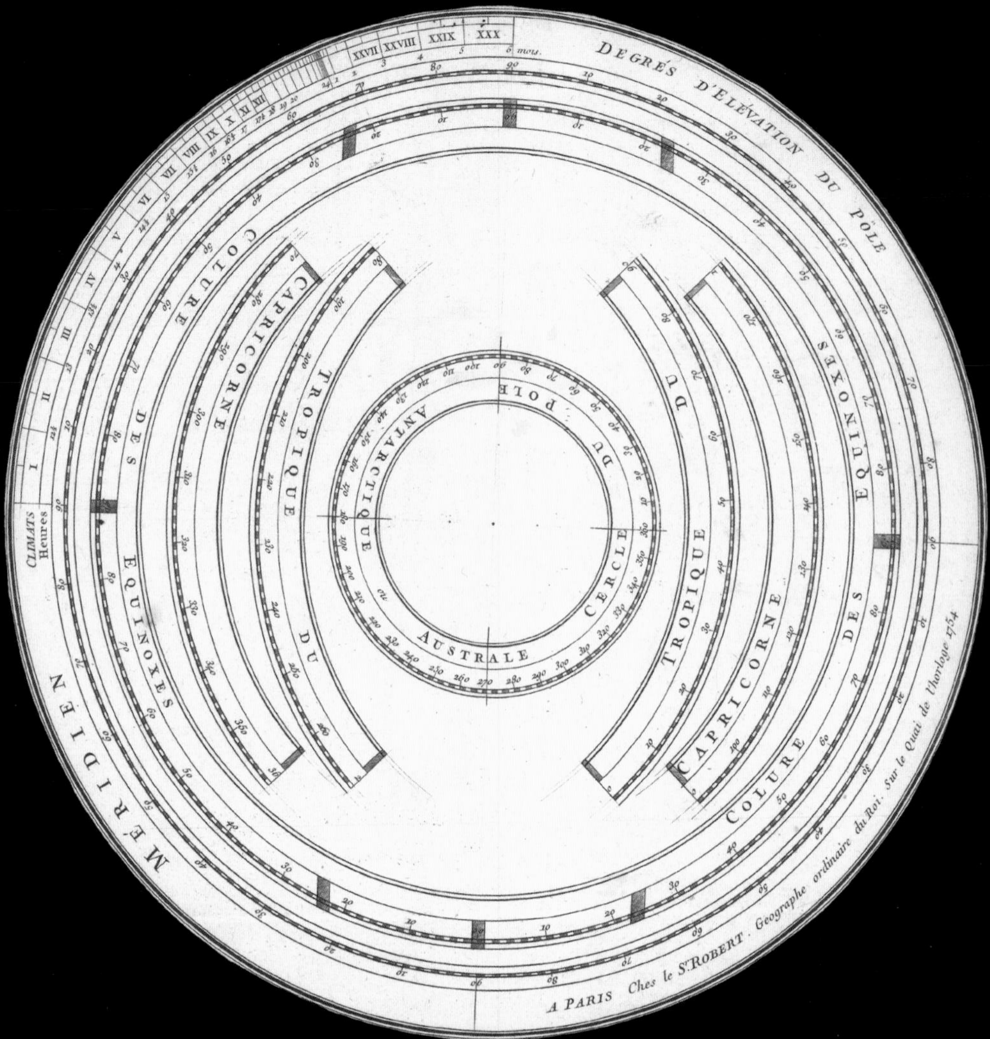
DEGRÉS D'ÉLÉVATION DU PÔLE
CLIMATS
Heures
MERIDIEN
COLURE DES EQUINOXES
TROPIQUE DU CAPRICORNE
CERCLE DU POLE ANTARCTIQUE
AUSTRALE
A PARIS Ches le Sr. ROBERT. Geographe ordinaire du Roi. Sur le Quai de l'horloge 1754

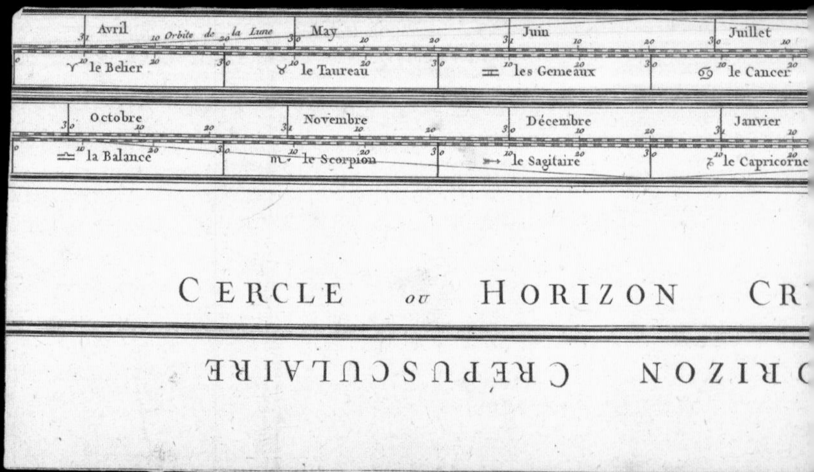
Avril
Orbite de la Lune
May
Juin
Juillet
le Belier
le Taureau
les Gemeaux
le Cancer
Octobre
Novembre
Décembre
Janvier
la Balance
le Scorpion
le Sagitaire
le Capricorne
CERCLE ou HORIZON CR
RIZON CRÉPUSCULAIRE

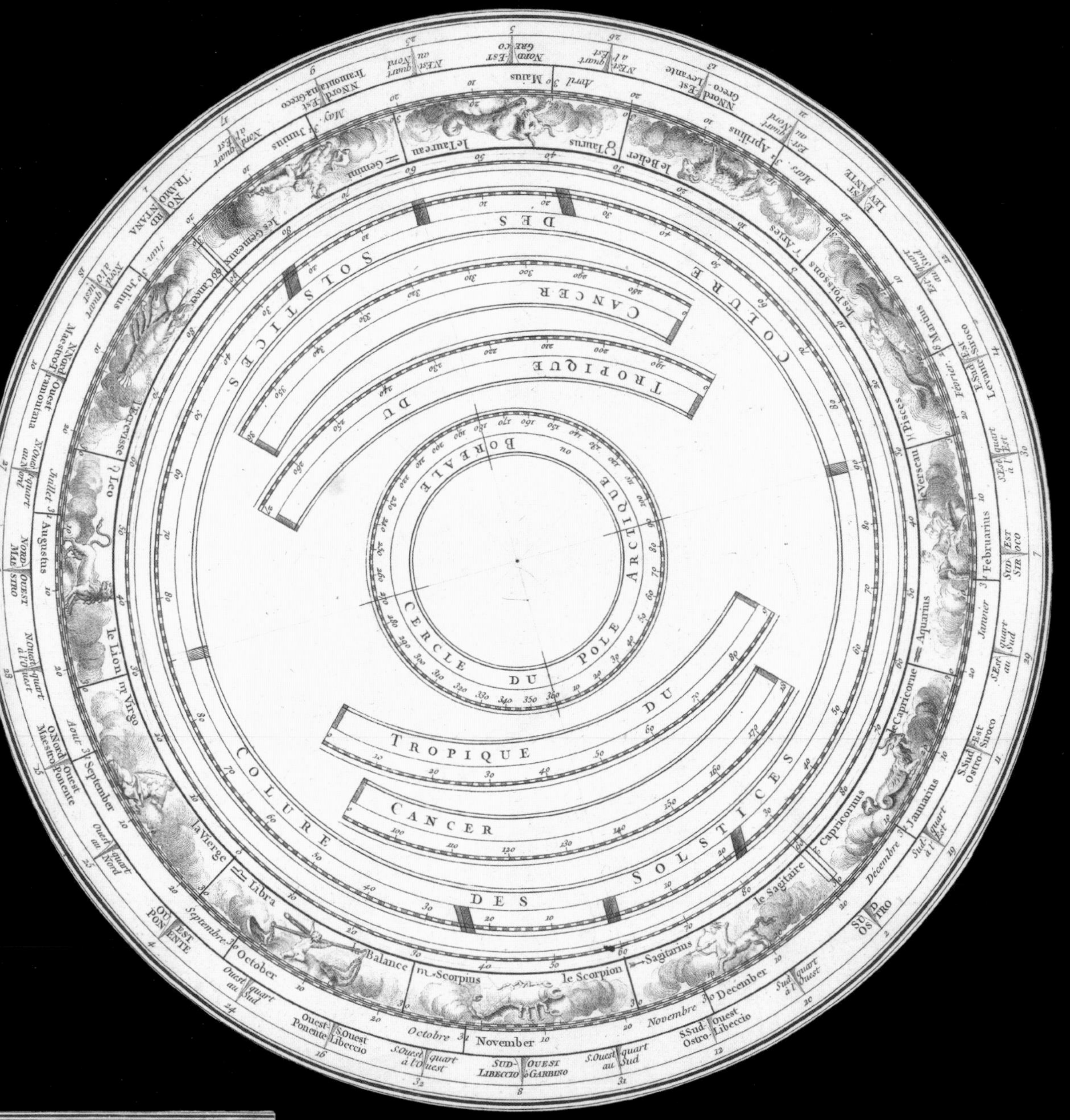
COLURE DES SOLSTICES
TROPIQUE DU CANCER
CERCLE DU POLE ARCTIQUE BOREALE
le Belier
le Taureau
Taurus
Gemini
les Gemeaux
Cancer
l'Ecrevisse
Leo
le Lion
Virgo
la Vierge
Libra
Balance
Scorpius
le Scorpion
Sagitarius
le Sagitaire
Capricornus
le Capricorne
Aquarius
le Verseau
Pisces
les Poissons
Aries
Aprilis
Maius
Junius
Julius
Augustus
September
October
November
December
Januarius
Februarius
Martius
Juillet
Aout
Septembre
Octobre
Novembre
Décembre
Janvier
Févier
Mars
Avril
Mai
Juin
Nord Est
Greco
Levante
Est
Sud Est
Siroco
Sud
Ostro
Ouest
Ponente
Sud Ouest
Libeccio
Garbino
Nord Ouest
Maestro
Tramontana

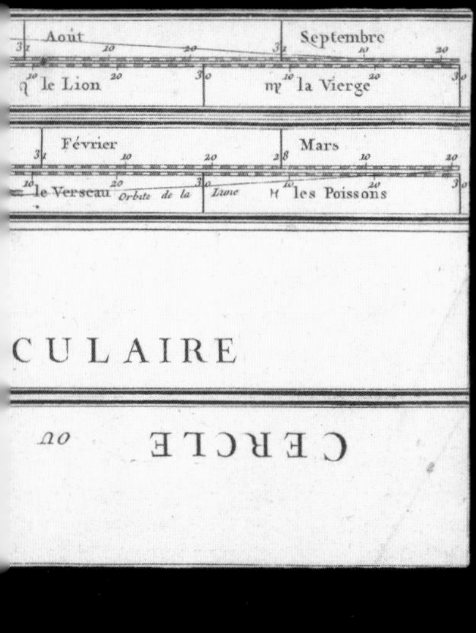
Aout
Septembre
le Lion
la Vierge
Février
Mars
le Verseau
Orbite de la Lune
les Poissons
CULAIRE
CERCLE ou

"The times of the rising, southing and setting of the Sun, Moon and Stars"

41 **FERGUSON, James**

A New Astronomical Instrument Shewing the Day of the Month, Change and Age of the Moon, the Places of the Sun and Moon in the Ecliptic, with the times of the rising, southing and setting of the Sun, Moon and Stars to the first, second and third Magnitude, from A.D. 1756 to 1805 inclusive.

Publication
London, James Ferguson, 29 August 1757.

Description
Two volvelles over an engraved circular scale.

Dimensions
450 by 315mm (17.75 by 12.5 inches).

References
Warner, James Ferguson 1; not mentioned in Millburn.

An extremely rare engraved paper astronomical instrument.

The instrument takes the form of two volvelles over a circular scale. The first volvelle is graduated around the circumference in hours, followed by age of the moon in days, with representations for quarter, full and new moons. The central section has an off-centre ellipse cut out to show constellations of the northern hemisphere on the volvelle beneath. The chart also shows the graduated ecliptic and equinoctial and is transversed by a scale on the top volvelle 0-90°-0. The remainder of the top volvelle shows tables for the dominical letter and mean time of the new moon in January and "The Days of the Months" forever.

The second volvelle has the star chart in the centre and scales around the circumference for days of the month and days of the houses of the zodiac, with the ages of the moon throughout the year with pictorial representations. Both volvelles rotate within a circular calendar scale on the main sheet. Below the instrument is an explanation of use.

An advertisement at the end of Ferguson's 'Description and use of the astronomical rotula' (1775) mentions:

"8. A New Astronomical Instrument. Showing all the problems of the ROTULA, except the Eclipses; and instead thereof, the Times of the Rising, Southing and Setting of the Sun, Moon and Stars" 5s 6d.

For a discussion of the life of James Ferguson, please see item 34.

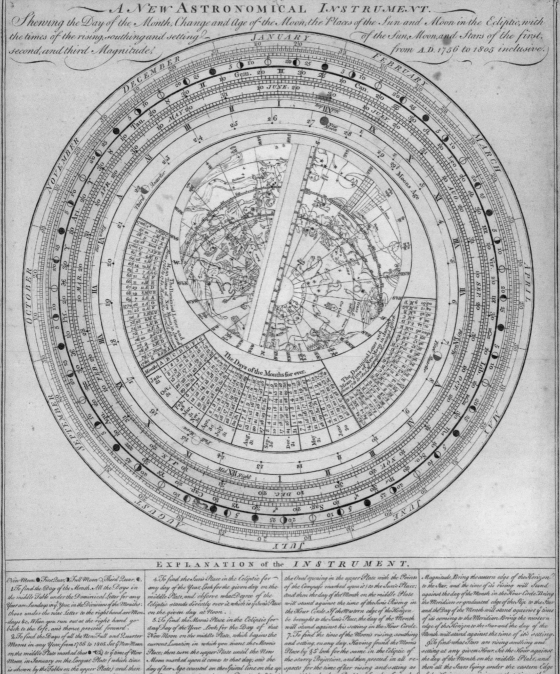

A NEW ASTRONOMICAL INSTRUMENT.

Shewing the Day of the Month, Change and Age of the Moon, the Places of the Sun and Moon in the Ecliptic, with the times of the rising, southing and setting of the Sun, Moon, and Stars of the first, second, and third Magnitude; from A.D. 1756 to 1805 inclusive.

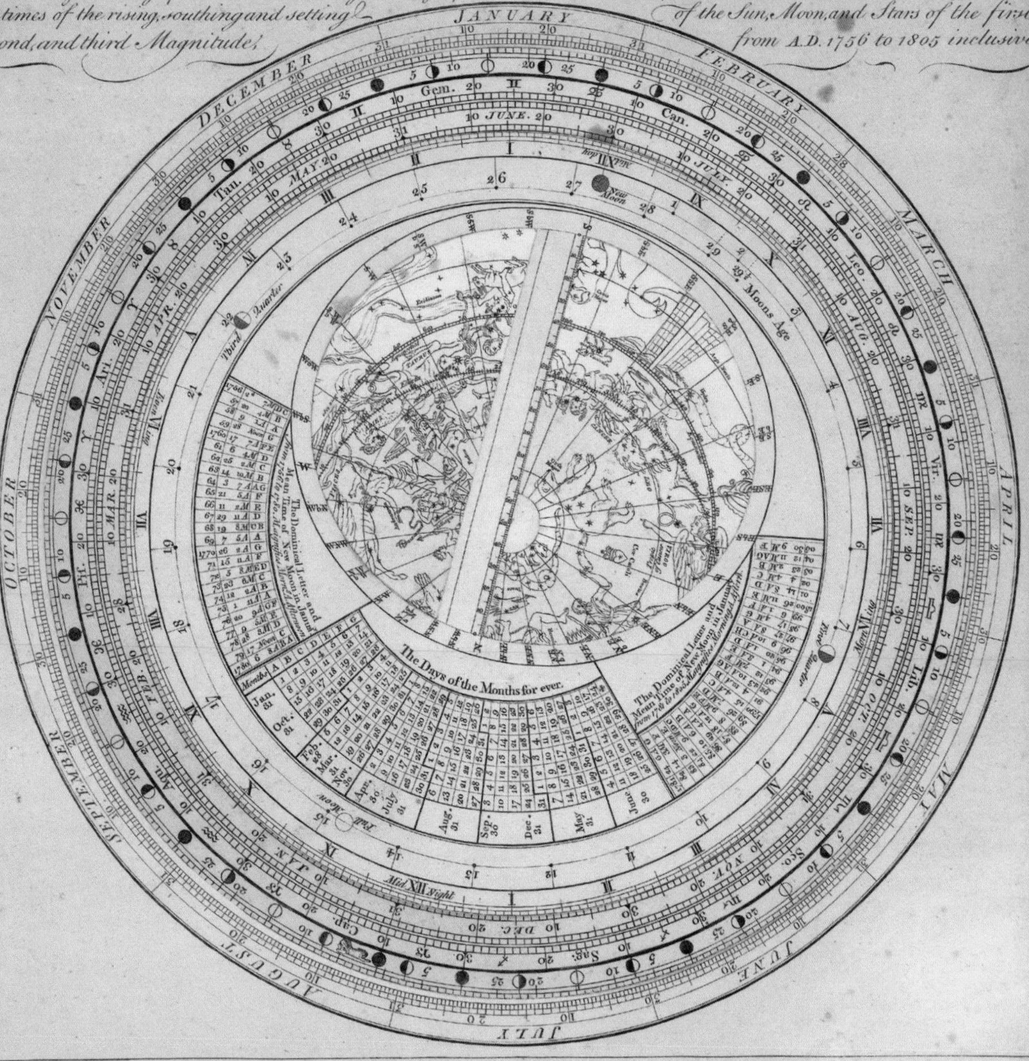

EXPLANATION of the *INSTRUMENT.*

New Moon ●. First Quar. ◑. Full Moon ○. Third Quar. ◐.

1. *To find the Day of the Month.* All the Days in the middle Table under the Dominical Letter for any Year are Sundays in ye Year, in the Divisions of the Months: those under the next Letter to the right hand are Mondays &c. When you run out at the right hand go back to the left, and thence proceed forward.

2. *To find the Days of all the New, Full and Quarter Moons in any Year, from 1756 to 1805.* Set ye New Moon on the middle Plate marked thus ● ☜ to ye time of New Moon in January on the Largest Plate (which time is shewn by the Tables on the upper Plate) and then all the following New, Full and Quarter Moons in that Year will stand against the days of the Months on which they fall. N.B. In Leap years after February the New Moon in January must be set to the day next before that on which it really falls.

3. *To find the Moon's Age on any given day of the Year.* Look for that day on the Largest Plate, and against it on the middle Plate you will find the Moon's Age for that day.

4. To

4. *To find the Sun's Place in the Ecliptic for any day of the Year.* Look for the given day on the middle Plate, and observe what Degree of the Ecliptic stands directly over it, which is ye Sun's Place on the given day at Noon.

5. *To find the Moon's Place in the Ecliptic for any Day of the Year.* Look for the Day of that New Moon on the middle Plate, which begins the current Lunation in which you want the Moon's Place; then turn the upper Plate until the New Moon marked upon it comes to that day; and the day of her Age counted on the Spiral line on the upper Plate will stand against her Place in the Ecliptic on the middle Plate.

6. *To find the time of the Sun's rising and setting on any day of the Year.* Having found the Sun's Place in the Ecliptic for the given day by § 4, look for the same Place of the Ecliptic or Oval Line divided by cross strokes with the Characters of the signs upon it in the Starry Projection, and bring the eastern edge of the Horizon, (which is the

the Oval opening in the upper Plate with the Points of the Compass marked upon it) to the Sun's Place: And then the day of the Month on the middle Plate will stand against the time of the Sun's Rising in the Hour Circle. If the Western edge of the Horizon be brought to the Sun's Place, the day of the Month will stand against his setting in the Hour Circle.

7. *To find the time of the Moon's rising, southing and setting, on any day.* Having found the Moon's Place by § 5 look for the same in the Ecliptic of the starry Projection, and then proceed in all respects for the time of her rising and setting as you did in the last Problem for the Sun's. And if to the Moon's Place you bring ye graduated Edge of the Slip which divides the Horizon in two equal parts, the day of the Month will stand over the time of her coming to the Meridian; And the Degrees thereon counted from the South at S will shew her mean Altitude on the Meridian.

8. *To find the time of the rising, southing and setting of any Star of the first, second or third Magnitude.* Bring the eastern edge of the Horizon to the Star, and the time of it's rising will stand against the day of the Month in the Hour Circle. Bring the Meridian or graduated edge of the Slip to the Star and the Day of the Month will stand against ye time of it's coming to the Meridian. Bring the western edge of the Horizon to the Star and the day of the Month will stand against the time of it's setting.

9. *To find what Stars are rising southing and setting at any given Hour.* Set the Hour against the day of the Month on the middle Plate, and then all the Stars lying under the eastern Edge of the Horizon are rising at that time: those under the western edge are then setting: and those under the graduated edge of the Slip which divides the Horizon in two equal parts are then on the Meridian.

10. *To find ye Meridian Altitude of the Sun or any Star on a given day.* Bring ye Sun's Place or the Star to the Meridian, and its Altitude will be cut among the Degrees counted from S.

J. Ferguson delin.

Published [illegible] Act of Parliament

One of the earliest Japanese books with volvelles

42 **NAKANISHI, Takafusa**

Konten min'yo seiu Benran [trans.: Practical Introduction to Meteorology].

Publication
Kyoto, Nakanishi, 1767.

Description
Two volumes, octavo, the first comprising 26 folded leaves, the second 30 folded leaves, numerous woodcuts in the text (two with moveable volvelles), two folded leaves of advertisements for books published by Nakanishi, original paper wrappers (a little rubbed, unimportant marginal worming in Vol. II), original block printed title label on each upper cover, new stitching.

Dimensions
265 by 165mm.

First edition, Kyoto issue (the book was also issued in Osaka in the same year) of this rare work on meteorology, astronomy, and astrology for laymen. It is the earliest attempt to present a scientific account of the meteorology of Japan based on local observations (and therefore not entirely based on Chinese meteorological theories). The book is also especially notable for being one of the earliest Japanese books to contain volvelles.

The first section of the book is astronomical and geographical: there are depictions of an armillary sphere, comets in the sky, constellations, and numerous diagrammatic maps. The second part is devoted to meteorology, in which the author explains how weather changes and describes the extremities of weather conditions, including rain storms, heavy snow, strong winds, thunder, lightning, etc. Nakanishi also explains how to predict the weather. There is much about the phenomenon of twinkling stars and their meaning regarding earthquakes, heavy winds and as a portent for epidemics. The author states that haloes, rainbows and severe weather can predict terrestrial events such as political instability, earthquakes, plagues, famine, etc.

One of the most interesting features is the author's explanation of the relationship between landscape and weather. There are numerous maps of regions of Japan – especially Kyoto, Tokyo, and Osaka – where Nakanishi describes in great detail the local weather patterns and how they have formed the landscape of the area.

Nakanishi (fl. 1754-72), a resident of Kyoto, was a disciple of the Seki school of mathematics and the author of many books. He was an astronomer, mathematician and calendar maker; he was also active as a publisher of science and medical books, as well as literature.

The Waseda University copy is also the Kyoto issue (no priority).

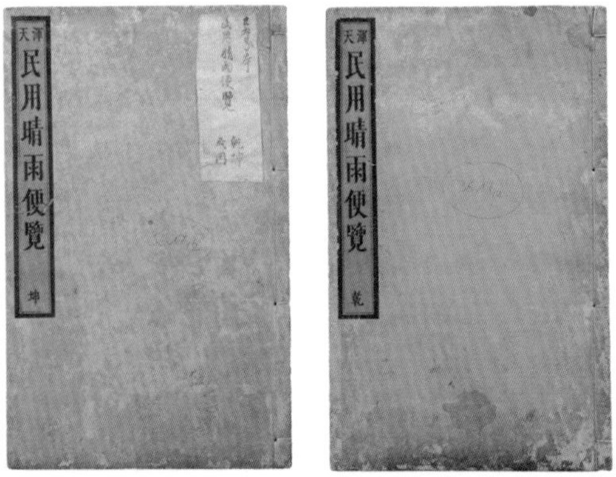

日ノ晴雨ヲ占フニハ天干ハ甲ノ木ニシテ地支ハ子ノ水ナリ是即チ水生木ト地支ヨリ天干ヲ相生ス 生尅ノ法ハ前ニ見タリ 扨後ニ備フル所ノ生尅晴雨占ノ中ニテ見合スレバ陰晦ニシテ雨フラザルノ日ナリト知ナリ○若甲午ノ日ナル寸ハ天干ハ甲ノ木ニシテ地支ハ午ノ火ナリ即チ木生火ト天干ヨリ地支ヲ生ズ此日晴テ風アリトス○若庚寅ノ日ナル寸ハ天干ハ庚ノ金ニシテ地支ハ寅ノ木ナリ是金尅木ト天干ヨリ地支ヲ尅ス

氣下降スル者盛ナラザル寸ハ天ノ氣ハ止リ地氣ハ住ラズ或ハ一惟ニ上騰シテ散ズ又何ゾ雨降ヿ有ンヤ是謂陰陽不和ニシテ雨降ザルナリ辞ニ曰ク密雲ニシテ雨フラズトハ是ナリ雨ハ惟陰陽ノ和スルニ在リ未ダ雲ノ盛ナルヲ以テ遂ニ雨アリトシ雲ノ盛ナラザルヲ以テ遂ニ雨ナシトスベカラズ

○日辰風知雨法。時辰亦同シ

知雨圖

●假令子ノ日風吹バ即チ圖中ノ風ノ字ヲ以テ子ノ方ニ當レバ雨ノ字卯ノ方ニアリ則チ卯ノ日雨フルト知ベシ

▲又丑ノ時ニ風吹バ圖中ノ風ノ字ヲ丑ノ方ニ當テ見レバ雨ノ字辰ノ方ニアリ則チ辰ノ時ニ雨フルト知ベシ

○天地説

夫天ノ性ハ圓ニシテ動キ地ノ性ハ方ニシテ静ナリ然モソノ本質ヲ考フル寸ハ天地倶ニ渾圓ナリ天ハ地外ヲ包ミ地ハ天ノ最中ニ居テ雞子ノ黄ナルモノ青キ内ニ在ガ如ク確然トシテ空ニ浮ミテ落ズ陰陽五行ハ精ヲ天ニ發シテ日月五星列布シ質ヲ地ニ顯シテ水火木金土成リ然シテ後ニ人ト禽獣ト其ノ間ニ交リ生ズ凡ソ頭ノ向フ所ヲ天トシ足ノ停ル所ヲ地トス渾倫一球ニシテ本ヨリ上下アルヿ無キナリ

天動運旋于外 地静處居于中

人常依附圓體 無有方隅上下

山海輿地圖

赤道下爲熱帶 兩極下爲寒帶

寒熱二帶之中 即是爲正帶也

○雨曜圖説

日 體

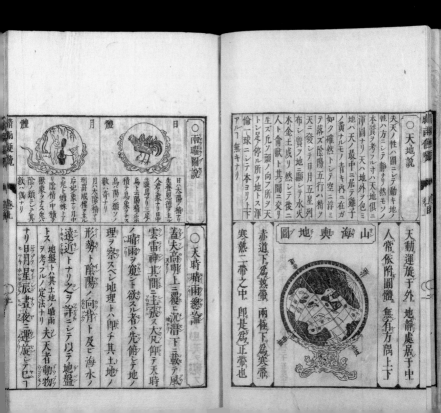

日ハ太陽ノ精ナリ生養恩德ヲ主ル人君ノ象ナリ日中ニ踆烏アリ三足ノ烏ト云陽精ノ宗積テ烏象ヲナス烏ハ陽ノ類ソノ數ハ奇ナリ

月 體

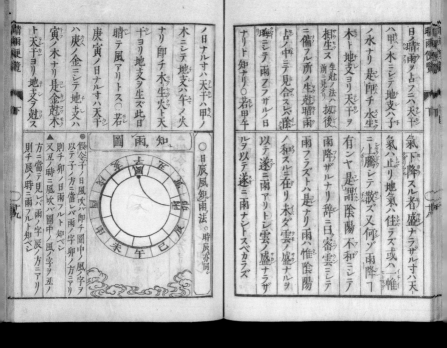

月ハ太陰ノ精ナリ刑罰威權ヲ主ル后妃ノ象ナリ月中ニ兎ト蟾蜍トアリ陰精ノ中積テ獣象ヲナス兎ハ陰ノ類ニシテ其數ハ偶ナリ

○天時晴雨總論

蓋夫高明上ニ覆ヒ沈潛下ニ載テ風雲雷神其間ニ主張ス大凡仰テ天時ノ晴雨ヲ窺ント欲スル者ハ先俯シテ地ノ理ヲ察スベシ地理トハ即チ其土地ノ形勢ト陰陽ノ向背ト及ビ海水ノ遠近トナリ之ヲ詳ニシテ以テ地盤トス 地盤トハ其土地ノ晴雨ヲ考フルノ定法ナリ 夫天者動物ナリ日月星辰晝夜ニ運旋シテ已ヿ

The "Cosmo-plane"

43 **DICQUEMARE, l'Abbé Jacques François**

Cosmo-Plane Inventé et Construit au Hâure de Grace en 1768 Par Mr. l'Abbé Dicquemare, dedié à Monsieur l'Abbé Nollet et exécuté par le Sr. Desnos.

Publication
Paris, Chez Desnos Ingénieur Géographe pour les Globes et Sphéres et Libraire de Sa Majeste le Roi de Dannemark, Rue Saint Jacques au Globe, 1768.

Description
Large wall hanging instrument, engraved on paper, fine original hand-colour, mounted on wood, and varnished, consisting of three moveable volvelles.

Dimensions
570mm (22.5 inches) in diameter.

A rare instrument intended to aid astronomical navigation at sea.

The instrument is a giant wall-mounted volvelle, consisting of three concentric discs, each one engraved and mounted on board.

To the centre of the instrument is a small diagram of the earth with the lines of the zodiac on the ecliptic – including the Tropics of Capricorn and Cancer; the Equator, Arctic and Antarctic circles; and the degrees of longitude and latitude. The next disc contains three diagrams of the Earth: the "Sphère Oblique", the "Sphère Paralelle", and the "Sphère droite". The spheres are said to demonstrate "the annual revolution of the sun, the solstices, the equinoxes, the seasons, etc.". Below are a list of the twelve signs of the zodiac, in French and Latin; a table of the standard unit of measurement in different countries; a key to the magnitude of the stars; and information concerning magnetic declination at the Paris Observatory on the 3 September 1767. To the left and right are two cartouches: to the left is an ecclesiastical and political map of France; to the right is a cut-out that, when the disc is revolved, reveals maps of the four continents (Europe, Africa, Asia and America). Several scale bars are engraved on the circumference to denote longitude based upon two prime meridians: the first at the "Isle de Fer" (Canary Islands) and the second at Paris. The next line denotes signs of the zodiac, together with the calendar; prominent stars through the year; and degrees of a circle. In this scale, the vernal equinox has been aligned with the prime meridian of the "Isle de Fer". The next scale shows the altitude of the sun throughout the year, with the last scale showing lines of latitude. Surrounding this are numerous tables providing information on the prime meridians; the revolution of the planets; prominent places with their latitude and longitude; comets; signs of the zodiac; a table of latitude and the change in climate; table of the declination of the stars upon the instrument; discussion of the frigid, temperate and torrid zones; declination of the sun in the northern and southern hemispheres; the seasons; and length of the days in each climate zone.

Father Jacques-François Dicquemare (1733-1789) was an astronomer and naturalist who lectured in natural science and natural history at the university in Havre. He is best known, with Nollet, as a popularizer of science in his book 'La connoissance de l'astronomie, rendue aisée & mise à la portée de tout le monde, 1769' and as the author of the 'cosmo-plane', the present work, which was intended, among other things, to solve the problems of nautical astronomical navigation.

COSMO-PLANE,
Inventé et Construit au Hâvre de Grace en 1768
PAR Mr. L'ABBÉ DICQUEMARE,
DÉDIÉ
À MONSIEUR L'ABBÉ NOLLET.
Longueur des Jours sous chaque Climat en Heures et demie heures
Sphère Parallele
Sphère droite
Sphère Oblique
Zenith
HORIZON
LA FRANCE
XII SIGNES DU ZODIAQUE
TABLE
Des mesures Géographiques des Pays les plus connus
A PARIS
Chez Desnos Ingénieur Géographe pour les Globes et Sphères et Libraire de Sa Majesté le Roi de Dannemarck
Rue Saint Jacques au Globe
A.P.D.R.

The work is dedicated to Jean-Antoine Nollet (19 November 1700-25 April 1770) a French clergyman and physicist, who was one of the great popularizers of science in the eighteenth century. Nollet was particularly interested in the new science of electricity, which he explored with the help of Du Fay and Réaumur. He joined the Royal Society of London in 1734 and later became the first professor of experimental physics at the University of Paris.

We are only able to trace one institutional example of the instrument; that held by the Stewart Museum, Montreal.

COSMO-PLANE,
Inventé et Construit au Hâvre de Grace en 1768.
PAR Mr. L'ABBÉ DICQUEMARE,
DEDIÉ
A MONSIEUR L'ABBÉ NOLLET
Longueur des Jours sous chaque Climat en Heures et demie
Zénith
Sphère droite
Sphère Parallele
HORISON
POLE NORD
PARIS
Sphère Oblique
Démonstration de la révolution annuelle du Soleil, des Solstices, des Equinoxes, des Saisons, &c.
LA FRANCE Ecclésiastique et Politique
L'EUROPE
OCCIDENTAL
PARTIE D'AFRIQUE
PARTIE DE L'ASIE
LES XII SIGNES DU ZODIAQUE
Septentrionaux
le Bélier
le Taureau
les Gémeaux
L'Ecrevisse
le Lion
la Vierge
Méridionaux
la Balance
le Scorpion
le Sagittaire
le Capricorne
le Verseau
les Poissons
En Latin
Aries, Taurus, Gemini, Cancer, Leo, Virgo, Libra, Scorpius, Sagittarius, Caper, Amphora Pisces.
TABLE
Des mesures Géographiques des Pays les plus connus réduites en pas Géométriques de 5 pieds chacun
Astres
Le Soleil
Etoiles
1re Grandeur
2me Grandeur
3me Grandeur
Une Aiguille aimantée de 4 pouces de longueur déclinoit de 19d. 30m. du Nord vers l'Ouest à l'Observatoire de Paris le 3. Septembre 1767.
TABLE De la Latitude où se termine chaque Climat
A PARIS
Chez Desnos Ingénieur Géographe pour les Globes et Sphères et Libraire de Sa Majesté le Roi de Dannemarck.
Rue Saint Jacques au Globe.
A.P.D.R.

An unrecorded analemma

44 **DONN, B[enjamin]**

The Analemma Improved by B Donn. Pr[ice] 3s. 6d.

Publication
Bristol & London, Published by the Author, According to Act of Parliament, Sold By B. Law & J. Johnson Booksellers: also by Heath & Wing Instrument Makers, Jany. 1st, 1770.

Description
Engraved analemma with rotating volvelle, calendar scales and principal stars' positions.

Dimensions
330 by 203mm (13 by 8 inches).

References
Daniel, Christopher, 'The Equation of Time: The Invention of the Analemma. A brief history of the subject', Monograph No. 1, January 2006.

The instrument consists of a rotating celestial planisphere graduated with right ascension and declination. Below is a list of the principal stars, with an analemma charting the sun's position throughout the year.

The analemma is nowadays considered to be the 'figure-of-eight' device employed in a mean-time sundial to correct for the equation of time. However, in late antiquity the term was applied to a subsidiary instrument, in the form of a graphical projection, which facilitated the construction of a principal work such as a sundial. This was usually a planispheric projection, i.e. an orthographic-stereographic projection of the celestial sphere, as explained by Dr John Twysden (1607-1688) in his work 'The Use of the Great Planisphere, called the Analemma', published in London in 1685.

An advertisement for the analemma appears in a pamphlet published by Donn entitled, 'The Description and Use of the Navigational Scale' (1772).

Benjamin Donn (1729-1798), sometimes known as Benjamin Donne, was a British cartographer, surveyor and mathematician. Born in Bideford, he was the heir to a long line of well-respected mathematicians, including his father and older brother, who ran a local school. In 1768 he was elected librarian of the Bristol Library, and, "in keeping with his taste for the binomial theorem and the book of Euclid, he conceived the idea of converting the establishment into a mathematical academy; but the corporation did not join in his enthusiasm, and students were not invited." Later he established his own private mathematical academy in Bristol near St Michael's Church. Cartographically, Donn's most significant work is his 1765 large format map of Devonshire, based upon a mile-for-mile survey he completed at his own expense. This was the first large-scale map of any British county to win the award of £100 from the Royal Society for the Arts. Donn later went on to publish a number of other less significant but popular maps, including a pocket map of Bristol, a map of western England, and several nautical charts of the Western Ocean, as well as various mathematical tables. A lifetime of study and dedication to mathematics earned Donn the title of Master of Mechanics to the King, an honorarium he would hold for only a short time. Donn died in 1798.

Designed to be used at sea, very few of these fragile card instruments survive. It may be that the present instrument is the only surviving example, as we have so far been unable to trace any others in institutional or private holdings.

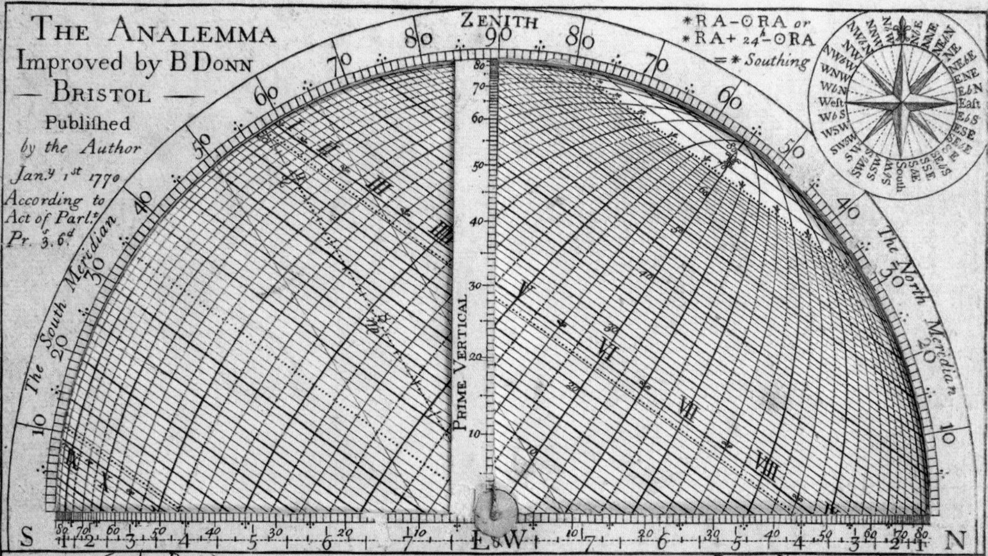

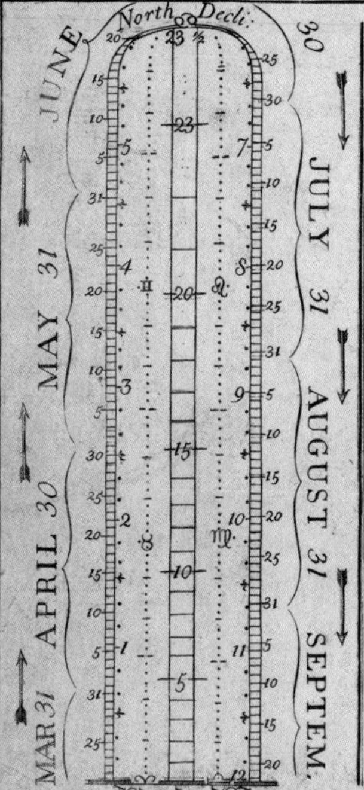

STARS	R:Aſcen: h	m	Declina d	m	
Achenar, *in Eridanus* α	1	29	58	25	S
∗ *over Aries* χ	1	54	22	21	N
Menkar, Whale's Jaw α	2	50	3	11	N
Algol, in Meduſa β	2	53	40	3	N
:*Pleiades, or 7 Stars* η	3	34	23	23	N
Aldebaran, *Bull's Eye* α	4	23	16	2	N
Capella, *in Auriga* α	5	0	45	44	N
Rigel, *Orion's* W. *Foot* β	5	4	8	29	S
Betelgeuſe, E. *Should:* α	5	43	7	21	N
Canopus, *Poop of Argo* α	6	19	52	35	S
Syrius, *Great Dog* α	6	35	16	25	S
Caſtor, *H: of* N. *Twin* α	7	20	32	22	N
Procyon, *Little Dog* α	7	27	5	48	N
Alphard, Hydra's ♡ α	9	16	7	40	S
Regulus, *Lyon's* ♡ α	9	56	13	5	N
Dubhe, N. *Pointer* α	10	49	62	59	N
Foot S.∗ *of the Croſier* α	12	14	61	49	S
Ariſta, *Virgin's Spike* α	13	13	9	57	S
Arcturus, *in Bootes* α	14	5	20	24	N
Antares, *Scorpion's* ♡ α	16	15	25	55	S
Lyra, *in the Harp* α	18	29	38	35	N
Altair, *in the Eagle* α	19	40	8	17	N
Fomalhaut, S. *Fiſh* α	22	45	30	50	S
Markab, Wing of Pega: α	22	53	13	58	N

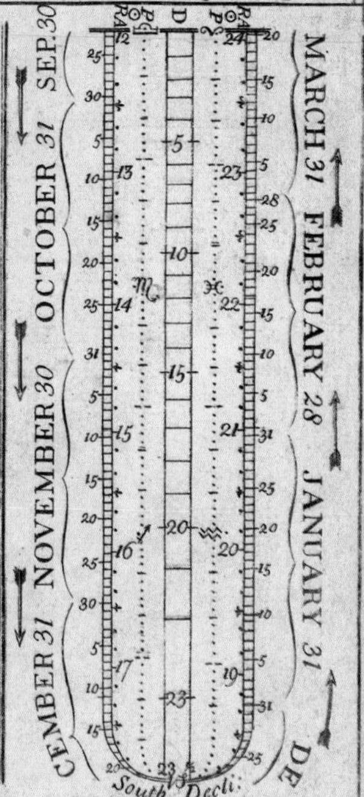

LONDON Sold by B. Law & J. Johnſon Bookſellers; alſo by Heath & Wing Inſtrument Makers.

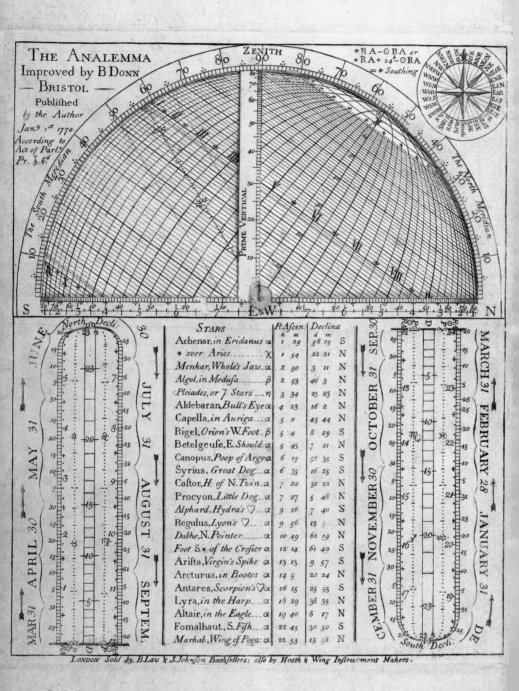

A previously unreported and possibly unique surviving example of this Ferguson nocturnal

45 **FERGUSON, James**

The Astronomical Time Keeper.

Publication
[London, James Ferguson, c. 1770].

Description
Engraved astronomical instrument on paper, volvelle over a circular scale.

Dimensions
450 by 315mm (17.75 by 12.5 inches).

References
Millburn, pp. 238 & 281.

A nocturnal or star dial comprising a rotating disc based on the northern circumpolar stars.

Millburn states that, "One of Ferguson's tracts includes an advertisement for the Astronomical Timekeeper ... [This] was evidently a printed version of the Nocturnal or Star Dial, but we have not found an extant specimen". The instrument to which he refers is, presumably, the present work, and the advertisement at the end of Ferguson's 'Description and use of the astronomical rotula' (1775) reads:

"9. The Astronomical Time-keeper. Shewing how to find the true Time of the Night by the Fixed Stars in all Latitudes. 5s 6d".

For a discussion of the life of James Ferguson, please see item 34.

The *ASTRONOMICAL* TIME KEEPER.

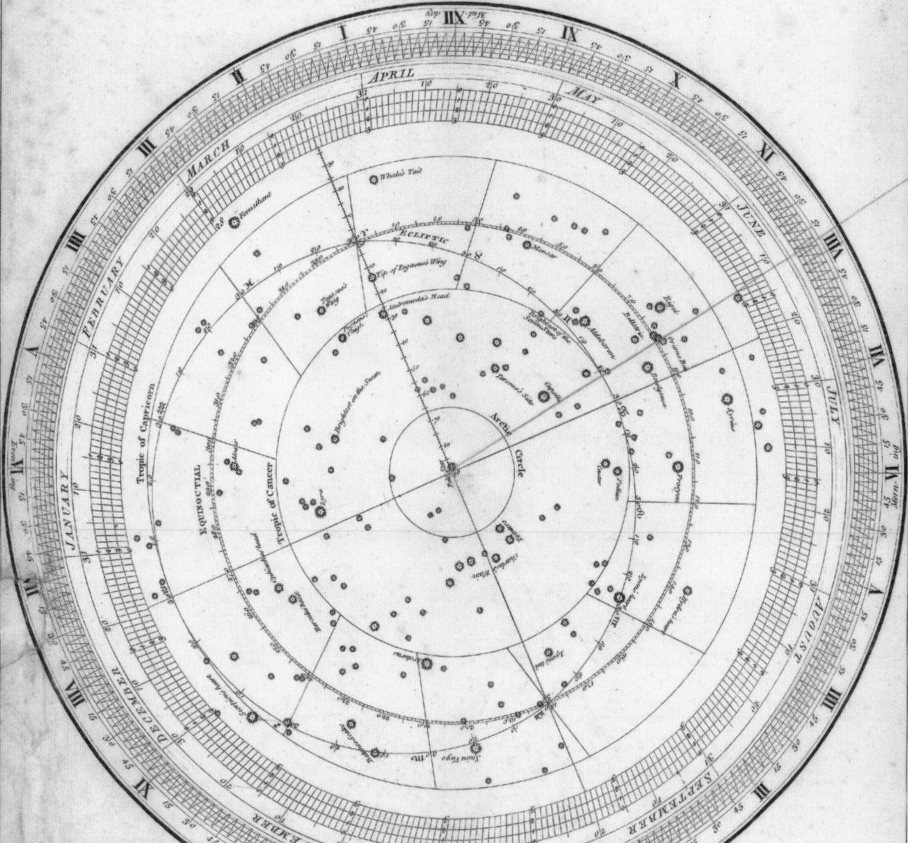

The Days of the Year are diagonally laid down in a Spiral of four Revolutions. Those in the Spiral marked 0 are for Leap Year, and those in the other Spirals, marked 1, 2, 3, are for ye first, second & third Years after Leap Year. By this method February has 29 Days in Leap Year, & only 28 in all other Years. Within these, the Stars are laid down according to their Right Ascensions & Declinations.

To shew the Positions of the Stars at any Hour of the Night of any given Day in the Year. Turn the Star-Plate till the given Day stands against the Hour of the Night; then hold the great Plate, with the XII for Mid-day uppermost, between you and the Pole Star; and then the Stars on the smallest Plate will have the same Positions, with respect to each other, that the Stars themselves have in the Heavens. And by this means, you may soon learn to know all the Stars of the first, second, and third Magnitudes.

To find the true equal Time of the Night. When you see any Star a little towards the left hand from being directly under the Pole Star, hang a Plumb line at Arm's length from you, between your Eye and the Pole Star, and watch till you see the Star below the Pole cut the Plumb line: then stretch the Thread from the center of the Star-Plate over the Midnight XII, and keeping the Thread there, turn the Star-Plate till the Star that cut the Plumb line comes under the Thread; and holding the Plate there, stretch the Thread over the Day of the Month, in the proper Spiral; and it will cut the true Time of the Night in in the Circle of 24 Hours: every Hour of which is diagonally divided into 60 minutes.

In this Operation, if the Pole Star be directly under the Thread or even with it above the Center of the Plate, when it is stretched over the Midnight XII, you have the time of the Night exactly. But if the Pole Star then lies either to the right or left hand of the Center, you must be careful in bringing the Star below the Pole toward the Thread, to place the Star-Plate so, as that Star may be as far to the right or left from the Thread as the Pole Star near the center is: and then, when the Thread is stretched over the Day of the Month, it will cut the true Time of the Night.

To find at what Time of the Night any given Star will be on the Meridian, on any Day of ye Year. Stretch the Thread over the Mid-day XII, and turn the Star-Plate till the given Star comes under the Thread: then, among the Months which stand against the night Hours, stretch the Thread over any Day, and it will cut the time of the Night when the like Star in the Heavens will be on the Meridian.

And thus, if you first find a Meridian Line by any of the common methods, and hang up two Plumb-lines in the Plane of the meridian, about two or three feet from each other, and place your Eye so, as ye one Line may just hide the other from your sight, and watch till you find any Star disappear beyond these Lines, that Star will then be on the Meridian. And if you stretch the Thread over the Midday XII and turn the Star-Plate till the like Star be just below the Thread, and then stretch the Thread over the Day of the Month in the proper Spiral, it will cut the true time of the Night in the Hour Circle.

On the 2d Day of April, the Pole Star will be directly below the Pole at Midnight, and on the 1st of October it will be on the Meridian at Midnight: On each Day afterward, it will be 3 minutes 56 seconds sooner below the Pole, or on the Meridian. Making this allowance each Day, if your Clock be within 10 minutes of the true equal time, you may find a Meridian by the Pole Star. For, at the time of its being on the Meridian by the Clock, hang up two Plumb lines so, as that when you put your Eye to the furthest Line from the Star, both the Lines may hide it from your sight at the same time, these Lines will be in the plane of the Meridian. For the Pole Star describes so small a Circle round the Pole, that its change of situation, or motion in 10 minutes is not perceptible.

Publish'd as the Act directs March 26. 1770.

A polyhedral sundial

46 **BERINGER, David**

[Polyhedral sundial].

Publication
Nurenberg, [1777-1821].

Description
Wooden polyhedral sundial, paper pasted to wooden furniture, hand-coloured and varnished, brass gnomon.

Dimensions
155 by 110 by 85mm (6 by 4.25 by 3.25 inches).

References
The Greenwich Maritime Museum collection includes two Beringer cube dials, reg. nos. AST0385 and AST0289; see H. Higton, 'Sundials at Greenwich', Oxford 2002, nos. 251 and 252, pp. 256-9.

David Beringer (1756-1821), a sundial maker in Nuremberg, was admitted as master of his craft in 1777 and is credited with inventing this particular type of polyhedral sundial, which became popular in South Germany towards the end of the eighteenth century.

The sundial is made up of an articulated arm, surmounted by a cube with sundials and gnomons to all five sides. The arm allows the user to incline the cube in a north-south direction; a plumb line on the eastern side that moves along a graduated scale can be used to adapt the instrument to the latitude of the user. To the base is set a compass in order to gain the correct bearing.

SUD

Rare planisphere

47 **FLECHEUX**

Planetaire ou Planisphere Nouveau, inventé et dessiné par M. Flecheux, approuvé par l'Academie Royale de Sciences. A Monsieur le Comte de Meslay le Vidame, Président Honoraire, de la Chambre des Compter de Paris.

Publication
Paris, [1778-1780].

Description
Engraving, with four volvelles, mounted on board and varnished.

Dimensions
600 by 585mm (23.5 by 23 inches).

References
Warner, Flecheux 1; FRBNF30440651.

A rare planisphere with moveable parts.

"Flecheux's map is intended to show the path of the sun, the daily equation of time, the path of the moon, the time of the lunar meridian passage, the places of the stars of magnitude 1-4 identified by Bayer numbers, their transits for a certain place, and the longitude at sea without recourse to further calculation. Accordingly, the coordinates are numerous: lines every 10 degrees r.a., the equinoctial and solstitial colures graduated every degree; dotted lines every 30 degrees longitude between ecliptic pole and ecliptic and over southern half of ecliptic, and dotted lines every 10 degrees longitude between equator and ecliptic over the northern half; meridian of the pole star; Arctic and orbit of the earth; Tropic of Cancer: circles every 10 degrees declination; ecliptic; equator graduated every 1 degree r.a. and every 1 degree longitude; circumference graduated every day. Finally there are lines indicating the days on which, and the extent to which, the mean-time clock is ahead of or behind the true sun" (Warner).

To the border of the work is a map of the world, an armillary sphere elevated to the latitude of Paris, a key to the magnitude of the stars upon the planisphere, and a diagram showing the equinoxes and the solstices.

The work is dedicated to Jérôme-Pélagie Masson de Meslay (1742-1798), the head of the Chambre des Comptes, the powerful courts which dealt with financial affairs, overseeing public spending and auditing the accounts of crown officials.

Flecheux (1738-1793) was an astronomer about whom little is known. We are only able to trace a handful of his works: the present planisphere (1778); a loxocosme (1784) for determining, among other things, the annual and diurnal movements of the earth; a map of the world (1782); and a table of planets passing the meridian (1789). His passing was mentioned by Jérôme Lalande in the 'History of Astronomy' (1794), who states he was "author of an ingenious planisphere".

Rare. We are only able to trace four institutional examples: those of the Adler Planetarium; Stanford University Library; Erfurt University; and the BNF.

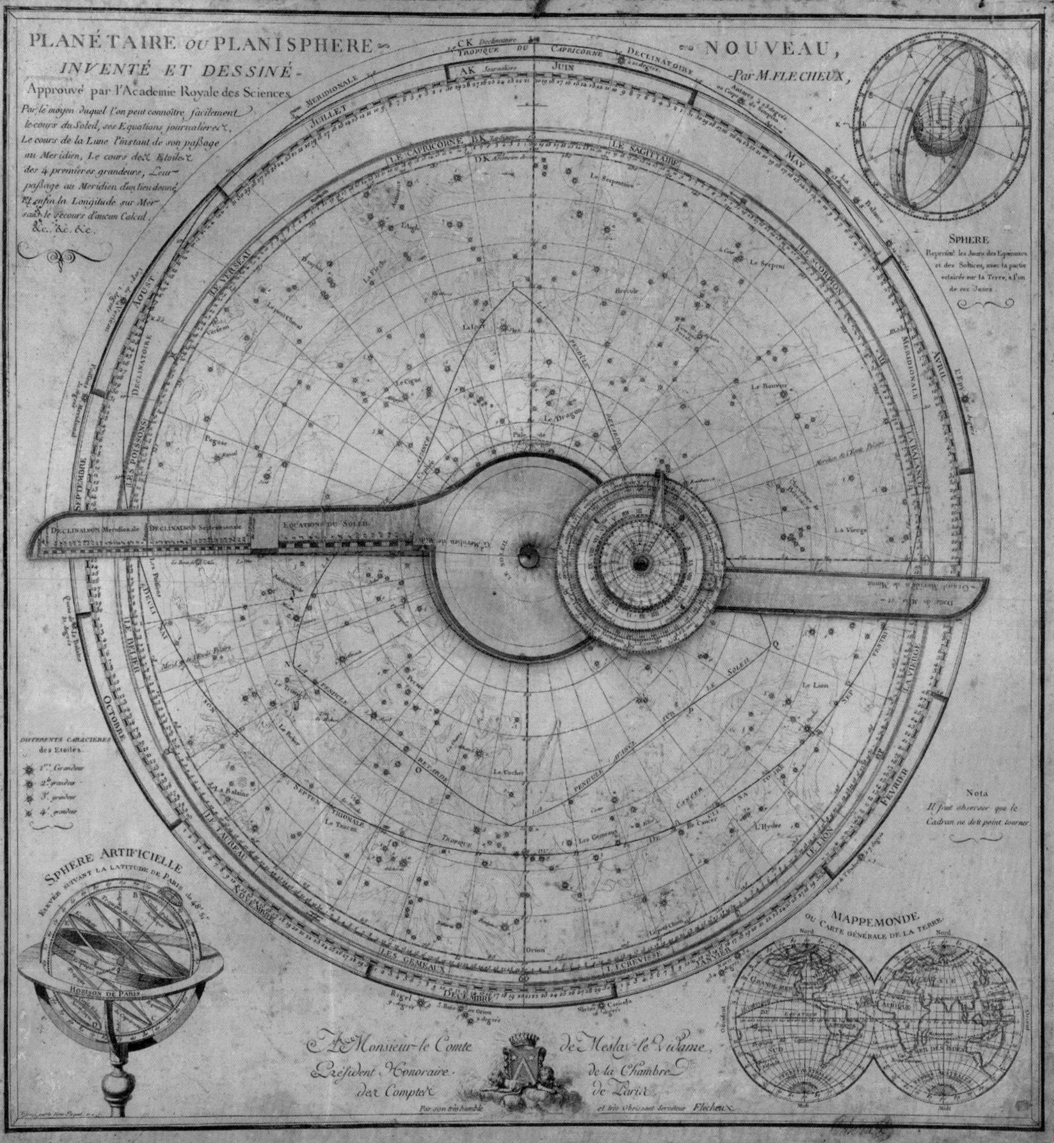
PLANÉTAIRE ou PLANISPHERE NOUVEAU,
INVENTÉ ET DESSINÉ Par M. FLECHEUX,
Approuvé par l'Academie Royale des Sciences
Par le moyen duquel l'on peut connoître facilement le cours du Soleil, ses Equations journalieres, Le cours de la Lune l'instant de son passage au Meridien, Le cours des Etoiles des 4 premières grandeurs, Leur passage au Meridien d'un lieu donné Et enfin la Longitude sur Mer sans le secours d'aucun Calcul. &c. &c. &c.
SPHERE
Represent. les Jours des Equinoxes et des Solstices, avec la partie eclairée sur la Terre, à l'un de ces Jours.
DIFFERENTS CARACTERES des Etoiles.
1.res Grandeur
2.de grandeur
3.e grandeur
4.e grandeur
Nota
Il faut observer que le Cadran ne doit point tourner.
SPHERE ARTIFICIELLE
ELEVÉE SUIVANT LA LATITUDE DE PARIS de 48° 51'
HORISON DE PARIS
MAPPEMONDE
OU CARTE GÉNÉRALE DE LA TERRE.
DECLINAISON Meridionale
DECLINAISON Septentrionale
EQUATIONS DU SOLEIL
JUILLET
JUIN
MAY
AVRIL
FEVRIER
JANVIER
DECEMBRE
NOVEMBRE
OCTOBRE
SEPTEMBRE
AOUST
LE CAPRICORNE
LE SAGITTAIRE
LE SCORPION
LA BALANCE
LA VIERGE
LE LION
L'ECREVISSE
LES GEMEAUX
LE TAUREAU
LE BELIER
LES POISSONS
LE VERSEAU
Le Serpentaire
Le Serpent
Le Bouvier
La Vierge
Le Lion
L'Hydre
Les Gemeaux
Le Taureau
Le Cocher
Orion
Le Dragon
Le Cygne
Pegase
Rigel
Sirius
A Monsieur le Comte de Meslay le Vidame,
Président Honoraire de la Chambre des Comptes de Paris
Par son très humble et très Obeissant Serviteur Flecheux

One of the first astronomers to introduce constellation boundaries

48 **[ANDRÉ, Noel] CHRYSOLOGUE de GY, Capuchin P.**

Extrait de l'Abrégé d'Astronomie Du P. Chrysologue de Gy, en Franche-Comté, Capuchin, pour servir d'instruction relativement à deux petits planisphères, Par le même Auteur. Ouvrage mis à la portée des Commerçans, & même des jeunes Gens qui désirent avoir.

Publication
Paris, chez Mérigot, Perrier & Verrier, 1779.

Description
Octavo (210 by 160mm), 23pp. pamphlet (190 by 125mm), two charts pasted to upper and lower pastedown (each 180 by 140mm), with moveable parts, some of which are metal, contemporary marbled paper boards, rubbed.

References
Warner, Andre 3; Tooley, 116.

This rare diminutive work was designed as a portable and more affordable version of André's maps of the heavens and the earth that he had published in the previous year, for use by travellers and the young. The text provides a detailed description of the planisphere and map, as well as the numerous problems that Andre encountered along the way.

Noel André (1728-1808), also known as Capuchin de Chrysologue de Gy, was a geographer and astronomer working in Paris. He lived for many years in the convent on rue Saint-Honoré in which Le Monnier's observatory was housed. He was one of the first astronomers to introduce constellation boundaries to his planispheres.

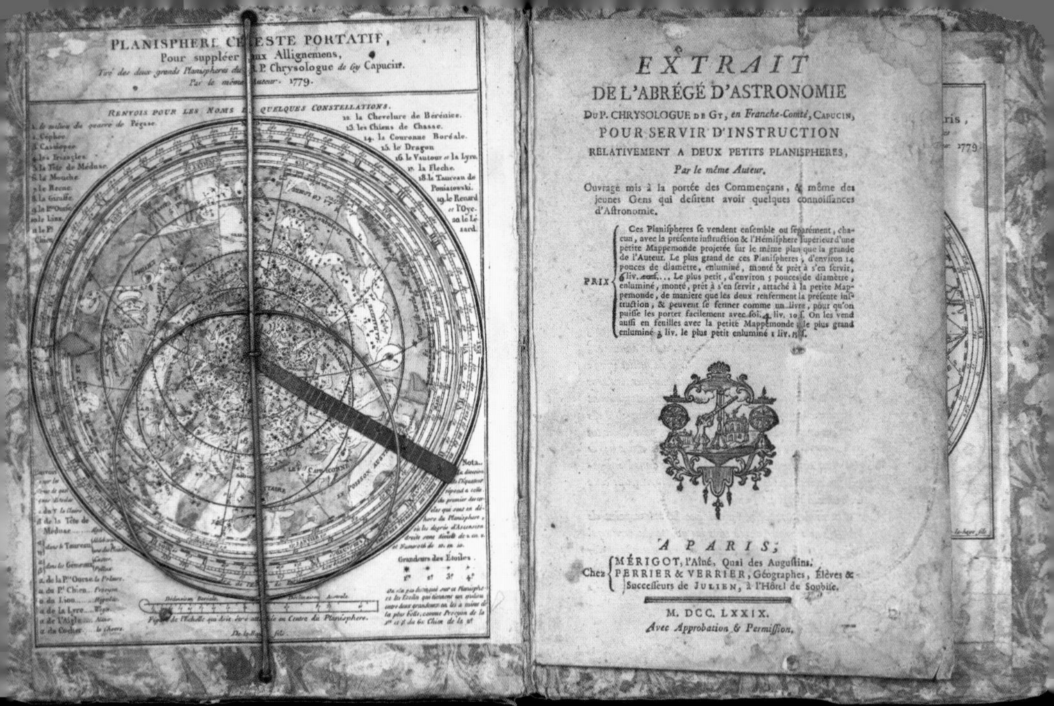
PLANISPHERE CELESTE PORTATIF,
Pour suppléer aux Allignemens,
Tiré des deux grands Planisphères du R.P. Chrysologue de Gy Capucin.
Par le même Auteur. 1779.
RENVOIS POUR LES NOMS DE QUELQUES CONSTELLATIONS.
12. la Chevelure de Bérénice.
13. les Chiens de Chasse.
14. la Couronne Boréale.
15. le Dragon
16. le Vautour et la Lyre.
17. la Fleche
18. le Taureau de Poniatowski.
19. le Renard et l'Oye.
20. le Lézard.
Grandeurs des Etoiles
Figure de l'Echelle qui doit être attachée au Centre du Planisphere.
EXTRAIT
DE L'ABRÉGÉ D'ASTRONOMIE
Du P. CHRYSOLOGUE DE GY, en Franche-Comté, CAPUCIN;
POUR SERVIR D'INSTRUCTION
RELATIVEMENT A DEUX PETITS PLANISPHERES,
Par le même Auteur.
Ouvrage mis à la portée des Commençans, & même des jeunes Gens qui desirent avoir quelques connoissances d'Astronomie.
PRIX
Ces Planispheres se vendent ensemble ou séparément, chacun, avec la présente instruction & l'Hémisphere Supérieur d'une petite Mappemonde projetée sur le même plan que la grande de l'Auteur. Le plus grand de ces Planispheres, d'environ 14 pouces de diamètre, enluminé, monté & prêt à s'en servir, 6 liv. ... Le plus petit, d'environ 5 pouces de diamètre, enluminé, monté, prêt à s'en servir, attaché à la petite Mappemonde, de maniere que les deux renferment la présente instruction, & peuvent se fermer comme un livre, pour qu'on puisse les porter facilement avec soi, 4 liv. 10 s. On les vend aussi en feuilles avec la petite Mappemonde; le plus grand enluminé 3 liv. le plus petit enluminé 1 liv. 10 s.
A PARIS;
Chez MÉRIGOT, l'Aîné, Quai des Augustins.
PERRIER & VERRIER, Géographes, Élèves & Successeurs de JULIEN, à l'Hôtel de Soubise.
M. DCC. LXXIX.
Avec Approbation & Permission.

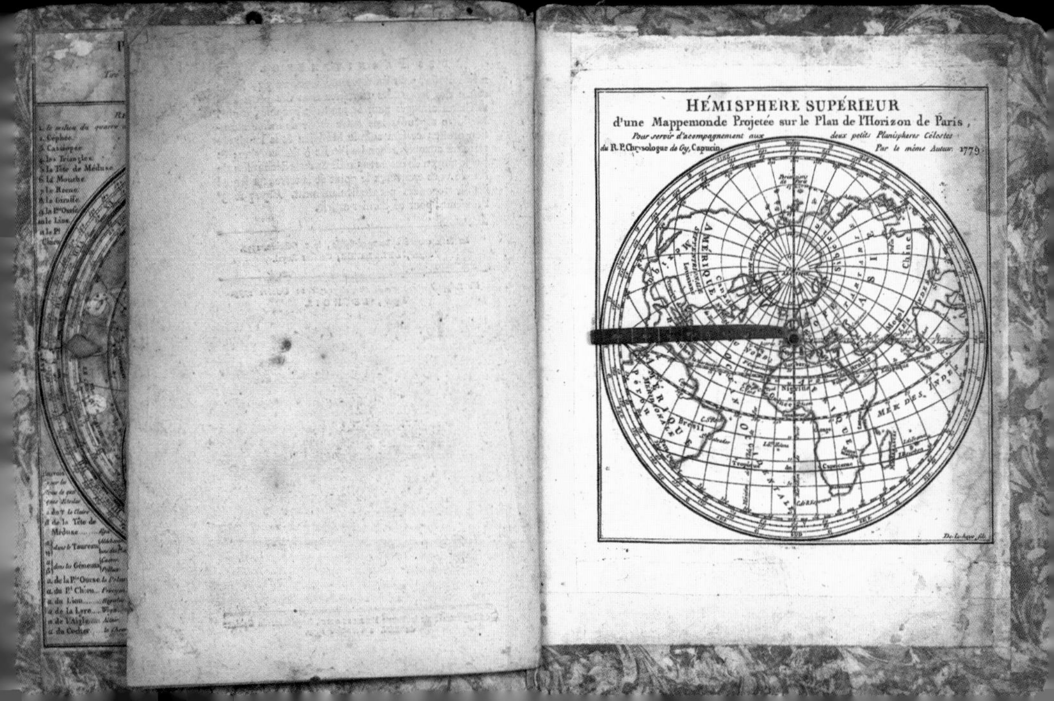
HÉMISPHERE SUPÉRIEUR
d'une Mappemonde Projetée sur le Plan de l'Horizon de Paris,
Pour servir d'accompagnement aux deux petits Planispheres Célestes
du R.P. Chrysologue de Gy, Capucin.
Par le même Auteur. 1779.
AMÉRIQUE
ASIE
MER DES INDES
Brésil
Chine

A unique manuscript lunar astrolabe

49 [Anonymous]

Planispherum Lunare cujus ope Locus medius Solis Lunae, ejusdemque Nodorum, Solis Declinatio, Lunaeque Latitudo Simplex, atque ejus Argumentum, necnon Novitunia et Plenitania Ecliptica simul inveniuntun.

Publication
[c. 1800].

Description
Ink and polychromy on paper over pine. The instrument comprises a circular base plate, and three rotatable cardboard volvelles, and a brass radius pointer attached to each other in the centre. A brass ring is attached to the base plate for suspending the instrument. All four paper covered discs are finely inscribed in manuscript with various scales and symbols.

Dimensions
470mm in diameter.

References
ODNB; Webster, R. & M., 'Western Astrolabes', Adler Planetarium & Astronomy Museum, 1998.

Content
1. The smallest volvelle bears a scale covering 12 hours on its outer ring. It also shows the ecliptical motion of the Sun, the Moon's orbit, the line of nodes, and the arguments of latitude (in other words, the distances from the nodes).
2. On the second volvelle, a scale covers the years from 1801 to 1825. Each year is subdivided in twelve months, with the abbreviated name written for each month.
3. The following volvelle carries a series of scales showing a monthly calendar, a zodiac calendar with skilfully drawn pictures and the symbols of the signs. Below the zodiac is a scale for the declination of the sun throughout the year, set in four sequences of three.
4. On the outside rim of the volvelle is another calendar scale in which the months are unevenly distributed. This scale presumably was to be used in conjunction with the outer scale on the circular base plate. In addition, the volvelle holds two brass studs that most probably helped the user turn the disc to the desired position. This latter scale gives the days, subdivided in hours. The days are numbered I to XXXI, with the number I coinciding with XXVII and 8 hours (the sidereal period of the Moon), which results in a double numbering from XXVIII to XXXI. Below this scale for days, there is a series of dates, all confined to the period 1801 to 1825, presumably for solar eclipses. The brass rule or pointer holds a horizontal scale from 5 to 0 (LA-southern declination) and from 0 to 5 (LB-northern declination), indicating the latitude of the moon with respect to the ecliptic. The closer to 0 at new moon or full moon, the likelier an eclipse is to occur. The rule is engraved with "Locus Lunae". The circular scales serve to set the moon's position and node relative to the sun, from which the user can then infer the lunar phase and whether an eclipse will occur at new moon or full moon.

Manuscript instruments of this type are rare, especially in such good condition, as no other exact copy is recorded to date. Similar instruments were produced at the end of the sixteenth century, mostly in brass. Sir Robert Dudley (1573-1649, see item 17) had a lunar calculator made by Charles Whitwell (c. 1568-1611) – a brass disc of 72 cm diameter overall, which was the most complex instrument made during the sixteenth century. Inscribed 'Sir Robert Dudley was the inventor of this instrument', its purpose was to calculate the place of the moon over a period of thirty years. It is now in the Museo di Storia della Scienza in Florence, Italy. Another similar paper device was printed, with detailed instructions, in 1786 in Vlissingen (Flushing) in the Netherlands, advertised as a "Starkundige Maan-Wyzer en Almanach" (Astronomical Moon Pointer and Almanac) by Henricus Schortinghuis.

Didactic astronomical playing cards

50 **PÂRIS [Louis-Michel]**

Cartes elementaires d'astronomie et de Geographie, par M. l'Abbé.

Publication
A Falaise, chez Brée frères, Et se trouve à Paris, chez Marcilly, rue St-Julien-le-Pauvre, no. 14, A Rouen, chez Lecrêne-Labbey. 1807.

Description
Set of 42 hand-coloured woodcut playing cards, of which three have moveable parts, text to verso, housed within original pull-off slipcase with publisher's label.

Dimensions
105 by 70mm (4.25 by 2.75 inches).

A rare set of cards that form an introduction to geography and astronomy, and the last known work of the author, Louis-Michel Pâris (1740-1806). The set includes three volvelles. The first (no. 23) shows the equatorial seconds and minutes as regards the oblique position of the globes.

1

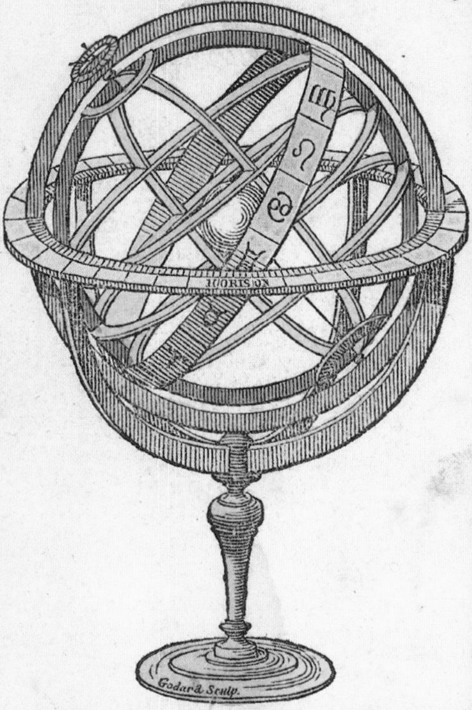

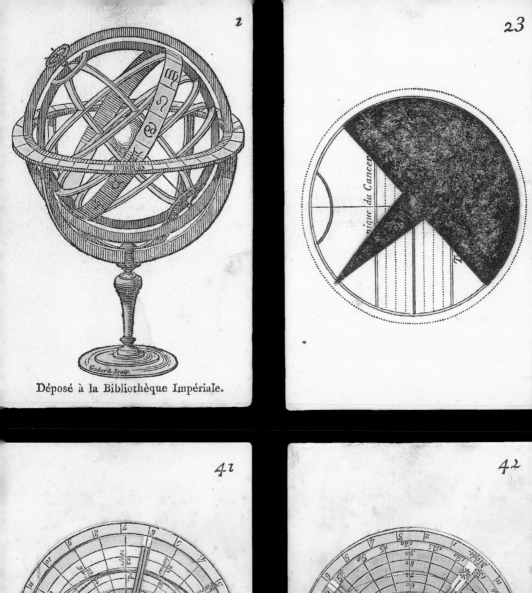

Déposé à la Bibliothèque Impériale.

23

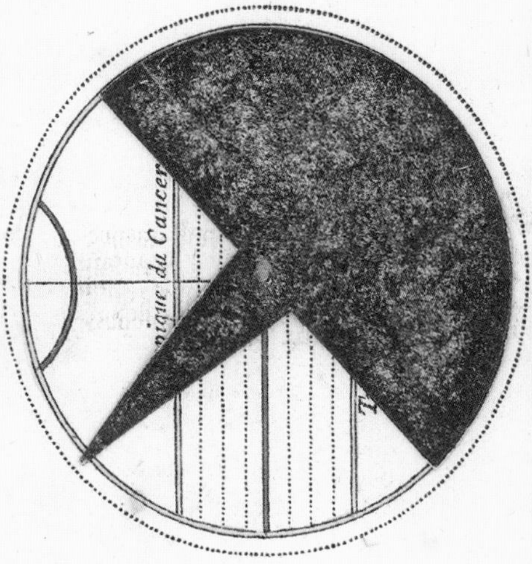

41

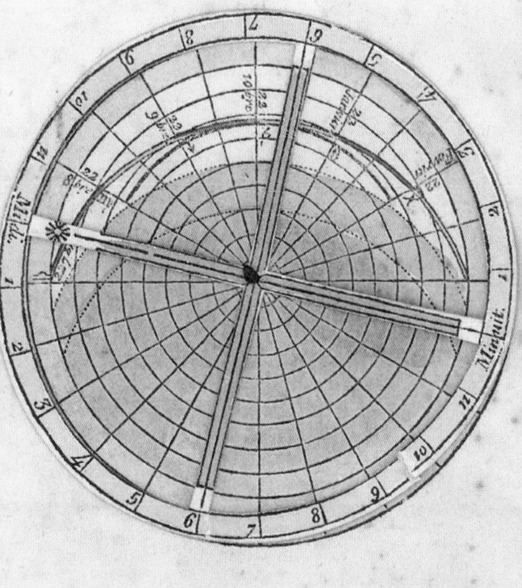

42

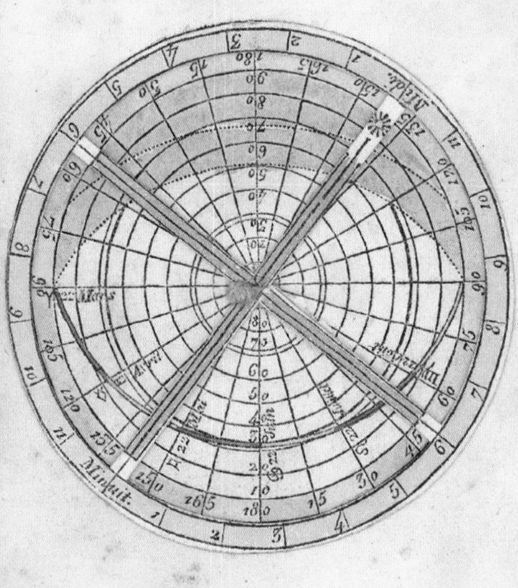

An early nineteenth century perpetual calendar

51 **GAUTIE: IR PS**

Calendrier Perpetuel.

Publication
[?Paris, 1812].

Description
Engraving with aquatint, with moveable parts, in original frame.

Dimensions
250 by 310mm (9.75 by 12.25 inches).

In the upper part of the plate is the title on a banderole held aloft by two cherubs; to the centre is a sphere which bears the year; below are two further spheres which contain information upon days, star signs, day and night times, and sunrise and sunset. Two further tables give lists of signs of the zodiac and the dates for the beginning of spring, summer, autumn and winter. Below the calendar is a copy of Guido Reni's 'Aurora'.

L'AURORE AUX CHEVEUX DE ROSE
chasse les ténèbres, ouvre les portes du Ciel; et le Soleil, dont la lumiere se répand partout, dissipe tous les Astres.

Miersch's "Star Clock"

52 **MIERSCH, J.G.**

Die Sternen-Uhr [instrument].

Publication
Leipzig im Magasin für Industrieu Literatur, 1822.

Description
Instrument: hand-coloured engraved base plate with aperture to reveal three hand-coloured engraved rotatable cardboard volvelles mounted on thick cruciform pasteboard knobs, [WITH explanatory booklet:] Octavo (210 by 130mm), 22pp. plus advertisement leaf, blue printed paper wrappers.

Dimensions
250 by 210mm.

A decorative portable nocturnal comprising a rotating disc based on the northern circumpolar stars and further volvelles for both the phases of the moon and date.

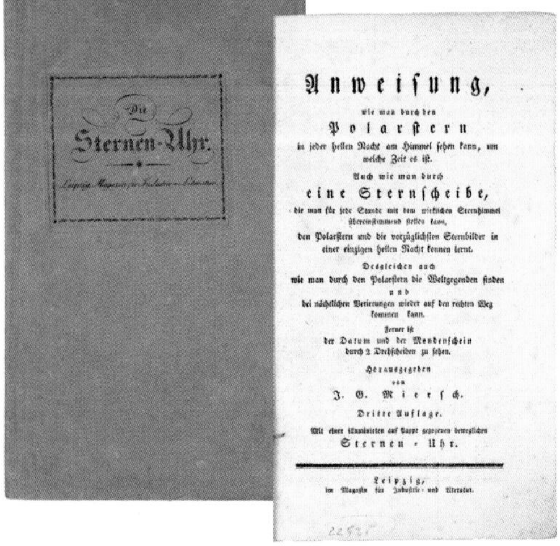

Nachtstunden
Morgenstunden
Abendstunden
Südwest
Südost
West
Ost
Milchstrasse
Pegasus
Andromeda
Cepheus
Cassiopea
Perseus
Fuhrmann
Drache
Kl. Bär
Gr. Bär
Herkules
Bootes
Polar=Kreis
Scheitelkreis
Horizont=Kreis
Untergang Nordwest
Nordost Aufgang
Erde
Nord
Nacht
Datum
Sonntag
Montag
Dienstag
Mittwoch
Donnerst:
Freitag
Soñab:
Mondenschein
Die Sternen-Uhr.
Leipzig, im Magazin für Industrie u. Literatur.

Navigating by the stars

53 **NORIE, John William**

Norie's Set of Celestial Maps, for finding The Principal Stars in the Heavens.

Publication
London, Published as the Act directs, by J.W. Norie & Co. at the Navigation Warehouse and Naval Academy, No. 157, Leadenhall Street, 1st March, 1825.

Description
Quarto (305 by 250mm), six engraved star charts of which two are folding, stamp of "Cox Opticians Devonport" to upper paste-down, black paper boards, with publisher's label, extremities rubbed.

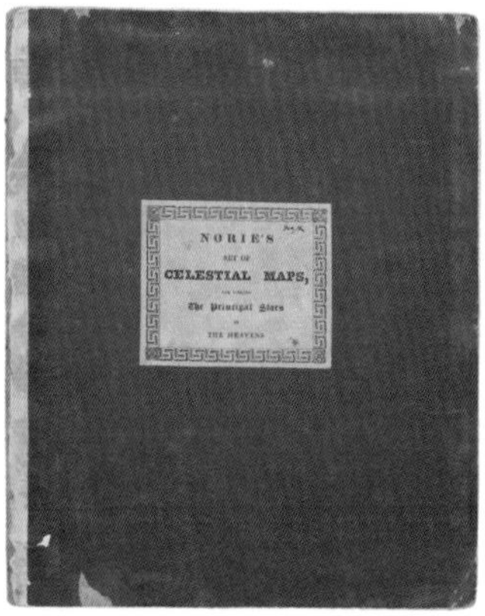

Norie's rare celestial chart book.

The book was produced in order for the student to develop a basic understanding of the heavens so that he may gain "a knowledge of the principal fixed stars in the heavens: and pecularly [sic] adapted to the purpose of finding the stars proper for ascertaining the latitude and apparent time at sea; the longitude by lunar observations" (Norie). This particular example bears the stamp of William Charles Cox, of Devonport, the noted scientific instrument maker and fellow of the Royal Astronomical Society.

John William Norie (1772-1843) was a mathematician, hydrographer, chart maker and publisher of nautical books. His most famous work was the 'Epitome of Practical Navigation' (1805), which became the standard work on navigation and went through many editions. Norie began his career working with William Heather, who ran the Naval Academy and Naval Warehouse in Leadenhall Street from 1795, which sold navigational instruments, charts, and books on navigation. Norie took over the Naval Warehouse after Heather's retirement and founded the company J.W. Norie and Company in 1813. After Norie's death the company became Norie and Wilson, then in 1903 Imray, Laurie, Norie & Wilson.

Rare. OCLC records only two institutional examples of the 1825 edition (Osher Map Library and Sydney University Library) with Copac recording another (The National Library of Wales).

List of Charts
I. & II. A Map of the Zodiacal Stars. Intended to assist Students in Astronomy in acquiring a Knowledge of the Principal Stars near the Ecliptic. Leadenhall Street By John Norie.
III. A Map of the Principal Stars from the North Pole to the Tropic of Cancer.
IV. A Map of the Principal Stars from the South Pole to the Tropic of Capricorn.
V. A Map of the Principal Stars from the North Pole to the Tropic of Cancer.
VI. A Map of the Principal Stars from the South Pole to the Tropic of Capricorn.

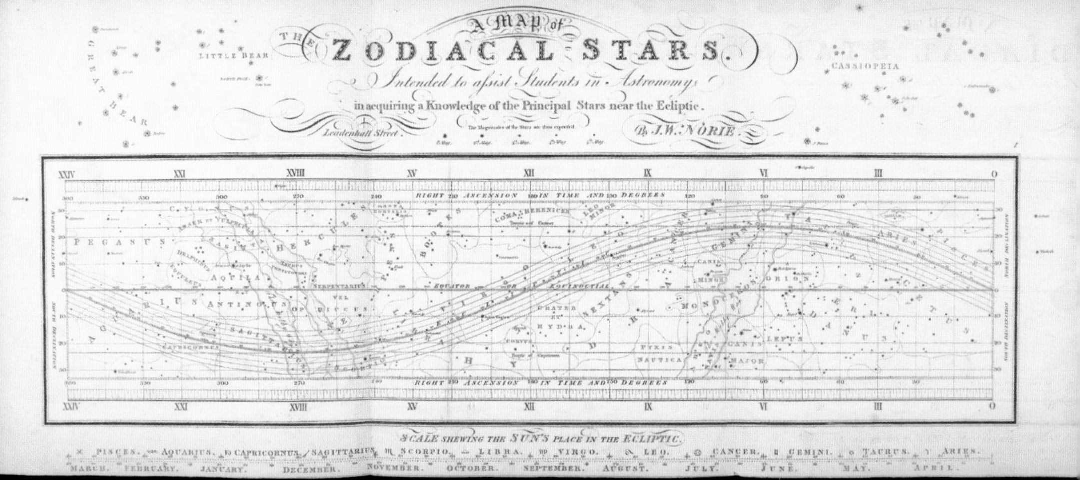

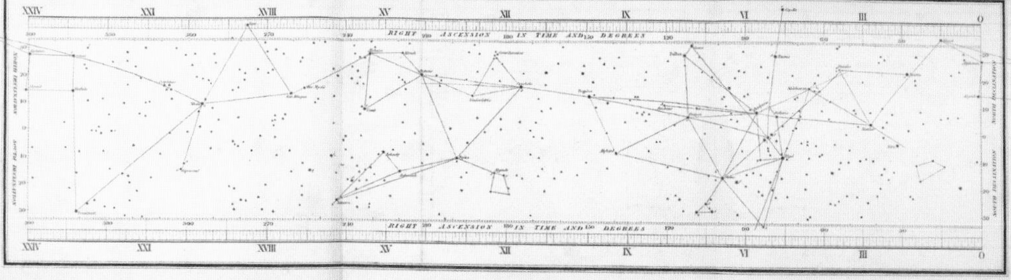

A NEW EDITION, Published as the Act directs, March 1st [illegible], by J.W. NORIE & C° at the Navigation Warehouse and Naval Academy, N° [illegible] Leadenhall Street, LONDON.

A rare folding paper globe

54 **BAUER, Carl Johann Sigmund**

Künstliche Erdkugel zur Verbreitung gemein nütziger Kentnisse über die Eintheilung u: Gestalt der Länder u: Meere unsers Wohnplatzes.

Publication
Nuremberg, 1825.

Description
Terrestrial folding globe comprising six ungraduated engraved gores with contemporary outline colouring, each mounted on contemporary card with cords to gore ends, contained in contemporary envelope style card folder with publisher's label to upper board, inside covers with engraved terrestrial and celestial diagrams, each with faint contemporary hand colouring, the central panel with fifteen lithographic costume plates, each with contemporary hand colouring, showing the world's inhabitants and displayed as a concertina folding strip.

Dimensions
Length 1560mm, retaining original linen ties; folded size 200 by 120mm; each gore 170mm in length.

The present work would appear to be an early example of Carl Johann's globes designed for the educational market. The globe itself is housed within paper covers, which contain information on the inside including the orbit of the earth, the cardinal points, the frigid, temperate, and torrid zones, the equinox, and the seasons. Pasted to the central panel is a concertina of 15 lithographs depicting indigenous people, from the Englishman to the Freundschaftsinsulaner (Friendly Islander, Tonga). The globe is backed upon blue card, with the original string attached to the north and south poles. The title gives prominence to the latest discoveries of William Parry, whose exploration of the Northwest Passage between 1819-1825 had been followed by cartographers with keen interest.

The format would appear to have proved popular, as the Bauer firm would continue to produce a miniature globe together with depictions of indigenous people well into the mid-nineteenth century. A version was published for the English market titled 'The Earth and Its Inhabitants'.

Johann Bernard Bauer (1752-1839) and his sons Carl Johann Sigmund (1780-1857) and Peter Bauer (1783-1847) were scientific instrument and globe makers working in Nuremberg. Johann is recorded as the engraver of a celestial globe by Georg Klinger in 1790; he also published some late editions of the Doppelmayr globes. His sons are best known for their miniature globes published for the educational market.

We are only able to trace three institutional examples: the Houghton Library at Harvard University; the Library of Australia; and the Danish National Library.

Verzeichniſs

der

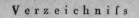

dabei befindlichen Abbildungen verschiedener Völker der Erde.

Europäer.

1. Engländer.
2. Tiroler.
3. Ungar.

Asiaten.

4. Türke.
5. Perser.
6. Chinese.

Afrikaner.

7. Neger der Goldküste.
8. Bewohner von Congo.
9. Hottentot.

Amerikaner.

10. Patagonier.
11. Grönländer.
12. Californier.

Australier.

13. Van Diemensländer.
14. Neuholländer.
15. Freundschaftsinsulaner.

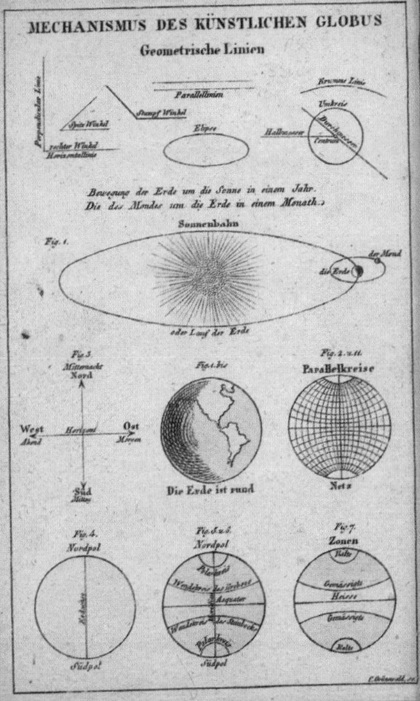

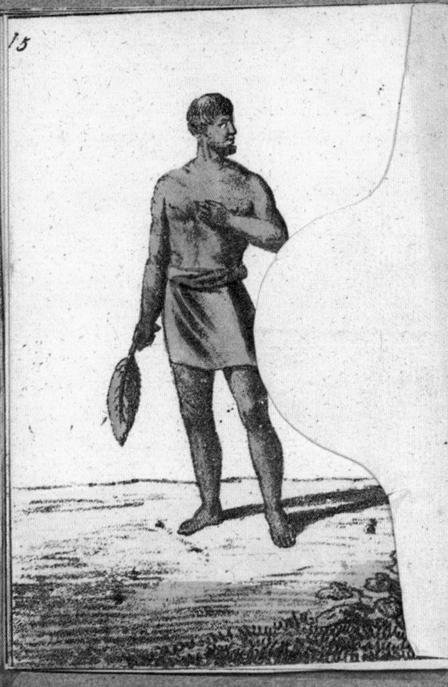

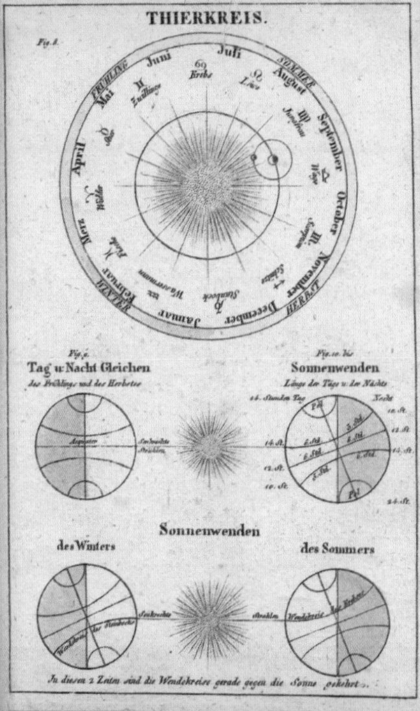

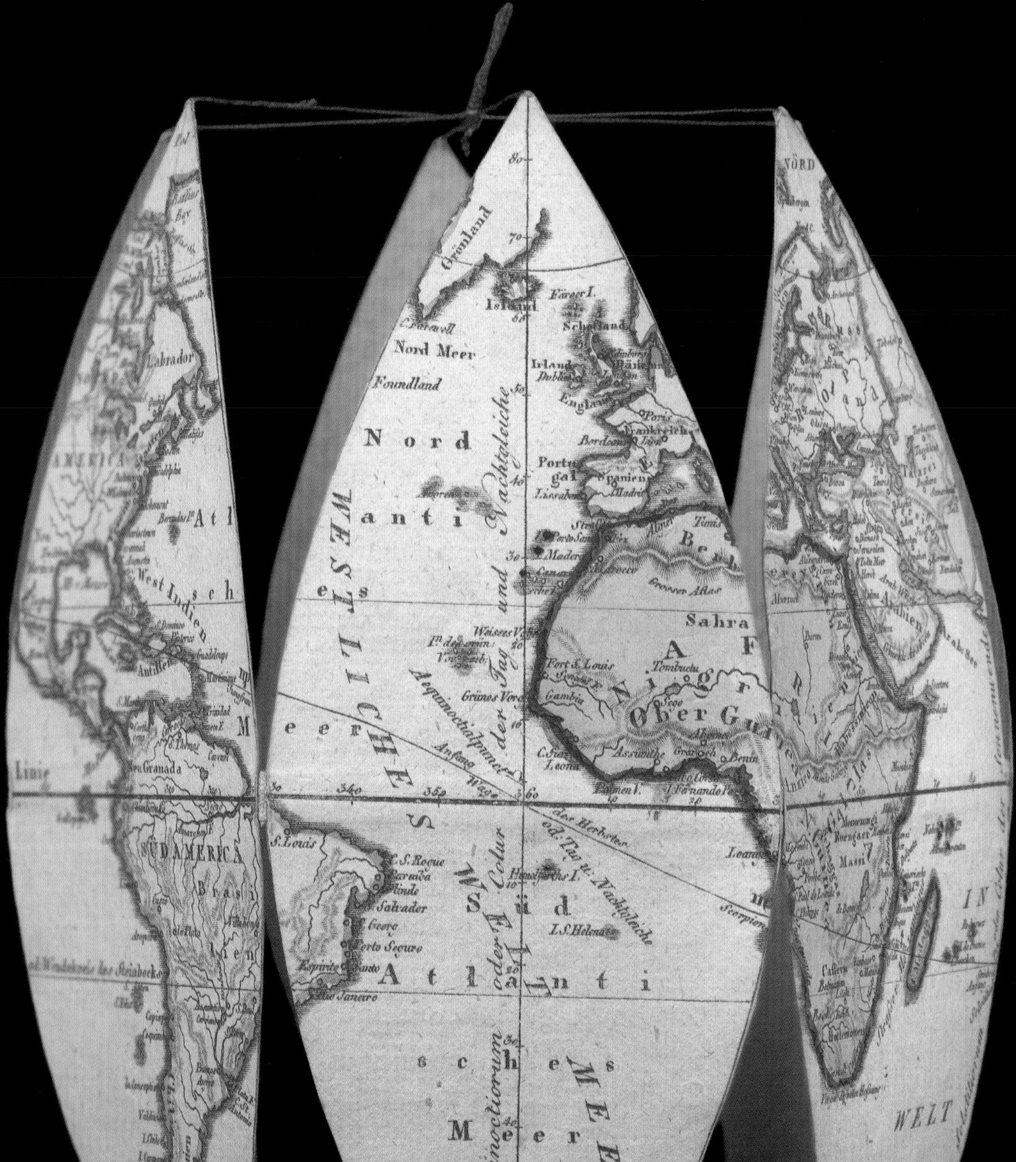

Grönland
Island
Färöer I.
Schetland
Nord Meer
Foundland
Irland
England
Portugal
Spanien
Nord
anti
es
Meer
WEST LICHES
Sahra
A F
Fort S. Louis
Tombuctu
Gambia
Grünes Vorg.
Ober Gui
Benin
Aequinoctialpunct
Colurus Aequinoctiorum oder Colur der Tag und Nachtgleiche
S.Louis
Süd
Atlanti
sches
Meer
MEER
S.Helena
Süd Georgien
Sandwich I.
SÜD
Labrador
AMERICA
West Indien
Linie
SÜDAMERICA
Feuerland
Pol
NÖRD
Loango
Massi
Caffern
WELT

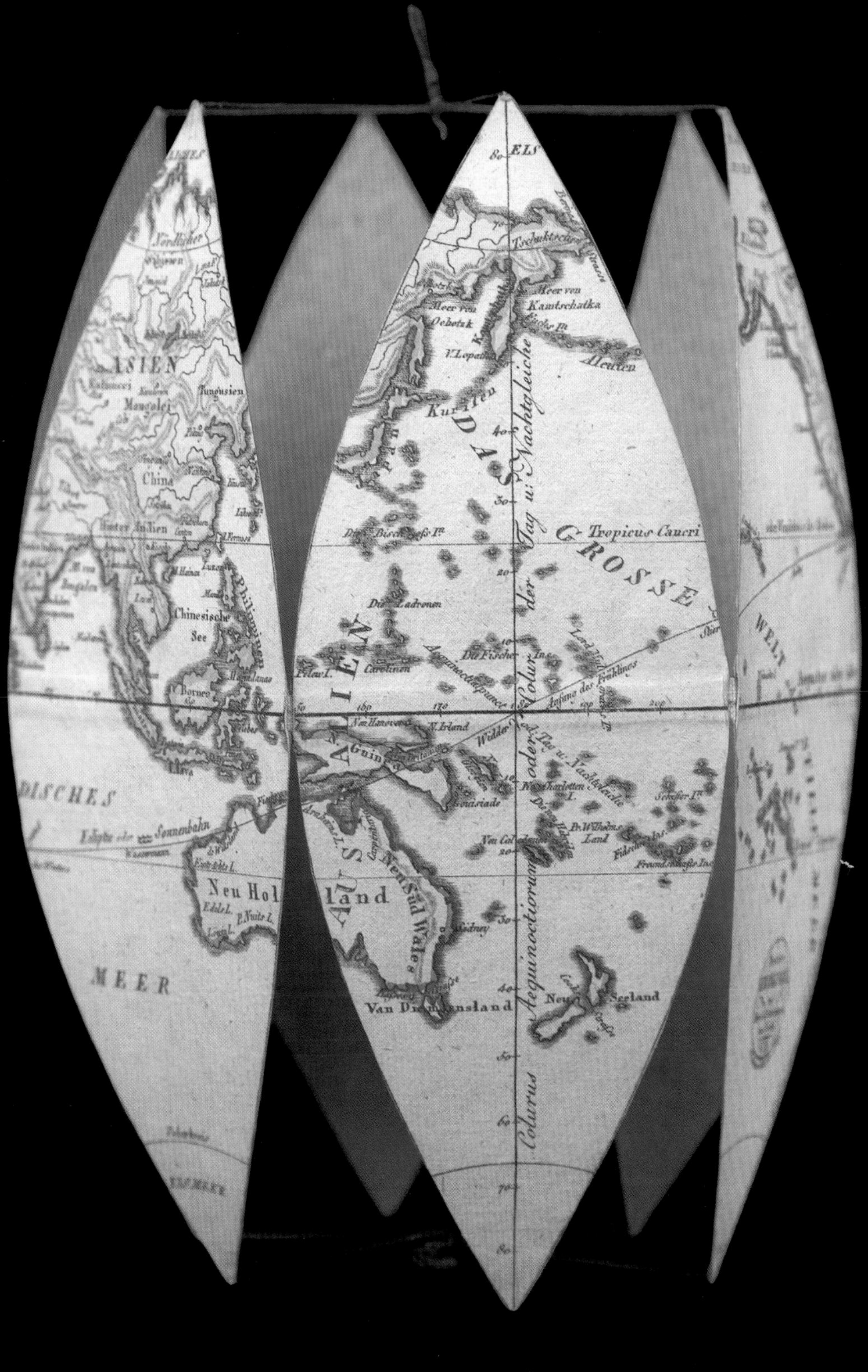
ASIEN
Mongolei
Tungusien
China
Hinter Indien
Chinesische See
Borneo
DISCHES
Neu Holland
MEER
Meer von Ochotsk
Meer von Kamtschatka
Aleuten
Kurilen
DAS
Tropicus Cancri
GROSSE
Die Ladronen
Carolinen
N. Irland
Neu Süd Wales
Van Diemensland
Neu Seeland
WELT

A unique nineteenth century nautical instrument maker's shop sign

55 Publication
[London, c. 1825-51].

Description
Heavily polychromed yellow pine in the form of an over-sized octant, inscribed on the 'T' bar "Stevens Lon[don]".

Dimensions
1120 by 940mm (44 by 37 inches).

There are two candidates for the original owner of this sign: Jeremiah Stevens (fl.1825-1840) or William Henry Stevens (fl.1849-1851), although little is known about either.

Jeremiah Stevens was a member of the Goldsmiths' Company and was recorded as a Mathematical and Philosophical Instrument Maker located at 5, Green Arbour Court, Doctor's Commons, London, in 1825, and at 2, Bell Court, Doctor's Commons, London, for the period 1831-1840. He served his apprenticeship under William Birkwood from 1809.

An Italian armillary sphere

56 [Anonymous]

[Armillary sphere].

Publication
[c. 1825].

Description
Wooden stand and rings, paper, brass, gores on terrestrial sphere.

Dimensions
Height: 350mm; diameter: 190mm.

References
Dekker, Globes, AST0631.

The outermost sphere measures 19 centimetres in diameter and is composed of two wooden circles, which are perpendicularly fixed to each other and represent latitude and longitude. One of them is inscribed with 'coluro de solstizj' and the other with 'coluro degli equinozj'. Both are also labeled with inscriptions for fixed stars, and at their intersections are the Poles.

Running horizontally is another circle, marked internally with 'circolo dell'eclittica', and enclosed by a zodiacal strip 2.6 centimetres wide. The strip is graduated and lists the zodiacal signs with their symbols above and the Gregorian calendar months below.

Six further rings (or "armillae", in Latin) are mounted inside the outer skeleton, at the heart of which is fixed the gilt sphere representing the Sun. Furthest away from this are the ring of Saturn, then Jupiter, Mars, Earth, Venus and Mercury. Earth's globe measures 2.5 centimetres in diameter and is connected to the main axis via one brass arm that also connects it to the small disc representing the Moon. All rings can be moved around to best describe and understand their orbits. Each planetary ring is filled with information regarding the planet's inclination, the revolution time in days, hours and minutes, and the distance to the Sun in 'Miriamenti o Leghe Nuove'.

A similar French-language example is kept at the National Maritime Museum in Greenwich, London.

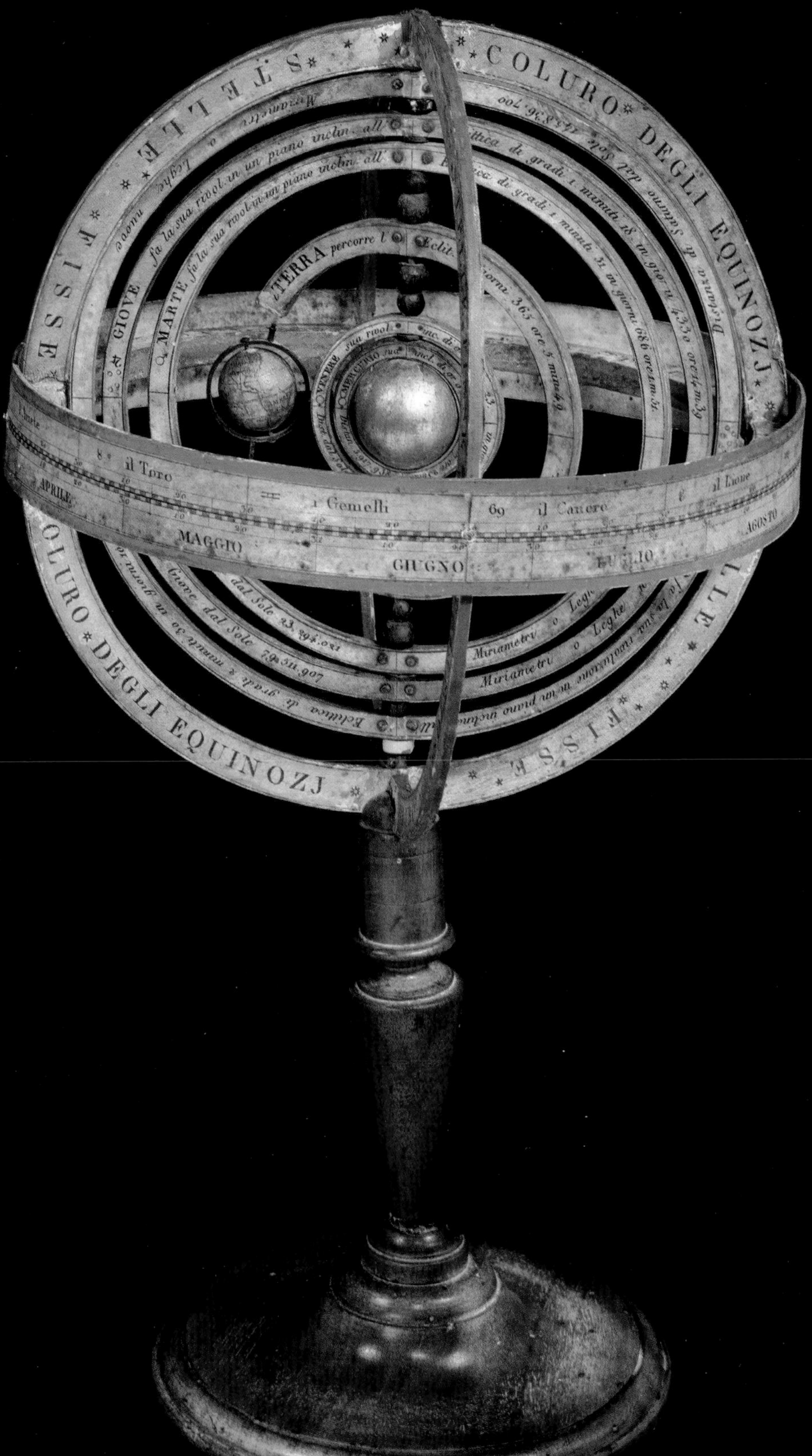

COLURO DEGLI EQUINOZJ
STELLE FISSE
GIOVE
MARTE
TERRA percorre l' Eclit.
il Toro
i Gemelli
il Cancro
il Lione
APRILE
MAGGIO
GIUGNO
LUGLIO
AGOSTO
COLURO DEGLI EQUINOZJ

Rare advertisement for Malby's 12 and 18 inch globes

57 **MALBY, Thomas**

Malby's Modern 18 & 12 Inch Globes Manufactured & Published under the Superintendence of the Society for the Diffusion of Useful Knowledge.

Publication
London, Malby & Co., Houghton St. and The Strand, [1843].

Description
Broadside advertisement.

Dimensions
140 by 85mm (5.5 by 3.25 inches).

A rare advertisement for Malby's 12 and 18 inch globes.

This small broadside shows the stock of Malby's 12 and 18 inch globes for the year 1843. The stock ranged from the cheapest "reference globes" and "slate globes" "for the use of Students in Geography", which could be had for as little as one guinea, to the 18 inch globe with Spanish mahogany furniture, which would set you back 15 guineas.

The firm of Malby & Co., publishers and map-and-print colourers, appears to have started with Malby Senior, who occupied premises at 22 Houghton Street, Clare Market, London, around 1839. Sometime afterward he moved to 3 Houghton Street. Later, the firm was directed by his son, Thomas Junior, as Malby & Son. A number of their globes – perhaps all – were engraved by C. Malby, but his precise relation to Thomas Senior is not clear.

One novelty introduced by Malby was the depiction of lines of magnetic variation on a globe. The firm was continued by Thomas Malby III, but it is not known for how long. After 1860, Malby's globes designed for the Society for the Diffusion of Useful Knowledge appear to have been published by Edward Stanford.

The 18 Inch GLOBES will be published March 1st 1843.
12 Inch GLOBES .... June 1st 1843

REFERENCE GLOBES

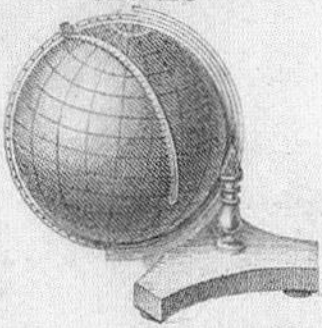

18 Inch ...... 3 ...... GUINEAS each
12 Inch ...... 1½ ...... GUINEAS

N° 1

18 Inch ...... 7 ...... GUINEAS
12 Inch ...... 3½ ...... GUINEAS

N° 2

18 Inch ...... 10 GUINEAS
12 Inch ...... 5½ GUINEAS

MALBY'S

MODERN

18 & 12 Inch GLOBES

MANUFACTURED & PUBLISHED,
under the Superintendence of the,
SOCIETY FOR THE DIFFUSION of USEFUL KNOWLEDGE.
by Malby & Co.
HOUGHTON St. NEWCASTLE St. STRAND, LONDON.
And Sold by CRADOCK & Co. Paternoster Row.

N° 3

18 Inch ...... 12 GUINEAS
12 Inch ...... 6 GUINEAS

N° 4

18 Inch ...... 15 ...... GUINEAS
12 Inch ...... 7½ ...... GUINEAS

The Celestial Globes may be had with or without the figures of the Constellations. The Publishers deem it necessary to inform the public that the Constellations are printed in a different color from the more important matter consequently they do not create that confusion necessarily attendant on their introduction on other Globes.

The Terrestrial Globes are Compiled from the latest and most authentic sources they will also contain a Table of the estimated Population of every Country in the World by G. L. Brent Fellow of the Statistical Society of London.

N° 5

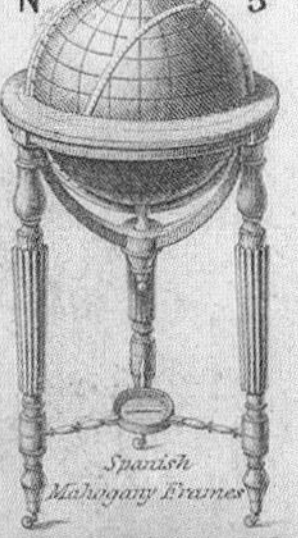

18 Inch ...... 15 ...... GUINEAS
12 Inch ...... 7½ ...... GUINEAS

N° 6

18 Inch ...... 15 ...... GUINEAS
12 Inch ...... 7½ ...... GUINEAS

SLATE GLOBES
For the use of Students in Geography

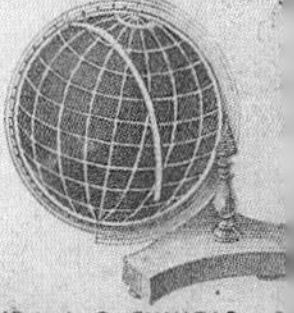

18 Inch ...... 3 ...... GUINEAS each
12 Inch ...... 1½ ...... GUINEAS
9 Inch ...... 1 ...... GUINEA

Engraved by Chs. Malby

A Cyrillic globe

58 **KROTOVII, V.K.**

[Russian Globe] [Terrestrial Globe established by V.K. Krotovii of the War and Topographical Office].

Publication
[St. Petersburg] V. Poliakov 1849.

Description
Set of eight globe gores, mounted on cloth, with fine original colour, some minor discolouration and loss at poles.

Dimensions
830 by 370mm (32.75 by 14.5 inches).

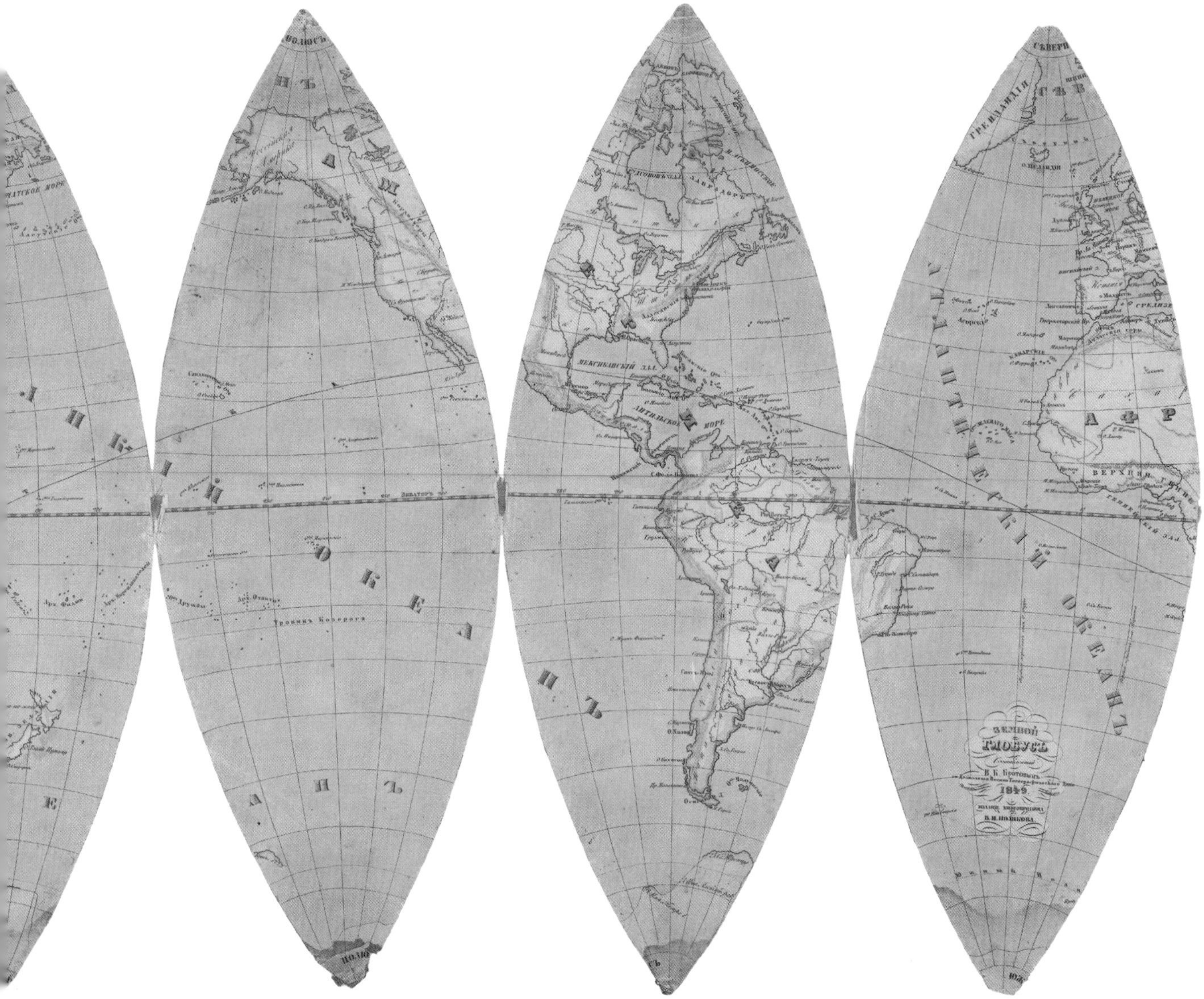

A very early example of the word "computer" to refer to a calculating instrument and "An application of American Genius to a British Principle"

59 **FULLER, John Emory**

Fuller's computing telegraph [cover title]. ... Telegraphic computer, a most wonderful and extraordinary instrument, by which business questions, of every possible variety, are instantly performed ... [pasted to inside upper cover].

Publication
New York, 1852.

Description
Quarto (283 by 285mm), letterpress title pasted to inside upper cover and 11 leaves of text, light toning, folding lithographed table, entitled 'Analytical table of mechanical movements', tipped to inside lower cover, original cloth, worn and re-backed, together with a separate double-sided volvelle (283 by 285mm) engraved by George G. Smith, mounted on heavy cardboard, containing "Fuller's Time Telegraph" on one side and "Palmer's Computing Scale" on the other, plus a separate broadsheet advertisement and list of subscribers for "Fuller's Telegraph Computer, for Readily Solving Business Questions. An application of American Genius to a British Principle".

References
Baxandall 1975, no. 147; Karpinski 1940, 471-72; Origins of Cyberspace 302.

Fuller's 'Telegraphic Computer' represents a very early example of the word "computer" to refer to a calculating instrument (rather than a person of exceptional mathematical facility). Until the invention of electronic computers in 1945, the term "computer" usually referred to a person who compiled mathematical tables with or without mechanical assistance. Sometimes the term referred to "lightning calculators" who performed remarkably fast computations in their heads. During the first decade of electronic computing, the term was apparently used interchangeably for people and machines. By about 1960 the word was generally applied only to machines.

The invocation of telegraphy in the title refers to the notion of instant communication associated with telegraphy, which had recently captured the public imagination. The computer is more properly referred to by the name of its original inventor Aaron Palmer: 'Palmer's Computing Scale' having been patented by him in 1843, and improved and produced in several versions by J.E. Fuller from 1847. This model is printed from the attractive and intricate original Palmer plate, with Fuller's name and own patent added to the engraving, printed by George C. Smith, 186 Washington St., Boston. The reverse side, 'Fuller's Time Telegraph', was patented in 1845. The invention was exhibited with some success at the Great Exhibition at Crystal Palace in 1851, as referred to in the preliminary advertisement.

'Palmer's Computing Scale', essentially an early and ingenious slide-rule, was used to calculate square measures, cubic measures, timber measures, grain measures, liquid measures and interest rates from 3 percent to 10 percent on a daily and monthly basis. The 'Time Telegraph' on the reverse was used to calculate time lapse in days or weeks between any two given dates.

FULLER'S
TIME TELEGRAPH.
JANUARY
FEBRUARY
MARCH
APRIL
MAY
JUNE
JULY
AUGUST
SEPTEMBER
OCTOBER
NOVEMBER
DECEMBER

PALMER'S
IMPROVED BY
FULLER.
COMPUTING SCALE.
Use the inner circle for Dollars, Cents & Mills,
or Pounds, Shillings & Pence

Flammarion's planisphere

60 **FLAMMARION, Camille**

[Celestial Planisphere] Planisphère céleste mobile pour l'Horizon de Paris dressé sous la direction de Camille Flammarion par Léon Fenet.

Publication
Paris, 44 Rue N.D. des Champs, Thomas, G., [c. 1888].

Description
Lithograph circular celestial chart printed in colours (500mm diameter) mounted on pine board rotating on a brass pin, with apertures for calendar and map of the heavens, the surround printed with instructions for use.

Dimensions
557 by 545mm (22 by 21.5 inches).

An uncommon planisphere of stars visible to the naked eye by the astronomer Camille Flammarion (1842-1925) and lithographed by Léon Fenet (1839-1898). The charts may be dated subsequent to the creation of the magazine "Astronomy" by Camille Flammarion (1887) and prior to his death (1925), as the printed description states that the chart includes all of the stars listed in Flammarion's catalogue, represented by their apparent magnitude.

The text in the four corners of the chart gives some example exercises in astronomical calculation, concluding: "In a word, this mobile Planisphère solves all issues related to the apparent position of the stars, the Sun, Moon and planets [to the horizon of Paris], and gives the simplest and easiest way to find these stars in the sky without having studied previously".

USAGES DU PLANISPHÈRE

Ce *Planisphère* est destiné à faire connaître l'aspect du ciel à une heure et à une date quelconque de l'année, son usage est des plus simples.

Le cercle dans lequel apparaissent successivement les constellations représente l'horizon. Le fil tendu du *nord au sud* est le méridien ; *l'est* est à gauche, *l'ouest* à droite. La jonction de ce fil et du cercle zénithal tracé sur la carte indique, pour Paris, les étoiles qui se trouvent juste au-dessus de nos têtes.

Pour se servir de ce *Planisphère*, l'observateur doit le supposer placé au-dessus de sa tête, les points cardinaux correspondant à ceux de l'horizon.

Il suffit pour trouver quelles sont les étoiles visibles à un moment donné, de faire tourner la carte céleste et de mettre en regard l'heure et la date ; on a, du côté gauche les étoiles qui se lèvent, sous le fil celles qui passent au méridien, et du côté droit celles qui se couchent.

Exemples :

1. *Qu'offre avoir l'aspect du ciel pour le 15 Novembre à 9 heures du soir ?*

Pour cela on fait tourner la carte et on amène le 15 Novembre au-dessous de 9 heures du soir. Par cette disposition on voit que les constellations de Cassiopée, d'Andromède, des Poissons et de la Baleine sont au méridien ; celles des Gémeaux, d'Orion, de l'Éridan, apparaissent du côté *est* et par conséquent se lèvent, tandis que Hercule, l'Aigle, le Capricorne, et le Poisson Austral se couchent à *l'ouest*.

On remarquera que le ciel visible le 15 Novembre à 9 heures du soir est également visible à toutes les heures correspondantes aux dates indiquées sur la carte ; par exemple, le 30 Septembre à minuit, le 15 Octobre à 11 heures du soir, le 31 Octobre à 10 heures, le 30 Novembre à 8 heures, le 15 Décembre à 7 heures, le 31 Décembre à 6 heures ; etc. il en est de même pour toutes les positions.

2. *Quel jour de l'année Arcturus passe-t-il au méridien à 10 heures du soir ?*

Cherchez Arcturus, étoile principale de la constellation du Bouvier, et faites tourner la carte jusqu'à ce qu'elle soit sous le fil qui représente le méridien, lisez la date correspondante à 10 heures du soir : 24 Mai, c'est la réponse à la question.

3. *A quelle heure le 15 Juillet, Véga passe-t-elle au méridien ?*

Véga est l'étoile la plus brillante de la Lyre, à gauche du Bouvier ; amenez-la sous le méridien comme on a fait pour Arcturus, et regardez sur la carte l'heure correspondante au 15 Juillet, vous trouverez 11 heures du soir, c'est l'heure de son passage au méridien le 15 juillet.

4. *Quel jour de l'année Sirius se lève-t-il à minuit.*

Faites tourner la carte jusqu'à ce que cette étoile, la plus belle du ciel, qui illustre la constellation du Grand Chien, au pied d'Orion à gauche, soit prête à se cacher sous le cercle qui figure l'horizon, du côté *est*. Voyez le jour correspondant à minuit. 21 Octobre, c'est la réponse à la question.

5. *A quelle heure se couchent les Pléiades le 11 Janvier ?* Amenez au bord de l'horizon, côté *ouest*, ce petit groupe d'étoiles, facilement visible à l'œil nu, qui fait partie de la constellation zodiacale du Taureau, puis cherchez l'heure qui correspond au 11 Janvier, vous trouverez 4 heures du matin.

On peut de même, savoir quel jour une étoile ou un groupe d'étoiles se couchent à une heure donnée.

6. *Combien de temps l'étoile de 1ère grandeur Altaïr de la constellation de l'Aigle, reste-t-elle visible au-dessus de l'horizon.*

Placez le centre du disque de cette étoile sur le bord du cercle de l'horizon, côté *est*, à son lever et lisez le chiffre qui se trouve en regard :13 heures sera le temps de la visibilité de cette étoile sur l'horizon de Paris.

De même, en transportant l'étoile Altaïr, côté *ouest*, à son coucher, le chiffre 11, complémentaire des 24 heures sidérales, donnera le temps de la disparition de l'astre au-dessous de cet horizon.

On remarquera qu'au fur et à mesure qu'on se rapproche du *nord*, les étoiles restent de plus en plus longtemps visibles sur l'horizon, tandis que la durée d'invisibilité diminue inversement. C'est ainsi que l'étoile Véga de la Lyre reste levée 20 heures pour ne disparaître que 4 heures et que la Chèvre, brillante étoile de la constellation du Cocher, reste perpétuellement visible à toutes les époques de l'année.

7. *Quelle est la position du Soleil dans le zodiaque un jour quelconque de l'année ?*

Présentez la carte de manière à ce que ce jour corresponde à l'heure du passage du Soleil au méridien à midi vrai ; alors, l'intersection du fil méridien avec la ligne de l'écliptique indiquera la position du Soleil à la date dont il s'agit.

Il n'y a que quatre époques dans l'année où le Soleil passe exactement au méridien à midi moyen : le 15 Avril, le le 14 Juin, le 31 Août et le 24 Décembre ; le 10 Février, le Soleil est au méridien à midi 15 minutes environ, temps moyen et le 16 Novembre à 11h.45

En se reportant sur la carte au premier méridien divisé, on pourra avoir en degrés, à l'aide d'une règle graduée ou d'un compas, la hauteur du Soleil au-dessus de l'horizon au moment de sa culmination.

Pour avoir la position de la Lune ou d'une planète, cherchez dans la *Connaissance des Temps* son ascension droite et sa déclinaison ; amenez le chiffre d'ascension droite au méridien puis, indiquez sur ce plan la déclinaison que vous aurez prise avec une règle ou un compas sur le premier méridien divisé ; ce point vous donnera la position de l'astre. On pourra ensuite, cette position étant marquée sur la carte, faire avec cet astre tous les problèmes de lever, de passage au méridien et de coucher donnés ci-dessus.

En un mot ce *Planisphère mobile* permet de résoudre toutes les questions relatives à la position apparente des étoiles, du Soleil, de la Lune et des planètes, et donne le moyen le plus simple et le plus facile de trouver ces astres dans le ciel sans avoir fait pour cela d'études préalables.

Les phénomènes célestes les plus intéressants à observer chaque mois sont publiés dans *l'Astronomie*, (Revue d'Astronomie populaire).

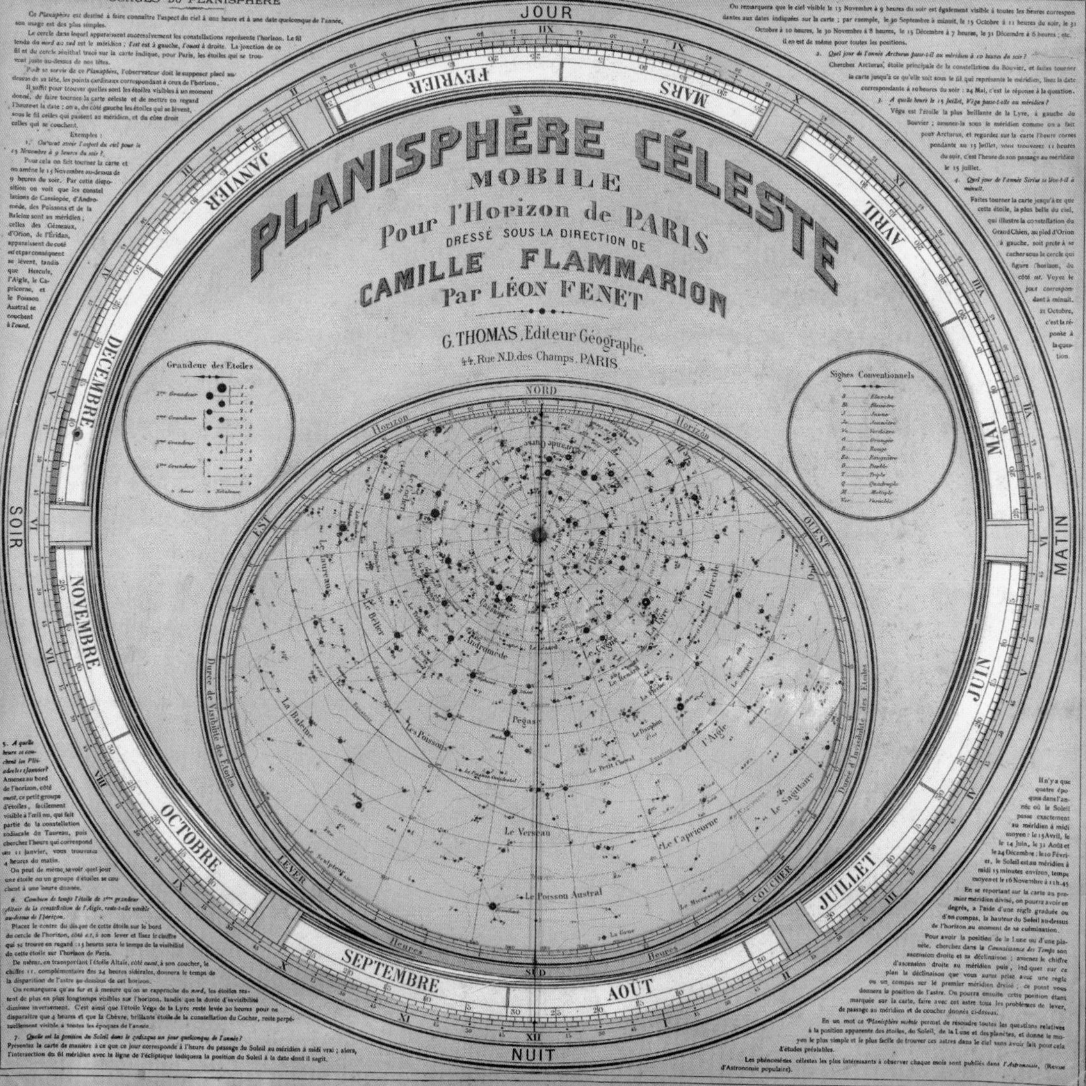

Glossary of the basic features of astronomy and time keeping

Ascension and Declination
Right ascension measures the angular distance of an object eastward along the celestial equator from the vernal equinox to the hour circle passing through the object. The vernal equinox point is one of the two where the ecliptic intersects the celestial equator. Analogous to terrestrial longitude, right ascension is usually measured in sidereal hours, minutes and seconds instead of degrees, a result of the method of measuring right ascensions by timing the passage of objects across the meridian as the Earth rotates.

There are 15 degrees in one hour of right ascension (360 degrees / 24 hours) and 24 hours of right ascension around the entire celestial equator.

Declination measures the angular distance of an object perpendicular to the celestial equator, positive to the north, negative to the south. For example, the north celestial pole has a declination of +90 degrees. The origin for declination is the celestial equator, which is the projection of the Earth's equator onto the celestial sphere. Declination is analogous to terrestrial latitude.

Astrolabe
An elaborate inclinometer, historically used by astronomers, navigators, and astrologers. Its many uses include locating and predicting the positions of the Sun, Moon, planets, and stars, determining local time given local latitude and vice-versa, surveying, triangulation, and to cast horoscopes.

Astronomical clock
A clock with special mechanisms and dials to display astronomical information, such as the relative positions of the sun, moon, zodiacal constellations, and sometimes major planets.

Celestial equator
A circle on the imaginary celestial sphere, in the same plane as the Earth's equator. In other words, it is a projection of the terrestrial equator out into space. As a result of the Earth's axial tilt, the celestial equator is inclined by 23.4 degrees with respect to the ecliptic plane.

Celestial sphere
An imaginary sphere of arbitrarily large radius, concentric with Earth. All objects in the observer's sky can be thought of as projected upon the inside surface of the celestial sphere, as if it were the underside of a dome or a hemispherical screen. The celestial sphere is a practical tool for spherical astronomy, allowing observers to plot positions of objects in the sky when their distances are unknown or unimportant.

Days
The rotation of the Earth on its own axis. One revolution of the planet Earth on its access occurs in a period of time divided into 24 hours; one full day. Any given place will be on the side of Earth towards the Sun for part of that period, daytime; and for part of the period it will be on the side opposite the Sun, night time; between day and night are intermediary periods of half-light: twilights following dawn and preceding dusk.

Dominical letters
The letters A-G assigned to days in a cycle of seven with the letter A always set against 1 January as an aid for finding the day of the week of a given calendar date and in calculating Easter.

A common year is assigned a single dominical letter, indicating which letter is Sunday. Thus, 2011 is B, indicating that B days are Sunday. Leap years are given two letters, the first indicating the dominical letter for January 1 - February 28 (or February 24, see below), the second indicating the dominical letter for the rest of the year.

Ecliptic
The apparent path of the Sun on the celestial sphere, and basis for the ecliptic coordinate system. It also refers to the plane of this path, which is coplanar with both the orbit of the Earth around the Sun and the apparent orbit of the Sun around the Earth. The path of the Sun is not normally noticeable from the Earth's surface because the Earth rotates, carrying the observer through the cycle of sunrise and sunset, obscuring the apparent motion of the Sun with respect to the stars.

Leap Years
The Earth (and its moon) rotates around the Sun once every approximately 365.25 days; one solar year. Every four years – a leap year – the four extra quarter days (the .25 in the above figure) add up to a whole day, requiring the insertion of an extra day, traditionally in February, the shortest calendar month.

Lunation
The rotation of the Moon around the Earth. The Moon rotates around the Earth approximately once every 29.53 days: one lunar month, or one lunation. As the Moon rotates around the Earth different amounts of it are illuminated by the Sun, relative to the Earth, causing the appearance of its waxing and waning: when the Moon appears not to be lit by the Sun it is a new moon, this is followed by an increasingly large crescent that becomes a full moon at the mid-point of the lunation (during the 14th day) and then wanes back to a crescent and another new moon. Because

lunations are each approximately 29 days long, in the Middle Ages lunar months were considered to alternate between of 29 and 30 days.

Metonic Cycle
Solar and lunar cycles combined. Although a solar year cannot be divided exactly into 12 or 13 lunations, 19 solar years can be divided almost exactly into 235 lunations:
19 years x 365.25 days = 6940 days (actually 6939.75 days)
235 lunations x 29.53 days = 6940 days (actually 6939.55 days)

Node
Points of intersection in the orbit of a celestial body with another body, or of a plane. The ascending and descending nodes of the lunar orbit refer to points where the Moon crosses the ecliptic to the North or South.

Planisphere
A star chart analog computing instrument in the form of two adjustable disks that rotate on a common pivot. It can be adjusted to display the visible stars for any time and date. It is an instrument to assist in learning how to recognize stars and constellations. The astrolabe, an instrument that has its origins in the Hellenistic civilization, is a predecessor of the modern planisphere.

Seasons
Because the Earth's axis is at an angle from the vertical, the northern hemisphere will always be tilted towards the Sun (and will therefore be hotter) and the southern hemisphere away from it (and therefore be colder), or vice versa, changing gradually as the Earth rotates around the Sun: this gradual change is manifest in the seasons, from hot to cold and back again, repeating the cycle. The 29.5-day length of a lunation does not divide exactly into the 365.25 days if the year: the closest approximation is 12 lunations (of alternately 29 and 30 days), which equals 354 days, 11 days shorter than a solar year. This means that the lunar cycles gets increasingly out of step with the solar cycle, by 11 days per solar year.

The lengths of these four periods vary according to the Earth's position relative to its rotation about the Sun. The longest day of winter is the Winter Solstice, the longest day of summer is the Summer Solstice, and when the length of daytime and night time are exactly equal in spring and autumn, these are the Vernal Equinox and the Autumnal Equinox, the two days when the equator is closest to the Sun.

Sidereal Months
A sidereal month is the time it takes for the Moon to rotate around the Earth and return to its position in relation to the background stars. Because the Earth itself has moved during this period, this length of time is somewhat less than the period of the lunation: approximately 27.3 days. Thus in the San Zeno calendar (item 2), each two sidereal months of 27 days are followed by one of 28 days, with ten days 'left over' at the end of December.

Volvelle
A paper construction with rotating parts. An early example of a paper analog computer.

Zodiac
The position of the sun's course in the sky relative to the earth. Because the Earth is always moving relative to the Sun, the Sun appears (from Earth) to be moving relative to its 'background', the galaxy. The stars in the night sky are grouped into constellations, including twelve known as the signs of the Zodiac, Aquarius, Pisces, Aries, etc. The changing path of the Sun through the sky was considered to be "in Aquarius", etc., if it was passing through that segment of the sky. Because the position of the Sun relative to the night sky is dictated by the rotation of the Earth around the Sun, the signs of the zodiac keep regular step with the days of the year and the seasons, but the precise date on which the sun enters each sign of the Zodiac depends on the observer's position on Earth.

Select Bibliography

Adams, H. M., *Catalogue of books printed on the continent of Europe, 1501-1600 in Cambridge Libraries, 2vols., Cambridge, University Press, 1967.*

Adams, T.R., & Water, D.W., *English Maritime Books printed before 1801, London, NMM, 1995.*

Armao, Ermanno, *Il catalogo degli di Vincenzo Coronelli: una bibliografia geografica del Seicento, Florence, Olschki, 1957.*

Baxandall, David, *Calculating Machines, exhib. cat., London, The Science Museum, 1926, reprinted 1975.*

Benezit, Emanuel, *Benezit Dictionary of Artists, 14 vols., Paris, Editions Gründ, 2006.*

Bedini, Silvio, *Science and Instruments in seventeenth-century Italy, Aldershot, Hampshire, Variorum, 1994.*

Boffito, Giuseppe, *Bibliografia galileiana, 1896-1940, Rome, La libreria dello Stato, 1943.*

Brown, Basil, *Astronomical Atlases, Maps & Charts: an historical and general guide, London, Dawsons of Pall Mall, 1968.*

Burden, Philip, *The Mapping of North America, 2 vols., Rickmansworth, Raleigh Publications, 1996-2007.*

Crom, Theodore, *Trade Catalogues 1542-1842, Melrose, Florida, 1989.*

Dackerman, Susan, *Prints and the Pursuit of Knowledge in Early Modern Europe, New Haven, Yale University Press, 2011.*

Daumas, Maurice, *Les instruments scientifiques aux XVIIème & XVIIIème siècles, Paris, Presses Universitaires de France, 1953.*

Dekker, Elly, *Globes at Greenwich: a catalogue of the globes and armillary spheres in the National Maritime Museum Greenwich, NMM, London, 1999.*

Dodgson, Campbell, *Catalogue of early German and Flemish woodcuts preserved in the Department of Prints and Drawings in the British Museum, 2 vols., London, BM, 1903.*

Gingerich, Owen, *Rara Astronomica, Harvard Library Bulletin, 1971.*

Gunther, R.T., *The Astrolabes of the World, Oxford, OUP, 1932.*

Higton, Hester, *Sundials at Greenwich: a catalogue of the sundials, nocturnals, and horary quadrants in the National Maritime Museum, Greenwich, London, NMM, 2002.*

Honeyman Collection of scientific books and manuscripts, London, Sotheby's, 1978.

Hook, Diana, & Norman Jeremy, *Origins of Cyberspace: a library of the history of computing..., Novato, 2002.*

Karpinski, Louis Charles, *Bibliography of Mathematical Works Printed in America through 1850, Ann Arbor, University of Michigan Press, 1940.*

Krogt, Peter van der, *Koeman's Atlantes Neerlandici, 7 vols., T Goy-Houten, HES & De Graaf, 1997-2012.*

Lalande, Joseph, *Catalogue des Livres Composant la Bibliothèque de Feu..., Paris, Leblanc & Mérault, 1808.*

Meder, Joseph, *Dürer-Katalog: ein Handbuch über Albrecht Dürers Stiche..., CT, Martino Publishing, 2003.*

Milburn, John R., *Wheelwright of the Heavens, London, Vade-Mecum Press, 1988.*

Nordenskiöld, A.E., *A. E. Nordenskiöld: facsimile-atlas to the early history of cartography..., New York, Dover Publications, 1979.*

Panofsky, Erwin, *Albrecht Dürer Vol. 2: handlist, concordances, and illustrations, London, OUP, 1948.*

Poggendorff, Johan Christian, *Biographisch-literarisches Handwörterbuch zur Geschichte der exacters Wissenschaften, 6 vols. in 11, Leipzig, 1863-1904, reprinted Ann Arbor, 1945, in 10 vols.*

Phillips, Philip Lee, A list of geographical atlases in the Library of Congress: with bibliographical notes, Washington, LC, 1909-1992.

Poulle, E., Les instruments de la théorie des planets selon Ptolémée, Geneva, Droz, 1980.

Rossi, Lorenzo Filippo de'. Indice Delle Stampe, Rome, 1729.

Schottenloher, Karl, Landshuter Buchdrucker des 16. Jahrhunderts: mit eimem anhang, Mainz, Gutenberg-Gesellschaft, 1930.

Shirley, Rodney, Maps in the Atlases of the British Library: a descriptive catalogue c. AD 850-1800, 2 vols., London, British Library, 2004.

Shirley, Rodney, The Mapping of the World: early printed world maps, 1472-1700, London, Holland Press, 1983.

Stillwell, Margaret, The Awakening Interest in Science during the First Century of Printing, New York, Bibliographical Society of America, 1970.

Solla Price, D. J. de, *Science since Babylon, New Haven, Yale University Press, 1975.*

Stevenson, Edward L., *Terrestrial and Celestial Globes: their history and construction..., New Haven, Yale University Press, 1921.*

Taylor, Eva G. R., *Mathematical Practitioners of Hanoverian England: 1714-1840, Cambridge, University Press, 1966.*

Thieme, Ulrich, & Becker, Felix, *Allgemeines Lexikon der bildenden Künstler von der Antike bis zur Gegenwart, Leipzig, W. Engelmann, 1907-50.*

Van Ortroy, Ferdinand, *Bibliographie de l'oeuvre de Pierre Apian, Amsterdam, Meridian Publishing, 1963.*

Warner, Deborah, *The Sky Explored: celestial cartography, 1500-1800, New York, A.R. Liss, 1979.*

Waters, David W., *The art of navigation in England in Elizabethan and early Stuart times, New Haven, Yale University Press, 1958.*

Wilshire, William Hughes, *A descriptive catalogue of playing cards and other cards in the British Museum..., London, British Museum, 1876.*

Zinner, Ernst, *Deutsche un Niederländische astronomische Instrumente des 11.-18., Munich, Beck, 1956.*

Abbreviations

DSB – Dictionary of Scientific Biography
STC – Short Title Catalogue
ESTC – English Short Title Catalogue
NMM – National Maritime Museum
BNF – Bibliotheque Nationale de France

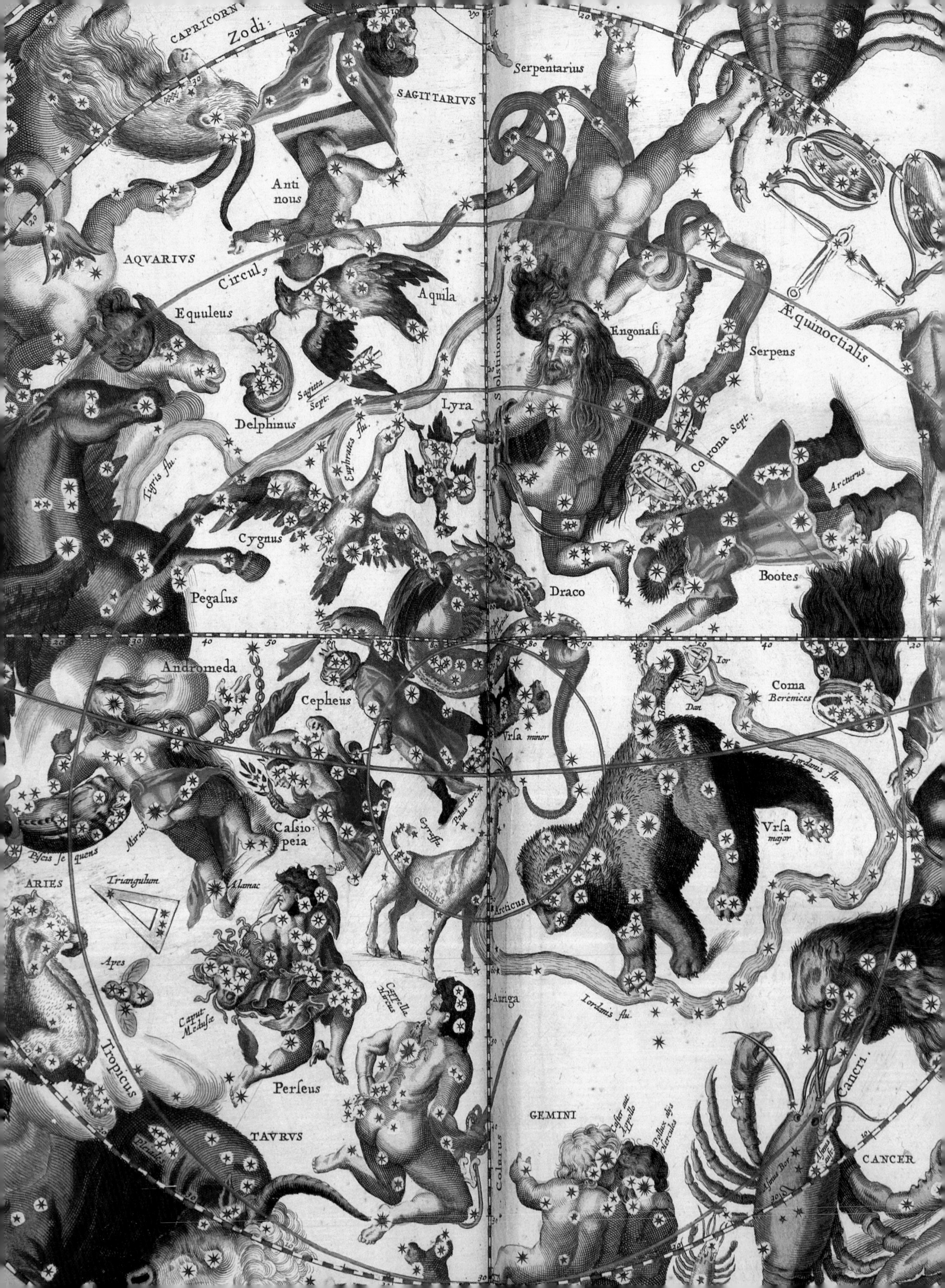

CAPRICORN
Zodi:
SAGITTARIVS
Serpentarius
Anti nous
AQVARIVS
Circul,
Aquila
Equuleus
Æquinoctialis.
Engonasi
Serpens
Solstitiorum
Sagitta Sept.
Lyra
Delphinus
Corona Sept.
Arcturus
Tigris flu.
Euphrates flu.
Cygnus
Bootes
Draco
Pegasus
Andromeda
Cepheus
Coma Berenices
Vrsa minor
Iordanis flu.
Casiopeia
Mirach
Vrsa major
ARIES
Triangulum
Alamac
Arcticus
Apes
Caput Medusæ
Auriga
Tropicus
Perseus
GEMINI
TAVRVS
Colurus
Cancri.
CANCER